Acknowledgments and credits appear on pages 342–344, which constitute an extension of this copyright page.
 Published by Scholastic Inc. Printed in the U.S.A.

ISBN 0-439-19864-X

8 9 10 09 09 08 07 06 05 04 03 02 01

CONTENTS

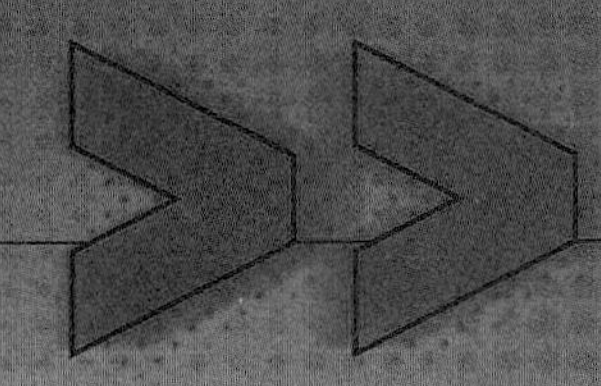

CONTENTS

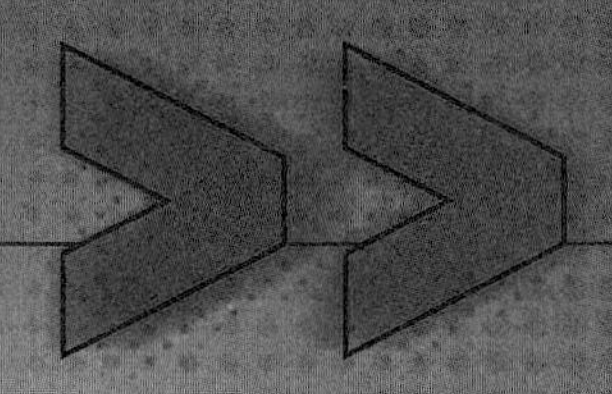

short story

Seventh Grade

by Gary Soto

It's the first day of seventh grade. Will Victor make a good impression on the girl of his dreams?

On the first day of school, Victor stood in line half an hour before he came to a wobbly card table. He was handed a packet of papers and a computer card on which he listed his one elective, French. He already spoke Spanish and English, but he thought some day he might travel to France, where it was cool; not like Fresno, where summer days reached 110 degrees in the shade. There were rivers in France, and huge churches, and fair-skinned people everywhere, the way there were brown people all around Victor.

Besides, Teresa, a girl he had liked since they were in catechism classes at Saint Theresa's, was taking French, too. With any luck they would be in the same class. Teresa is going to be my girl this year, he promised himself as he left the gym full of students in their new fall clothes. She was cute. And good in math, too, Victor thought as he walked down the hall to his homeroom. He ran into his friend, Michael Torres, by the water fountain that never turned off.

They shook hands, *raza*-style, and jerked their heads at one another in a *saludo de vato.* "How come you're making a face?" asked Victor.

"I ain't making a face, *ese.* This *is* my face." Michael said his face had changed during the summer. He had read a magazine that his older brother had borrowed from the Book Mobile and noticed that the male models all had the same look on their faces. They would stand, one arm around a beautiful woman, and *scowl.* They would sit at a pool, their rippled stomachs dark with shadow, and *scowl.* They would sit at dinner tables, cool drinks in their hands, and *scowl.*

"I think it works," Michael said. He scowled and let his upper lip quiver. His teeth showed along with the ferocity of his soul. "Belinda Reyes walked by a while ago and looked at me," he said.

Victor didn't say anything, though he thought his friend looked pretty strange. They talked about recent movies, baseball, their parents, and the horrors of picking grapes in order to buy their fall clothes. Picking grapes was like living in Siberia, except hot and more boring.

"What classes are you taking?" Michael said, scowling.

"French. How 'bout you?"

"Spanish. I ain't so good at it, even if I'm Mexican."

"I'm not either, but I'm better at it than math, that's for sure."

A tinny, three-beat bell propelled students to their homerooms. The two friends socked each other in the arm and went their ways, Victor thinking, man, that's weird. Michael thinks making a face makes him handsome.

On the way to his homeroom, Victor tried a scowl. He felt foolish, until out of the corner of his eye he saw a girl looking at him. Umm, he thought, maybe it does work. He scowled with greater **conviction.**

Glossary

raza-style: according to custom

saludo de vato: greeting

ese: man

Bonjour: hello

Très bien. Parlez-vous français?: Very good. Do you speak French?

Le bateau est sur l'eau: The boat is on the water.

In homeroom, roll was taken, emergency cards were passed out, and they were given a bulletin to take home to their parents. The principal, Mr. Belton, spoke over the crackling loudspeaker, welcoming the students to a new year, new experiences, and new friendships. The students squirmed in their chairs and ignored him. They were anxious to go to first period. Victor sat calmly, thinking of Teresa, who sat two rows away, reading a paperback novel. This would be his lucky year. She was in his homeroom, and would probably be in his English and math classes. And, of course, French.

The bell rang for first period, and the students herded noisily through the door. Only Teresa **lingered,** talking with the homeroom teacher.

"So you think I should talk to Mrs. Gaines?" she asked the teacher. "She would know about ballet?"

"She would be a good bet," the teacher said. Then he added, "Or the gym teacher, Mrs. Garza."

Victor lingered, keeping his head down and staring at his desk. He wanted to leave when she did so he could bump into her and say something clever.

He watched her on the sly. As she turned to leave, he stood up and hurried to the door, where he managed to catch her eye. She smiled and said, "Hi, Victor."

He smiled back and said, "Yeah, that's me." His brown face blushed. Why hadn't he said, "Hi, Teresa," or "How was your summer?" or something nice?

As Teresa walked down the hall, Victor walked the other way, looking back, admiring how gracefully she walked, one foot in front of the other. So much for being in the same class, he thought. As he **trudged** to English, he practiced scowling.

In English they reviewed the parts of speech. Mr. Lucas, a **portly** man, waddled down the aisle, asking, "What is a noun?"

"A person, place, or thing," said the class in unison.

"Yes, now somebody give me an example of a person—you, Victor Rodriguez."

"Teresa," Victor said automatically. Some of the girls giggled. They knew he had a crush on Teresa. He felt himself blushing again.

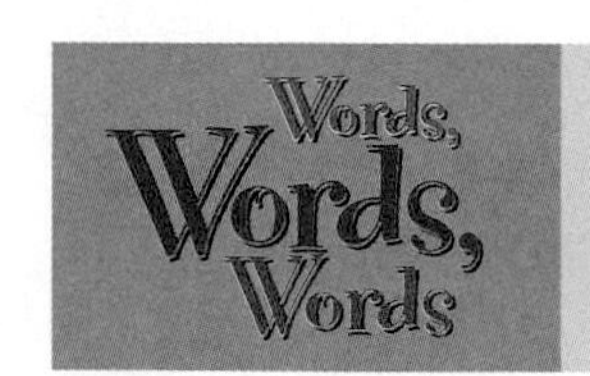

conviction: a strong belief in something
lingered: stayed or waited around
trudged: walked slowly with effort
portly: heavy or stout

Victor raised his hand, wanting to impress Teresa. . . . The room grew silent.

"Correct," Mr. Lucas said. "Now provide me with a place."

Mr. Lucas called on a freckled kid who answered, "Teresa's house with a kitchen full of big brothers."

After English, Victor had math, his weakest subject. He sat in the back by the window, hoping that he would not be called on. Victor understood most of the problems, but some of the stuff looked like the teacher made it up as she went along. It was confusing, like the inside of a watch.

After math he had a fifteen-minute break, then social studies, and, finally, lunch. He bought a tuna casserole with buttered rolls, some fruit cocktail, and milk. He sat with Michael, who practiced scowling between bites.

Girls walked by and looked at him.

"See what I mean, Vic?" Michael scowled. "They love it."

"Yeah, I guess so."

They ate slowly, Victor scanning the horizon for a glimpse of Teresa. He didn't see her. She must have brought lunch, he thought, and is eating outside. Victor scraped his plate and left Michael, who was busy scowling at a girl two tables away.

The small, triangle-shaped campus bustled with students talking about their new classes. Everyone was in a sunny mood. Victor hurried to the bag lunch area, where he sat down and opened his math book. He moved his lips as if he were reading, but his mind was somewhere else. He raised his eyes slowly and looked around. No Teresa.

He lowered his eyes, pretending to study, then looked slowly to the left. No Teresa. He turned a page in the book and stared at some math problems that scared him because he knew he would have to do them eventually. He looked to the right. Still no sign of her. He stretched out lazily in an attempt to disguise his snooping.

Then he saw her. She was sitting with a girlfriend under a plum tree. Victor moved to a table near her and daydreamed about taking her to a movie. When the bell sounded, Teresa looked up, and their eyes met. She smiled sweetly and gathered her books. Her next class was French, same as Victor's.

They were among the last students to arrive in class, so all the good desks in the back had already been taken. Victor was forced to sit near the front, a few desks away from Teresa, while Mr. Bueller wrote French words on the chalkboard. The bell rang, and Mr. Bueller wiped his hands, turned to the class, and said, "*Bonjour.*"

"*Bonjour,*" braved a few students.

"*Bonjour,*" Victor whispered. He wondered if Teresa heard him.

Mr. Bueller said that if the students studied hard, at the end of the year they could go to France and be understood by the populace.

One kid raised his hand and asked, "What's 'populace'?"

"The people, the people of France."

Mr. Bueller asked if anyone knew French. Victor raised his hand, wanting to impress Teresa. The teacher beamed and said, "*Très bien. Parlez-vous français?*"

Victor didn't know what to say. The teacher wet his lips and asked something else in French. The room

ASK Yourself

- Why do you think Victor acts so strangely around Teresa?

Consider what you know about Victor and how he feels.

grew silent. Victor felt all eyes staring at him. He tried to bluff his way out by making noises that sounded French.

"La me vave me con le grandma," he said uncertainly.

Mr. Bueller, wrinkling his face in curiosity, asked him to speak up.

Great rosebushes of red bloomed on Victor's cheeks. A river of nervous sweat ran down his palms. He felt awful. Teresa sat a few desks away, no doubt thinking he was a fool. Without looking at Mr. Bueller, Victor mumbled, "Frenchie oh wewe gee in September."

Mr. Bueller asked Victor to repeat what he said.

"Frenchie oh wewe gee in September," Victor repeated.

Mr. Bueller understood that the boy didn't know French and turned away. He walked to the blackboard and pointed to the words on the board with his steel-edged ruler.

"*Le bateau,*" he sang.

"*Le bateau,*" the students repeated.

"*Le bateau est sur l'eau,*" he sang.

"*Le bateau est sur l'eau.*"

ASK Yourself

- If you wanted to impress someone, what would you do?

Decide how you would handle a situation like this in your own life.

Victor was too weak from failure to join the class. He stared at the board and wished he had taken Spanish, not French. Better yet, he wished he could start his life over. He had never been so embarrassed. He bit his thumb until he tore off a sliver of skin.

The bell sounded for fifth period, and Victor shot out of the room, avoiding the stares of the other kids, but had to return for his math book. He looked **sheepishly** at the teacher, who was erasing the board, then widened his eyes in terror at Teresa who stood in front of him. "I didn't know you knew French," she said. "That was good."

Mr. Bueller looked at Victor, and Victor looked back. Oh please, don't say anything, Victor pleaded with his eyes. I'll wash your car, mow your lawn, walk your dog—anything! I'll be your best student, and I'll clean your erasers after school.

Mr. Bueller shuffled through the papers on his desk. He smiled and hummed as he sat down to work. He remembered his college years when he dated a girlfriend in borrowed cars. She thought he was rich because each time he picked her up he had a different car. It was fun until he had spent all his money on her and had to write home to his parents because he was broke.

Victor couldn't stand to look at Teresa. He was sweaty with shame. "Yeah, well, I picked up a few things from movies and books and stuff like that." They left the class together. Teresa asked him if he would help her with her French.

"Sure, anytime," Victor said.

"I won't be bothering you, will I?"

"Oh no, I like being bothered."

"*Bonjour,*" Teresa said, leaving him outside her next class. She smiled and pushed wisps of hair from her face.

"Yeah, right, *bonjour,*" Victor said. He turned and headed to his class. The rosebushes of shame on his face became bouquets of love. Teresa is a great girl, he thought. And Mr. Bueller is a good guy.

He raced to metal shop. After metal shop there was biology, and after biology a long **sprint** to the public library, where he checked out three French textbooks.

He was going to like seventh grade. ●

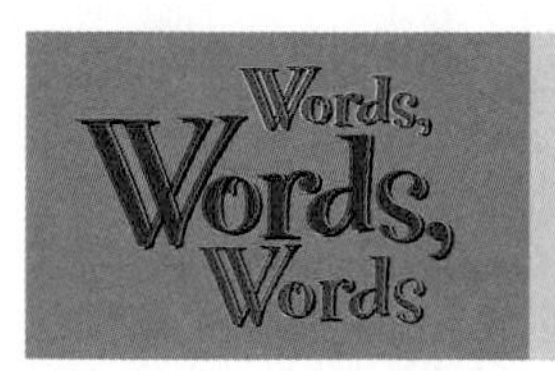

sheepishly: acting in an embarrassed way for having done something foolish
sprint: a fast run for a short distance

Gary Soto

Gary Soto remembers what it's like to be a seventh grader. He brings his memories to life in his stories.

Growing up in Fresno, California, Gary Soto was a lot like the kids in his stories. He never thought about becoming a writer. In fact, he says, "we didn't have any books around and no one really encouraged me to read." Soto headed for college with plans of becoming a scientist. Then one day, he discovered a book of poetry in the college library. Soto enjoyed it so much that he began to write his own poems. Soon after, he switched his major to English and went on to get an advanced degree in Creative Writing. He's been writing poems, short stories, and novels ever since. Recently, Soto talked about his life and work.

So, is Victor in "Seventh Grade" based on you?
Luckily, no. Believe me, I did do some foolish things as a seventh grader. But Victor's story actually came from my wife. When she was in junior high, this kid in her class tried to impress people by pretending to speak a foreign language. It wound up being really embarrassing for him because he kept rattling nonsense and everyone was laughing at him.

What were you like in the seventh grade?
I was pretty goofy. I liked girls, but I was very shy. I remember a bunch of girls liking me and thinking I was really cute. I was terrified. The girls were following me around school and I just kept running away from them.

Are any of your stories based on your own life?
Absolutely! Almost all of my stories are based on my own memories—either that, or they're imaginary stories that easily *could* have happened in my own life.

I'll bet your life today is different from what you imagined growing up. Can you describe a typical workday as a writer?
My life did turn out a lot different than I thought. In junior high, I figured I might become a scientist who studies dinosaur bones! Still, writing is no different from any other kind of work. Writing demands focus, concentration, and energy. To achieve those things, I need rest. I try to get eight or nine hours of sleep each night. Then I spend at least three or four hours a day writing. ●

Other Books by Gary Soto

Pacific Crossing

Martial-arts student Lincoln Mendoza visits Japan and discovers a whole new world.

Crazy Weekend

Hector visits his Uncle Julio for the weekend and has an adventure of a lifetime.

Talk About It

Now that you've read "Seventh Grade" and the author profile, what do you have to say about these questions?

▶ Victor tried very hard to impress Teresa. What really impresses *you* about other people?

▶ What are some things that might make people nervous on the first day of school? Explain.

Comprehension Check

Write your answers to the questions below. Use information from the story and the author profile to support your answers.

1. What does Mr. Bueller do when he realizes that Victor cannot speak French?
2. Why does Mr. Bueller help keep Victor's secret?
3. What often happens to people who pretend to know something they don't?
4. When did Gary Soto decide he wanted to be a writer?
5. How is Victor's story different from the real-life experience it was based on?

Vocabulary Check

Complete each sentence with the correct vocabulary word below.

lingered **sheepishly** **conviction**
sprint **trudged**

1. In order to catch the bus to school, we had to _______.
2. After we missed the bus, we stopped running and _______ the rest of the way.
3. We felt bad and handed our late passes _______ to the teacher.
4. It is the teacher's _______ that we all get to class on time.
5. After class was over, we _______ for a minute so that we could apologize.

Write About It

Choose one of the writing prompts below.

- Write five to eight tips that would help any new seventh grader to be successful in school.
- Think about how Victor feels about Teresa. Then write a note from Victor to Teresa. Make sure that you clearly explain Victor's feelings.
- Write a thank-you note from Victor to Mr. Bueller. In the note, have Victor tell his teacher how he feels about what happened in class.

More to READ

Did you enjoy reading about seventh graders? If so, you might also like these books.

Crash
by Jerry Spinelli

Crash is a bully from way back. This is most unfortunate for Penn Webb, the friendly, peace-loving kid who lives down the block. But Crash's whole world changes when his beloved grandfather has a stroke. After that, Crash begins to see things differently. And this turns out to be most fortunate for his new friend, Penn!

P.S. Longer Letter Later
by Paula Danziger and Ann M. Martin

Best friends, Elizabeth and Tara*Starr, are separated after Tara*Starr moves away. Elizabeth is quiet and shy, while Tara*Starr will do anything for attention. Then things change for them both. Tara's life settles down, and Elizabeth's world turns upside down. Their letters back and forth tell the story.

Reading Movie Schedules

You're going to the new horror movie. But when you get to the multiplex at 7P.M., you find out that the movie started at 6:40!

Everything would have been great if only you'd read the movie schedule correctly. Check out the schedule below. Then get ready to go to the movies.

A Movie Schedule

Some schedules list movie times for several theaters. Be sure to check times for the right theater.

When movie times are this close together, it means the film is playing in two separate theaters at the same location.

Some theaters offer bargain prices on early shows. Theaters often offer discount tickets for children, too.

WESTSIDE MULTIPLEX 1350 Hepburn Blvd.
555-8777
- **Cab Driver IV, R** 12:30, 3:25, 6:20, 9:15
- **The Mouse That Stole Christmas, G** 12:00, 2:10, 4:20
- **Seven Seconds 'Til Midnight, R** 7:00, 9:50
- **Rocko XVIII, PG-13** 12:30, 1:20, 2:50, 3:45, 5:15, 6:10, 7:40, 8:30, 10:00
- **StarGazer, PG-13** 12:50, 3:30, 6:10, 9:00
- **Here With the Wind, PG** 12:10, 3:30, 7:00, 10:20

SOUTHSIDE MEGAPLEX 527 Wayne Hwy.
555-3000
- **The Mouse That Stole Christmas, G** 12:00, 2:10, 4:20, 6:30, 8:40
- **Rocko XVIII, PG-13** 1:00, 2:15, 3:15, 4:30, 5:30, 6:45, 7:45, 9:00, 10:00
- **Cab Driver IV, R** 1:30, 2:15, 3:15, 4:20, 6:15, 7:15, 9:20, 10:10
- **StarGazer, PG-13** 1:00, 3:50, 7:40, 10:20
- **Here With the Wind, PG** 1:00, 4:30, 8:00
- **Germinator IV, R** 12:15, 3:45, 6:15, 8:15, 10:40
- **Fly Story, PG** 12:00, 2:15, 4:30, 6:40, 8:45

BARGAIN CINEMAS 122 Cagney Road
555-5610
$7.00 adults
$4.50 under 12
$4.50 all shows before 3:00

- **Cab Driver IV, R** 12:50, 3:50, 6:50, 9:50
- **Here With the Wind, PG** 12:00, 3:20, 6:45, 10:00
- **Rocko XVIII, PG-13** 1:00, 3:15, 5:30, 7:45, 10:00
- **StarGazer, PG-13** 1:15, 4:00, 7:10, 9:40

RATINGS GUIDE
G = all ages; **PG** = parental guidance suggested
PG-13 = parents strongly cautioned
R = no one under 17 admitted without adult

"Check the date on your newspaper. Most cinemas change their schedules on Fridays, so a Thursday paper won't do if you're going to the movies on Friday night."

See a Movie

Here's your chance to make sure you get to the movies on time. Use the schedule to answer the questions below. Write your answers on your own paper.

1. You're going to Bargain Cinemas with your 11-year-old brother. How much would it cost the two of you to see the first showing of *Here With the Wind*?
a. $7.00 **c.** $14.00
b. $9.00 **d.** $14.50

2. John is 15. It's Saturday. He really wants to go to the movies at the Westside Multiplex. But he can't get to the theater until 7 P.M. Which movies could he see?

3. You want to see *StarGazer* after school. School gets out at 3 P.M. All the theaters are about 30 minutes from your school. At which theaters can you see the movie? What is the first showing you could make at each theater?

4. Which of these movies is not playing at the Southside Megaplex?
a. *Cab Driver IV* **c.** *StarGazer*
b. *Seven Seconds 'Til Midnight* **d.** *Fly Story*

5. It's Friday night. You and your friends are going to the Westside Multiplex after work. Which movies can you see if you get to the theater at 7 P.M.?

Now Playing . . .
Hollywood is always looking for good movie titles. Make up a list of three titles that you are sure would become big hits!

Sneak Preview
Pick one of the movies from the schedule to the left. Imagine what this movie is about. First, write down the main characters. Next, say what happens. Finally, tell why audiences will like this movie.

"Want to make sure the movie doesn't sell out before you get there? Order tickets in advance over the phone or online."

admitted: to be allowed in
cinema: a movie theater
guidance: supervision, care

personal narrative

Fighting Fire

As one of San Francisco's first women firefighters, Caroline Paul was prepared for anything to happen. Just not this.

by Caroline Paul

The alarm comes in near midnight. My squad responds to a house fire. William Costanzo is driving today. Because the fire is in Hunter's Point we take the freeway. The fire rig shakes and groans from the strain of going so fast. As we ride, I hold my hands in front of me and try to flex them. My gloves are stiff with ash from a previous fire. Coat, belt, helmet—they are all in place. All I can do is sit and wait.

Our rig lunges onto the sidewalk before the house and noses to a halt. I don't see the flames, but I see that the two-story family residence is haloed in orange light. The sky is murky with smoke.

William and I throw a quick salute to a chief who stands in the middle of the street, bent over the radio in his left hand. It is hard to hear anything above the roar of wood giving way and the shouts for more water, more ladders, more axes. Hoses lie everywhere. Fire vehicles jam the streets.

"Rescue 3 is here, Chief," William says.

"Okay, we got a report of two people still in the back room," the chief answers matter-of-factly. "A baby and an adult."

Pause, look, I say to myself as I walk quickly toward the fire. I try to remain calm, but the word "baby" pounds in my head. The garage door, at street level, is twisted and burned. Smoke cartwheels from the opening, and two hose lines disappear into the darkness. "Front door," I breathe to William and bound up the steps. There is already a hose snaking its way inside: an engine company's attack.

My mask is on, and I turn to make sure that William has followed me inside. I do not want to lose him or be lost by him; tonight we need to do everything perfectly. Instead, to my surprise, I find a civilian behind me. He is wringing his hands and pointing. There is black all over his face, and I wonder if he has been burned. He grabs my coat. I see that he is crying. I cannot understand a word he says—it's not English—but I know what is going on. It is his baby inside—in the back room of the house.

By this time William is past me and near the engine crew. They have not made much headway, and something has stopped them at a small hall.

I push the father back as gently as I can and join William. It is hot, very hot. "We need to get through," I say to the engine crew. "There are two people in the back." "Stay back," hisses the rear firefighter. "Don't push us forward!"

"Don't worry. We'll get them. I promise." His eyes pin mine. I push him away from the smoke and darkness toward the outside. *I promise.*

The **urgency** in his voice makes me step away. The fire must be back there, and he is afraid we'll shove them into it. I quickly check an **adjacent** room, but there is no access to any other place. I grab the father. "Is there any other way to the back?"

He points frantically again to the far wall of the room amid a hail of words I can't understand. "Any . . . other . . . way?" I repeat in that exaggerated, idiotic way that people try to speak through language barriers. "It's your kid, I know. Please, can you tell me—" and then I let go of his shoulders and say, "Don't worry. We'll get them. I promise." His eyes pin mine. I push him away from the smoke and darkness toward the outside. *I promise.*

When the father has been dragged to the front door, William and I fly down the stairs. We dive into the garage. As my air hose gets caught on the bumper of a car, William melts into the dark ahead of me. I disentangle myself and crawl farther in. Near the front wheel, William reappears. "Can't get through! All fire!" he yells.

"The rear. Get to the rear," I answer, and we take off again, holding each other's coat sleeves. The way to the back has already been trampled by axes, chain saws, and well-aimed kicks.

The neighbors say nothing as we follow the destruction through their house, out to their yard and through a yawning hole in what was once a neat, tall fence. The smoke in the back is thick, but I can just make out a window above me. But the whole bottom of the house roils in flame. How can we get to that window?

Someone grabs my shoulder and I turn to see another chief, his white helmet gleaming against the flames. "There's a lady here who's jumped; we need some medical help for her."

Several firefighters surround a ghostly white face. **Simultaneously,** William reaches and jumps at a fence that lines the other side of the yard. I grab a foot and a knee and push him up. He teeters at the top and then shimmies to a small roof next to the burning building. I grab a chain saw and pass it up to him.

The chief pulls at me again. "Chief," I say, and there is apology in my voice, "we are going for someone else." Everyone is trained in medical work, and someone else can take care of the woman. It is our job now to get to the baby. William, an astonishingly good firefighter, has managed to get into position to cut into the room from the outside.

"Oh no," he mutters. "This roof won't hold." He is balanced **precariously** on a plastic greenhouse-like structure, but manages to expertly start the chain saw anyway. By now I have his belt buckle to steady him, and I crouch on the fence like a gymnast new to the balance beam.

Suddenly, William shouts above the saw's whine. "The whole wall is metal!" He revs the saw and tries to cut through it anyway, to no avail. I start to feel more frantic than I want to. I can still see the father's wide eyes and his stretched, grief-stricken face.

Another eight feet away, bordering the greenhouse roof is a second-floor window leading into a different house.

William treads carefully and reaches the window. I follow him,

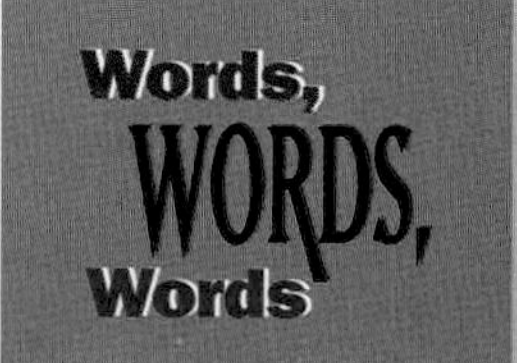

urgency: needing immediate attention
adjacent: close or next to something
simultaneously: happening at the same time
precariously: in an unsafe and risky way
anguish: a strong feeling of sadness and nervousness

but I am less careful. When the roof gives way, I am not thinking that I may get hurt, but that I may not be able to keep my promise. At the last second I wedge my arms out and catch myself on the beams. I hang there for a moment while William yells, "Are you okay?"

I assure him I am fine, that I am going to lower myself and climb back up. Meanwhile, I think about the weight I am wearing. Air pack, turnout coat, crash ax, flashlight. Fifty or so pounds extra. I hear the **anguish** in William's voice. "Are you okay?" he keeps saying over and over. He is unable to see me well in the dark and smoke. I tell him to go ahead. There is nothing he can do on this thin, uncertain roof. Meanwhile, I scream to myself, *You idiot!*

Carefully, I half-slither, half-drop to the ground. Nothing broken, just a bruise or two and this pounding heart. My heart pounds. *Don't worry, we'll get them. I promise.*

I force my body up the fence. Then I'm on the roof again. This time, I move gingerly toward the window around the garage hole I made. William hauls me in. Then he picks up the chain saw and turns the blade into the wall. The hole seems to take forever to cut, but it can only be a minute till he pushes the blade through one house and into the next. I can only think of the small body of a baby waiting on the other side—waiting for this act of desperation to reach her.

I drop my air pack and scramble to get into the hole. Suddenly the beam of a flashlight hits my eyes. It is the firefighters from below. "They're here," I tell William. "They got the fire out, and they're getting into the room." William turns away, head down.

The body is found a few minutes later. It is of a four-year-old boy, not a baby. He was found not in the room we had labored so hard to enter, but in the garage.

I lean against the wall. Could we have saved him? Did I make a wrong step, a wrong turn, a wrong decision? I want to weep. I think of the father. He had looked to me to save the most important person in his life, and I failed.

We walk through the front door slowly. William's face is frozen in stunned quiet.

There is a crowd outside. I step onto the sidewalk. Even though my head is down, I see three people huddled together. A small woman is in the middle. Her eyes are fixed on me. I stop suddenly. To her left is the father. I want to say something, but what would it be? "Sorry"?

Sorry, but your son is dead. I hesitate, then turn away. I feel sick. I do not look back. ●

ASK Yourself

- What do the two firefighters do to try to find the child?

Go back and list all the steps the firefighters took.

HELP IS HERE!

from *Emergency!* by Joy Masoff

As in firefighting, medical workers in emergency rooms and ambulances have almost impossible jobs to do. Here's what some workers told Joy Masoff about their jobs and lives.

Q. WHO ARE THE MOST DIFFICULT PATIENTS TO WORK WITH?

A. Since so many emergency medical workers are parents themselves, sick kids always touch them in a special way. Most ambulances keep a supply of stuffed animals on board to help EMTs (Emergency Medical Technicians) comfort young children who might be frightened. In the ER (emergency room), the nurses always spend extra time cuddling and reassuring their youngest patients. And many doctors let kids bring a favorite stuffed animal or blanket into the OR (operating room) if they need surgery. No one likes it when a child is hurt or ill.

Q. HOW DO YOU TAKE CARE OF SOMEONE WHO'S MEAN OR BAD?

A. That's one of the hardest things the ER team has to deal with. Should they give the best possible care to a known criminal? How do they keep from walking away when a patient starts yelling at them? They try to look past the personality and focus instead on simply healing a human body. They also try to remember that the patient is someone's son or daughter, or someone's father or mother. And that some people get nasty when they're scared. Remembering these things always helps.

Q. WHAT'S THE HARDEST PART OF EMERGENCY WORK?

A. The ER and the ambulances have to be staffed 24 hours a day, 365 days a year. Because of that, many medical workers find themselves at work in the middle of the night and during holidays.

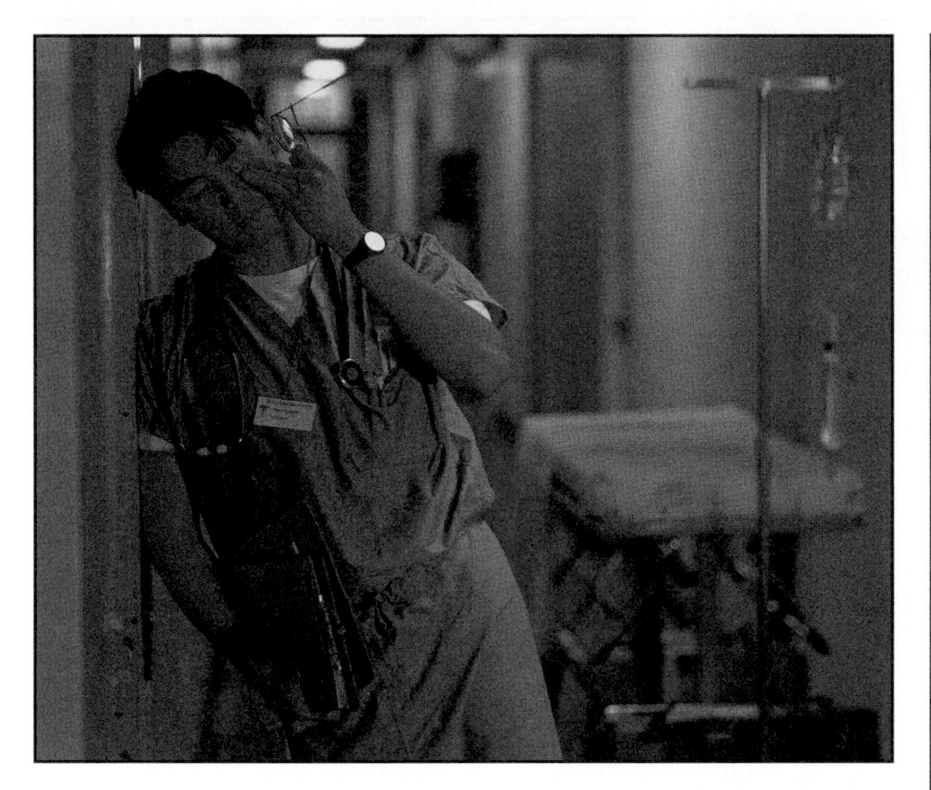

To be fair, everyone takes turns working the night shifts. Still, being tired comes with the job. Spending 12 hours on your feet with barely enough time for a bathroom stop is really exhausting. In busy ERs, pagers beep constantly, and meals are grabbed from vending machines. Family events such as Thanksgiving dinner often have to be missed.

Q. IS IT EVER SCARY?

A. EMTs often risk their lives working in terrible weather or in dangerous conditions. For them, work is sometimes very frightening. One EMT put it this way. "Imagine periods of intense boredom waiting for the next call, followed by moments of sheer terror answering it." Difficult rescues—where just reaching the victim can be a challenge—are tests of both physical and mental strength.

Q. HOW DO YOU DEAL WITH DEATH?

A. Most of the time, medicine is wonderfully rewarding. People who need help can be made well. Lives can be saved. But from time to time, no matter how hard everyone tries, it's impossible to help a patient. That's always hard for the emergency team. They meet once a week to talk about these cases, to learn from them and to be reassured that they did everything humanly possible. ●

IN THEIR OWN WORDS

A paramedic describes the job like this. "We go from hanging out to total chaos in one minute flat. I always say that being an EMT involves three things. Panic, fear, and regret. Panic when the call comes in—*will I be able to help?* Fear when we get there—*what if I can't?* And regret when it's over, because helping someone is so cool!"

A nurse shares her feelings. "At the end of my shift, all I can think of is how much my feet hurt and how good my heart and soul feel."

A doctor sums it all up. "Sometimes it feels a little like a Wild West stampede here. There will be 50 people waiting in the hallways, and I'll be thinking, 'No way am I getting out of here tonight.' And then, somehow, they're all treated and sent home . . . and that feels good!"

Talk About It

Now that you've read "Fighting Fire" and "Help Is Here!" what do you have to say about these questions?

- ▶ Should emergency workers like firefighters be willing to risk their own lives to save others? Explain.
- ▶ Do you think you would want to be an emergency worker? Why or why not?

Comprehension Check

Write your answers to the questions below. Use information from the personal narrative and the interview to support your answers.

1. Why are Caroline Paul and her partner trying so hard to enter the back room of the burning house?
2. Why does Caroline Paul feel sick at the end?
3. Would you ever make a promise that you weren't sure you could keep?
4. What are some good and bad points about emergency work?
5. Do you think Caroline Paul would agree with what the emergency workers say in "Help Is Here!"? Why or why not?

Vocabulary Check

Answer each question below with a complete sentence. Before you answer, think about the meaning of the vocabulary word in bold.

1. What would make someone speak with **urgency**?
2. Whose seats are **adjacent** to yours in class?
3. What would happen if you and your best friend called each other **simultaneously**?
4. What might cause someone to feel **anguish**?
5. What would you do if you saw a cat **precariously** balanced on a window ledge?

Write About It

Choose one of the writing prompts below.

- ▶ Caroline Paul obviously feels bad that she couldn't keep her promise. Write about a time that you weren't able to keep a promise that you made.
- ▶ Write a short news story about the attempted rescue as if you were a reporter on the scene.
- ▶ Describe an imaginary case in the ER. What happens? Who is trying to help? What is the outcome?

Fact FILE

Firefighting is a dangerous and difficult business. That's why not just anyone can be a firefighter. People who want to be firefighters first must pass a very difficult physical test. Here's a sample of what some aspiring firefighters are required to do.

- Drag a 140-pound sandbag while walking backwards.
- Crawl through an attic where there is no floor, only beams two feet apart.
- Open a fire hydrant and attach a valve.
- Raise and lower a 24-foot extension ladder.
- Break into a house using an eight-and-a-half-pound sledgehammer.
- Carry a 16-foot ladder.
- Extend a 200-foot fire hose.

Interpreting Medicine Labels

Sometimes reading medicine labels—and following their instructions—can be a matter of life or death. Here are two typical labels. Look them over. Can you figure them out?

Over-the-Counter and Prescription Medicine Labels

Rx DelRoy Pharmacy Rx
RX# 12345 Dr. Getbetter
12/1/03

Iva Cold
445 Flu Street
Cough, Wisconsin

Claritox 25 MG.
One (1) tablet three times a day.
12 tablets
No refills.

Take only if prescribed by doctor.
Take only as directed.

Take 2 hours after eating

Bactaid
Antiseptic • Anesthetic
first aid spray
For cuts, scratches, sunburn, minor burns, insect bites

Warning: For external use only.

Caution: Harmful if swallowed.
Avoid contact with eyes.
Keep out of reach of children.

If swallowed, administer large quantities of milk.
Call physician immediately.

What problems does this product treat? Be sure you choose the right product for *your* problem.

These instructions tell you how and when to take your medication. They also tell you how much to take.

Medicines can be harmful if taken incorrectly. Warning labels like this one tell you how to stay safe.

"Medicine labels aren't always easy to understand. Check them over before you leave the drugstore. If you see anything confusing, ask the pharmacist."

Taking Your Medicine

Unless you're a doctor, it can take time to understand medicine labels. Reread the labels and the tips that go with them. Then use them to answer the questions below. Write your answers on your own paper.

1. **True or false?** When you spray Bactaid on a cut, you should then drink a lot of milk.

2. Look at the Bactaid bottle. What do you think "external use" means?
   a. Use this product outside.
   b. Spray Bactaid on your skin.
   c. Swallow this product.
   d. Use this product if you have a sore throat.

3. You have a cough, and your friend does, too. Her doctor prescribed some medication that really works. She offered to share it with you. Should you take it? Why or why not? (Hint: Check the tip to the right.)

4. You had a fever. Your doctor prescribed some Claritox. How many times each day should you take the medicine? For how many days should you take it?

5. Which of the following is Bactaid **not** good for?
   a. cuts
   b. sore throats
   c. insect bites
   d. sunburn

Make a Plan

Your doctor wants you to take Claritox. Plan a four-day schedule for taking your medicine. Tell when you will eat and when you will take your medicine.

Look It Up

Look up three of these words in a dictionary and write what they mean: antidote, dosage, external, internal, pharmacist, physician, side effects.

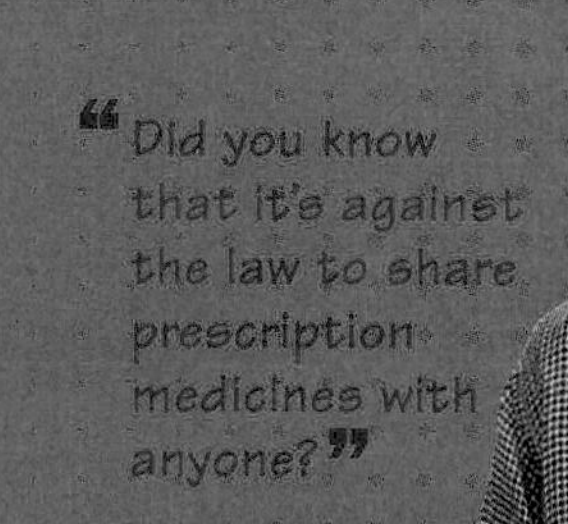

anesthetic: a medicine that helps make pain go away
antiseptic: a medicine that kills germs and prevents infection
prescription: an order for medicine, written by a doctor

The three stories you are about to read feature young people struggling with difficult decisions. As you read, think about what you might do in each of these situations . . . where there are no easy answers.

Only a Dollar's Worth

**Should you always treat people the way they treat you?
For some, that's a tough decision.**

by Herma Werner

It was Mr. Watts again.

Isabel sighed and grabbed the hose. She took the cap from the gas tank and called through the car window, "A whole dollar's worth again, Mr. Watts?" She knew she sounded nasty, but she didn't care.

Mr. Watts got out of his old car. "Watch your smart mouth, little girl," he said. "You ought to know by now what I want. Maybe you ought to get a job a girl can do right."

Isabel knew the whole routine from start to finish, including the insults. Mr. Watts watched like a hawk as she ran a dollar's worth of gas into the tank. He didn't take his eyes off her. He watched to make sure that every drop of gas he paid for got into the tank.

Then the old man opened a beat-up wallet and fished out a dollar bill. He held on to the money as if it were a fortune in diamonds.

"Get that windshield clean," he said. "And the rear glass, too. How come I have to remind you every time? The boy that was here before never forgot."

Isabel looked at Mr. Watts with scorn. Every couple of days, he came around for a dollar's worth of gas. For a dollar, he felt he was entitled to a window cleaning—front, rear, and sides. His dollar's worth included water in the radiator once a week. And water for the battery once a month.

Every two weeks, Isabel gave the old car an oil check. But if the car needed oil, Mr. Watts would order it from an auto-supply store. Then

he'd have his grandson add it for him. Cheap! Isabel thought to herself. She wished the old man could read her mind.

She finished polishing the glass. "OK, Mr. Watts? That the way you want it?" she asked.

Mr. Watts shrugged and gave Isabel the money. "Do I have a choice?" he muttered. He climbed back in his car and drove off at about ten miles per hour.

Isabel turned and saw that her boss, Mr. Kirkland, had been watching. She handed him the dollar bill.

"Mr. Watts just paid off your mortgage," Isabel said sarcastically. Mr. Kirkland laughed, but Isabel just looked disgusted. "Why do you put up with him, Mr. Kirkland?" she asked.

"Oh, he's been doing that for years," Mr. Kirkland said. "He's old. He has nothing else to do all day. Let him have his fun."

"I wish he'd have his fun with somebody else," Isabel said. She had been working at Kirkland's Gas Station for a few months. She liked the job, but she had come to dread the sight of Mr. Watts. "I know he's not broke," she went on. "I heard he has a lot of money."

"Not true," said Mr. Kirkland. "Mr. Watts has a small pension. If he didn't live with his daughters, I don't know what he'd do." He turned to go back to

Isabel felt her face grow hot. Why was he always so quick to blame her and put her down? He must know he gave her a dollar. So why lie about it?

the office. “Don’t let it get to you, Isabel,” he added. “It’s just one of those things. There’s nothing we can do.”

“No?” Isabel thought to herself. “Just once I’d like to tell that old cheapskate what I think of him. I bet we wouldn’t see him again after that.”

She went back to the pumps. And there, right where the old man had stood, Isabel saw it. It was green and beautiful. It was a $20 bill. She scooped it up and stared at it for a while to make sure it was real. She figured that it had to belong to Mr. Watts.

She looked down the street. Mr. Watts would be coming back for it any minute. Quickly, she stuffed the bill into the pocket of her jeans.

Half an hour passed. Mr. Watts did not return. After an hour, Isabel felt that the $20 was really hers. She began to make all kinds of plans for it. She could see herself adding it to the money she’d saved for a car. After an hour and a half, she had switched to buying a new jacket. After two hours, she watched herself listening to the new tapes she wanted. Just then, Mr. Watts came driving into the station.

Isabel slipped a hand into her pocket and touched the bill. There was no way Mr. Watts could know she had it. After all, he could have lost it anyplace. She thought of all his insults—about girls working at gas stations, about how dumb she was. Maybe he deserved to pay for the way he treated her.

The old car sputtered to a halt in front of the gas pumps. Isabel stood with the hose in her hand. For the first time she really noticed the torn **upholstery** inside the car. She got a look at the old empty crate that always sat on the backseat.

Mr. Watts got out of the car. He seemed even slower than usual, and he stared down at the ground for what seemed a long time. Then he looked hard at Isabel.

“Listen here, Missy. That wasn’t a dollar bill I gave you before. It was a 20.”

Isabel felt her face grow hot. Why was he always so quick to blame her and put her down? He must know he gave her a dollar. So why lie about it? All of Isabel’s doubts dissolved. Now she knew she had a right to the $20, but she was afraid he might make her empty her pockets.

“You give me the same thing every time you’re here, Mr. Watts,” she said. She met his eyes and stared him down. She was telling the truth, and he knew it.

“Today was different,” said Mr. Watts. “You forgot to give me change, Miss Know-It-All. I want my money.”

"You gave me a dollar bill," Isabel insisted. "That's the truth."

Mr. Kirkland came over to them, wiping his hands on a rag. "What's the trouble?" he asked.

"When I was here before I gave this . . . this girl of yours a $20 bill. She didn't give me my change," Mr. Watts said.

"No," Mr. Kirkland said. "Isabel handed me the money right after you left. It was a dollar bill. You're wrong, Mr. Watts. I hope you're not calling *me* a liar."

Mr. Watts stared at Mr. Kirkland. Then he shook his head sadly and seemed to fold up into a tiny gray package right before Isabel's eyes. She tried to blink the image away, but it stayed.

She had never thought of Mr. Watts as anything but mean and cheap and nasty. But suddenly, she understood him better. She was young and strong and able to do what he **considered** a man's work. He was old and poor. He didn't like buying a dollar's worth of gas at a time. He had to be **frugal.** But he still had pride, so he covered up what he had to do with a lot of noise.

Isabel went over to the old car. She opened the door and looked into the back where the crate was.

"Hey, you, get out of there!" Mr. Watts called. It was the old nasty voice, but Isabel heard something else under the sharp words. Fear.

She stood up and turned. The $20 bill was in her hand. "Is this what you're looking for?" she said. She walked over to the two men.

Mr. Watts grabbed the bill and waved it under Mr. Kirkland's nose. His voice was loud and mean again.

"See?" Mr. Watts said. "I don't go around saying things that aren't true."

Mr. Watts grabbed the bill. . . . Without even a thank you, he climbed into his car and drove away.

Without even a thank you, he climbed into his car and drove away. Mr. Kirkland gave Isabel a long, thoughtful look.

Isabel felt her face growing hot again, but she returned the look. After all, her only crime had been to dream a little.

"Think he'll be back?" she asked after a while.

"He'll be back," Mr. Kirkland said.

"For a dollar's worth?"

"I'm afraid so," laughed Mr. Kirkland.

And this time, Isabel laughed too.

ASK YOURSELF

- Why does Mr. Watts lie about the $20 bill?

Recall what you know about Mr. Watts and about people in general.

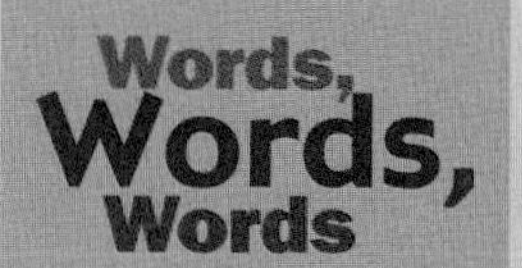

upholstery: the stuffing, springs, and covering put on furniture
considered: believed that something is true
frugal: careful not to waste money

Just a Pigeon

Not everyone thought Terrence's decision was the right one. See what you think.

by Dennis Brindell Fradin

It was rough—going to high school, pumping gas after school and Saturdays, and studying late into the night. He often had to tell himself, "You've got to keep at it to go to college."

But now, a Friday, Terrence McCray felt good. He was walking home after work with a paycheck in his pocket.

He was thinking about his date the next night with Deborah, when he saw the injured pigeon. It was in the gutter. Several people were hurrying by.

It's just a pigeon with a busted wing, he told himself. Some people walk by *people* in trouble. So why should I do anything for a pigeon? But it looked so helpless and scared.

He didn't want to pick it up, because he knew that pigeons sometimes carry diseases. So he went inside a grocery store and got a paper bag. When he came back outside, he hoped the pigeon would be gone. But it was still there.

"Come on, pigeon," he said, bending over with the bag. He felt like a fool, because some people had stopped to stare. But he picked up a twig and gently pushed the bird into the bag and carried it to his house.

Terrence's mother hadn't gotten angry when she saw the bird. She hardly ever got angry at him. She just said, "You're good-hearted, Terrence. But you can't take the **burden** of the world on your shoulders. You can try to help that bird. But get it out of my kitchen."

After dinner, his mother got ready for work. Terrence rushed out and bought some birdseed.

When he got back, his mother was in her nurse's uniform. She said, "You brought the bird here. So you decide what to do with it."

Terrence fed the pigeon. Then he put the bird in the shoebox out on the porch.

Later, he could hear the bird **cooing** sadly. "Maybe I should have left it in the street," he said to himself. "It will probably die, anyway."

On Monday, between classes, Terrence went to a pay phone. He looked up **"Veterinarians"** in the phone book, and dialed a number.

"Pigeon?" the doctor said. "Broken wing? I could try to fix it."

"How much will it cost?" Terrence asked.

"I couldn't tell. It could be expensive. If I can fix the wing, the bird will have to stay here a while. But you would have to pay me all at once."

After history class, Willie Barnes asked

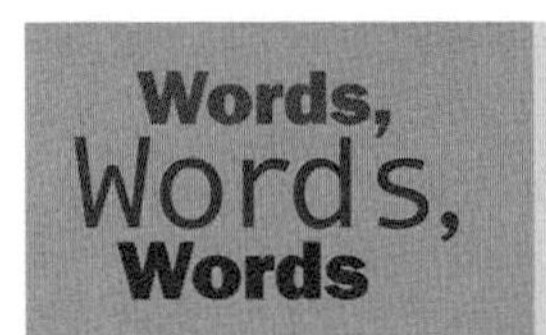

burden: a heavy load
cooing: the sound a pigeon makes
veterinarians: doctors who take care of sick animals
remarks: comments about something

Terrence to shoot baskets in the gym.

"I can't, Willie," he said. "See, I found this pigeon with a busted wing. I've got to take it to the vet before work."

"What?" Willie said. "Spending money on a pigeon?"

Thad Lanier had stopped to listen. He stared at Terrence and said, "So many people need help. And you spend money on a pigeon?"

"I saw it in a gutter," Terrence tried to explain. "I couldn't help it."

But Thad had turned and walked off with Willie, shaking his head.

Terrence took the pigeon to the vet. Dr. Landis said, "I've got to admit, this is my first pigeon. But I think I can fix its wing. Give me a call tomorrow."

The next day, Terrence called Dr. Landis. He learned that the bird's wing had been set, and it was doing well.

Terrence was glad about the bird. But he was worried about the money. Besides that, Thad kept making **remarks.** One afternoon, just before history class started, Thad went too far.

"Talk about your future black leaders!" Thad said. "How about Terrence here? He's spending his money on a pigeon."

"A what?" Deborah asked. "Is that why we couldn't go to the movies, Terrence?"

"Yeah," Thad said. "He found a sick pigeon, and he's paying for it to get well. Meanwhile, poor people don't have enough to eat." Excited by his own voice, Thad added, "Hey, who's the pigeon?"

Terrence got out of his seat and rushed at Thad. Just then, the teacher walked in. Terrence didn't care. He raised his fist. But as he saw Thad's frightened face, he felt sorry for him. He also knew why he had saved the pigeon.

"It was in trouble," he said. "It was alive, like us. If you walk past an animal, next thing you might walk past a person."

"What's all this?" the teacher asked.

"Nothing," Terrence said.

When Terrence went back to the vet he had plenty of money with him. But he kept hoping that somehow Dr. Landis would say, "Since you're so kind, you don't have to pay."

Dr. Landis took him back to where the animals were kept in cages. There was the pigeon, looking as healthy as any pigeon.

Dr. Landis took it out of the cage. Then they went out through the back door, and Dr. Landis set the pigeon down gently on the ground.

Terrence half expected the pigeon to thank them somehow. But it just fluttered its wings and flew up to a window ledge.

Terrence reached for his wallet.

"That will be twenty dollars," Dr. Landis said.

Terrence counted out the money. Then he looked for the pigeon. But it had flown out of sight.

ASK YOURSELF

- Why should anyone help a pigeon?

Think about Terrence's reason plus any reasons of your own.

A MATTER OF HONOR

Tina wants to do the right thing.
But will she lose a friend in the process?

BY BARBARA SEIGER

I was shocked. Well, maybe surprised is a better word. Yes, I was definitely surprised.

After class, Rachel looked at me and laughed. "Tina, you look funny with your mouth open like that," she said.

Embarassed, I closed my mouth.

"It's simple," Rachel said. "I didn't have time to study. And I had to pass that exam. OK?"

I looked at my feet, then I looked at the wall. I looked down the hall that was full of kids on their way to class. Finally, I looked at Rachel. "It's not OK." The bell rang for the next class.

It was Rachel's turn to be surprised. "You're not going to give me a bad time, are you? You're my best friend!" I didn't say anything as Rachel looked at me again—hard. Then she turned and ran down the hall.

That afternoon was the first time all year we didn't leave school together. No one was home, and I was desperate to talk to someone. So I called Amy. Amy's three years older than I am and totally boy crazy, but she's intelligent and I like her.

"What's the problem?" Amy asked.

"We had a big exam today and Rachel cheated. She had a book on her lap the whole time."

"You have to be **realistic,** Tina," Amy said. "Everyone cheats once in a while."

"You don't understand," I said. "Miss Lopez just **initiated** an **honor** system. She doesn't stay in the room when we take a test."

"Miss Lopez isn't realistic either," Amy said.

"The point is, we're all on our honor. That means we're supposed to report anyone who cheats."

"The point is, Rachel's your best friend, and you never report your best friend."

"No matter what?"

"It's not like she stole a car or something," said Amy.

"Wait a minute," I said. "Are you telling me it's not OK to steal a car but it's OK to steal answers?"

"I have to get off the phone," Amy said. "I'm expecting a call."

I hung up the phone thinking Amy hadn't been much help. But then I had to ask myself a question: What advice did I *want* to hear?

Mom was working late, so I made spaghetti and meatballs for me and my brother. My brother Shawn is a royal pain, and I never listen to anything he has to say. But I felt anxious and needed to talk, so I told him what had happened.

"Did anyone in your class ever report someone for cheating before?" he asked. Actually, that was a

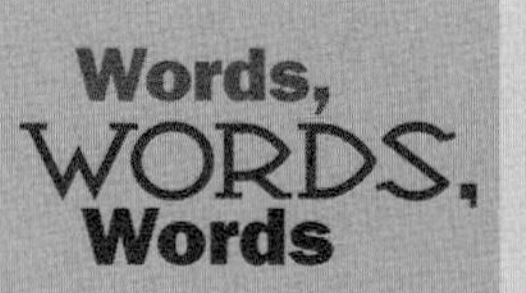

realistic: concerned with the way things really are
initiated: started
honor: honesty and fairness
opportunity: a chance to do something

pretty good question, because I had been thinking all along I didn't want to be the first.

"No," I answered.

"It's bad to be the first one," Shawn said.

"I know," I agreed. "But the whole point of the honor system is not to cheat. I mean, what's the point of having an honor system if someone cheats?"

"Cheating is wrong," Shawn said. "On the other hand, no one likes a rat. If you report Rachel, everyone in the class is going to hate you."

"No one will think I did the right thing?"

"They might think it, but don't expect them to say it."

"What would you do?" I asked.

"I don't know. Luckily, I don't have to decide because I don't have Miss Lopez," Shawn said with a grin.

"Just wait," I said. "You will and, when you do, I won't help you!"

The next morning, I saw Miss Lopez in the hall. I realized this was the perfect **opportunity** to tell her about Rachel cheating on the exam but I still hadn't made up my mind what to do.

My anxiety must have shown on my face, because Miss Lopez suddenly asked, "Tina, is everything OK? You look like something's bothering you."

My heart was pounding. "Oh . . . Really? Well, I . . ." ●

ASK YOURSELF

- What do you think Tina will do?

Think about what you might do in Tina's place.

Talk About It

Now that you've read "Only a Dollar's Worth," "A Matter of Honor," and "Just a Pigeon," what do you have to say about these questions?

- ▶ Is it ever okay to tell a lie? Why or why not?
- ▶ What are some things that are more important than money? Explain.

Comprehension Check

Write your answers to the questions below. Use information from the three stories to support your answers.

1. Where did Isabel really find the $20 bill that belonged to Mr. Watts?
2. When Rachel admitted to cheating on the test, what was she counting on Tina to do?
3. Why might a person who stops to help a pigeon be more likely to stop and help another human being?
4. Who do you think faced the most difficult decision—Isabel, Tina, or Terrence? Why?
5. What makes some decisions difficult?

Vocabulary Check

Complete each sentence with the correct vocabulary word below.

frugal **considered** **realistic**
opportunity **remarks**

1. Our class had the _______ to volunteer for a good cause.
2. We wanted to be _______ so we shopped at a discount store.
3. A bake sale was something we _______ to raise money for the school.
4. Our idea for the science project had to be _______.
5. Our teacher's _______ weren't leading us to a decision.

Write About It

Choose one of the writing prompts below.

- If you were Isabel, would you have kept the money? Write a paragraph explaining what you would have done with the $20 bill you found. Give your reasons.
- If you were Tina, would you have protected Rachel's secret? Write a letter from Tina to Rachel. In the letter, explain what Tina did and why she did it.
- If you were Terrence, would you have spent your own money to help that pigeon? Make a list of three reasons that explain your choice.

Take ACTION

All three of the stories you have read are about teens who care enough to do the right thing. Volunteering is a great way to show you care. Here are some ideas:

- **At senior citizen centers, volunteers might help with arts and crafts, entertainment, or just plain visiting. Call a senior citizen center in your neighborhood for more information. Bonus for you: Talking to a senior can make history come alive.**
- **Many animal shelters depend on volunteers to help take care of animals, give them lots of affection, and keep their cages clean. Check to see which organizations have locations near you. Bonus for you: You might make some new furry or feathered friends.**
- **Schools are always looking for teens to help out with younger students. You can volunteer as a tutor, a sports instructor, or just be a "big brother or sister." Bonus for you: It will feel good to be a role model.**

Completing a Job Application

Do you want to get a part-time job? First you have to know how to fill out a job application. That's an important way to show employers that you're the right person for the job.

Here is a standard job application. Do you know what you would write on each line?

Standard Job Application

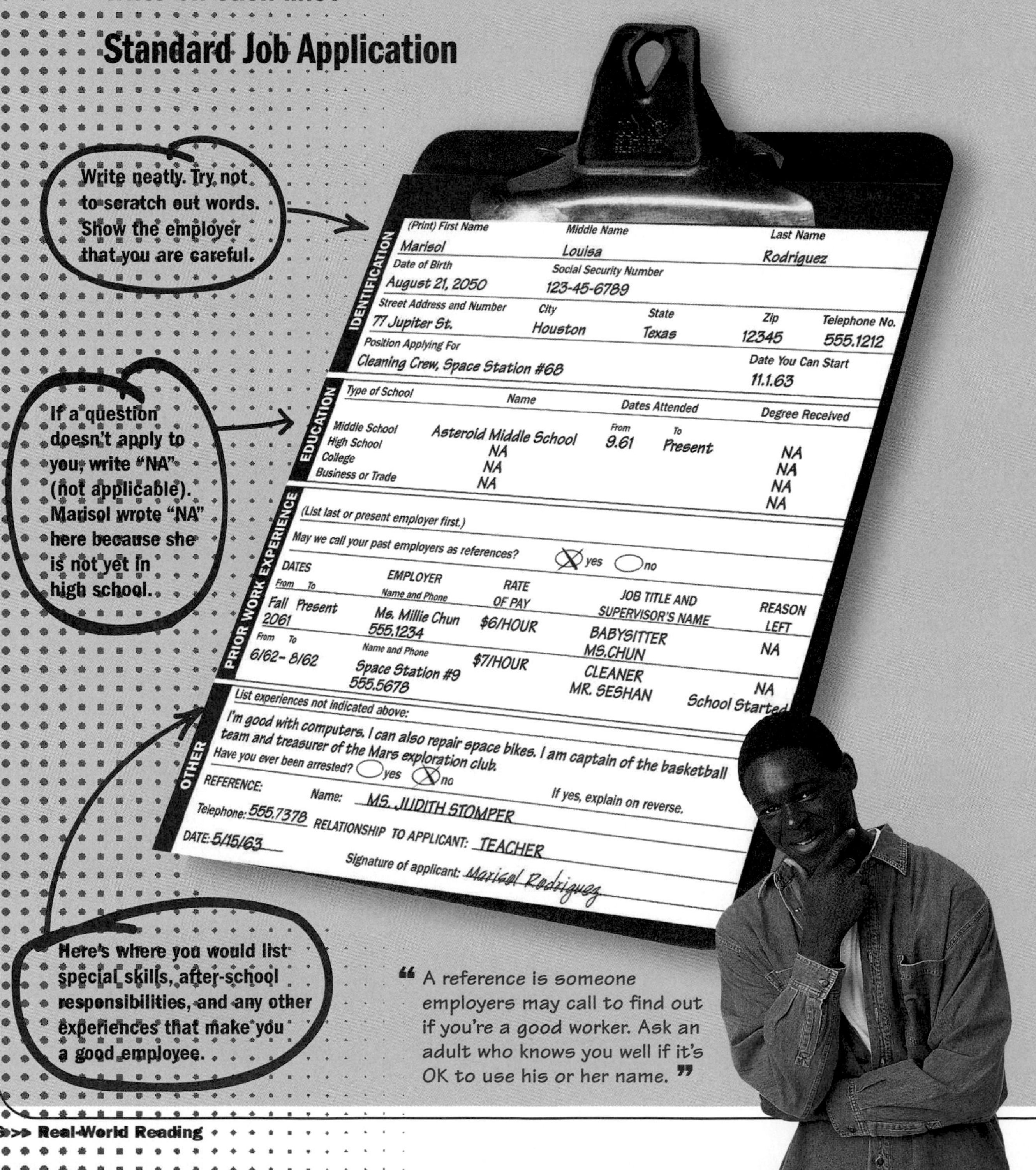

IDENTIFICATION

(Print) First Name: Marisol | Middle Name: Louisa | Last Name: Rodriguez

Date of Birth: August 21, 2050 | Social Security Number: 123-45-6789

Street Address and Number: 77 Jupiter St. | City: Houston | State: Texas | Zip: 12345 | Telephone No.: 555.1212

Position Applying For: Cleaning Crew, Space Station #68 | Date You Can Start: 11.1.63

EDUCATION

Type of School	Name	Dates Attended From	To	Degree Received
Middle School	Asteroid Middle School	9.61	Present	NA
High School	NA			NA
College	NA			NA
Business or Trade	NA			NA

PRIOR WORK EXPERIENCE

(List last or present employer first.)

May we call your past employers as references? ☒ yes ○ no

DATES From	To	EMPLOYER Name and Phone	RATE OF PAY	JOB TITLE AND SUPERVISOR'S NAME	REASON LEFT
Fall 2061	Present	Ms. Millie Chun 555.1234	$6/HOUR	BABYSITTER MS.CHUN	NA
6/62	8/62	Space Station #9 555.5678	$7/HOUR	CLEANER MR. SESHAN	NA School Started

OTHER

List experiences not indicated above:
I'm good with computers. I can also repair space bikes. I am captain of the basketball team and treasurer of the Mars exploration club.

Have you ever been arrested? ○ yes ☒ no — If yes, explain on reverse.

REFERENCE: Name: MS. JUDITH STOMPER

Telephone: 555.7378 RELATIONSHIP TO APPLICANT: TEACHER

DATE: 5/15/63 Signature of applicant: Marisol Rodriguez

Write neatly. Try not to scratch out words. Show the employer that you are careful.

If a question doesn't apply to you, write "NA" (not applicable). Marisol wrote "NA" here because she is not yet in high school.

Here's where you would list special skills, after-school responsibilities, and any other experiences that make you a good employee.

"A reference is someone employers may call to find out if you're a good worker. Ask an adult who knows you well if it's OK to use his or her name."

Apply Yourself

Are you ready to start your job hunt? Filling out an application correctly is the first step to landing a job. Reread the application on the left and review the tips that go with it. Then read the questions below and use the application to help you answer them. Write your answers on your own paper.

1. "NA" stands for "not applicable." What does that mean? Choose one of the following answers.
   a. never mind
   b. not again
   c. does not apply to me
   d. none of your business

2. Write down the name and address of your school.

3. Write down the name of someone you could use as a reference. What should you do before listing that person on a job application?

4. Do you volunteer, play a sport, or belong to a club? List two experiences that you could include in the "Other" section of a job application.

5. List three things that are important to do when you fill out a job application.

Top Jobs

List three summer jobs that you would love to have. Compare your list with the lists of other students in your class.

Write About It

You are a manager at the local swimming pool. Write three questions that you would ask someone applying to be a lifeguard at your pool.

applicant: a person who is looking for a job
employers: people or companies that pay you to work for them

play

CONFESSIONS OF A GYM-CLASS DROPOUT

BY
CHUCK RANBERG AND PATRICK DALEY

CHARACTERS

Travis Underwood* - a kid

Narrator* - an older Travis

Mr. Underwood* - Travis's father

Ralph - Travis's friend

Rocco - a big bodybuilder

Coach Willis - the gym coach

Al B.* - a trainer at the YMCA

Sheryl - Travis's girlfriend

Felicia - Rocco's girlfriend

Travis's gym class

*starred parts are major roles

SCENE ONE

Narrator: I always liked gym class, except for two things: the semi-annual physical fitness tests and the guys who never washed their gym clothes.

Coach Willis: Hello, wimps! Today we're testing to see how many pull-ups you can do.

Narrator: Make that three things. Our gym coach, Coach Willis, always called everyone a wimp. He probably thought it gave him a tough-guy image.

Coach Willis: Hurry up, Underwood! You're next.

Travis: Okay, Coach. Here I go.

Narrator: I jumped and grasped the pull-up bar, imagining I was in the Olympics, going for the gold. I could almost hear the crowd roar.

Travis: Ugh! Ah!

Narrator: Two and a half. Yep, that was it. My face was red. I was gasping for air.

Coach Willis: That's pitiful, Underwood. Next time take those rocks out of your pockets. Ha ha.

Travis: Yeah. Okay, Coach.

Narrator: Coach Willis thought he had a sense of humor, but he was mistaken.

Rocco: Step aside, Underwood. Let a man go next!

Narrator: That was Ed Rocovitch, whom everybody called Rocco. Rocco was built like a tank in tennis shoes. This guy was a serious bodybuilder. He was also a serious jerk.

Rocco: With those pipe-cleaner arms, I'm amazed you can even lift a fork to your face!

Narrator: The rest of the class laughed. Coach Willis beamed. He thought Rocco was really funny.

Coach Willis: Come on, Rocco. Show these wimps how it's done.

Narrator: Rocco walked over to the pull-up bar. I was hoping the bar would break.

Coach Willis: Come on, big guy!

Narrator: Coach Willis always called his favorite students "big guy." I, of course, was one of the ones he called "wimp."

Coach Willis: That's it, big guy!

Narrator: Rocco continued as if he were weightless. Eighteen, 19, 20 . . . Hadn't we been humiliated enough? Twenty-three, 24, 25. Finally, he stopped. He wasn't even breathing hard.

Rocco *(looking at Travis):* Top that, ladies!

Narrator: Of course no one could. Rocco went to Ultrabodies, the best gym in town. He always wore his Ultrabodies T-shirt in gym class, just in case we forgot. You could really hate a guy like that. I know I did.

SCENE TWO

Narrator: That night, at home, I took my shirt off and stood in front of a mirror. Rocco's words still stung. My arms were thin, even when I made a muscle. I had to do something. My honor was at stake.

Mr. Underwood: What are you doing, Travis? Practicing to be Arnold Schwarzenegger?

Narrator: Geez! Why do parents always embarrass you at your weakest moments? I tried to change the subject.

Travis: Uh, Dad, could you give me a lift to Java Joe's tonight?

Mr. Underwood: Is your homework done?

Travis: Of course it is, Dad.

Mr. Underwood: Sorry, Travis, I'm low on gas.

Narrator: Dad liked to toy with my **emotions.**

Travis: We could stop by a gas station on the way. I'll pump. Please? Sheryl and I are supposed to meet Ralph.

Narrator: Sheryl was my girlfriend. Ralph was a friend of ours. He worked behind the counter at Java Joe's, which was a popular hangout. Even Rocco and his pals went there.

Mr. Underwood: Okay, Travis. But make sure you call at a **reasonable** hour for a ride home.

Travis: Sure thing, Dad. Thanks.

Narrator: Sometimes Dad could be nice. You just never knew when.

SCENE THREE

Narrator: Later, I met Sheryl and Ralph at Java Joe's.

Travis: Sheryl, what are you doing this summer?

Sheryl: You know, I was thinking about starting a car wash. Why?

Ralph: Hey, guys. Another milkshake, another piece of pie?

Travis: Sure, Ralph. Hey, what makes the pie here so good?

Ralph: It's Joe's secret recipe. He sneezes in the filling.

Sheryl: Ralph, that's gross!

Ralph: Reality hurts, guys.

Sheryl *(to Ralph):* We're talking about the summer. What are your plans?

Ralph: I plan to keep working here, followed by a long life of more of the same. How about you, Travis?

Travis: I'm thinking of joining Ultrabodies.

Ralph: Ultrabodies?!

Travis: Well, I didn't do so well on the last gym test, and I think I need to get in shape.

Sheryl: You're not in bad shape, Travis.

Ralph: No, not for a guy who thinks life is a spectator sport. In fact, Travis is the Schwarzenegger of couch potatoes.

Sheryl: I think Travis is just fine the way he is.

Travis *(to Sheryl):* That's why you're such a wonderful person, and *(to Ralph)* you're not.

Ralph: Hey, reality—

Travis: I know, reality hurts.

Narrator: At that moment Rocco walked through the door. He was with his girlfriend, Felicia, the most beautiful girl on the planet. The fact that she preferred a guy like Rocco to me only proved how shallow she was. I kept reminding myself of that, and sometimes I even believed it.

Ralph *(rudely):* Oh look. It's the sweetest couple on earth.

Narrator: They sat in a corner booth. I sneaked a few glances at them. Rocco ordered his usual protein shake and fresh fruit platter. How could he eat that stuff? Rocco looked up suddenly, and I pretended to be inspecting the overhead lights. They were dirty. I saw Rocco whisper something to Felicia, and she laughed.

Ralph: More pie, Travis?

Travis: No thanks. Just the check.

ASK YOURSELF

- What's Travis's problem and how does he plan to solve it?

Think about Travis's plan for the summer.

SCENE FOUR

Narrator: School was ending, and it was time to discuss my training program with Dad. I knew that since money was involved, I had to be smart.

Travis: Dad, I've decided that I need to get in shape this summer.

Mr. Underwood: Oh, really? Good for you.

Travis: I want to **improve** my gym scores and my muscles.

Narrator: Dad was always a sucker for words like "improve."

Mr. Underwood: That sounds great. I know just what you can do.

Travis: You do?

Mr. Underwood: There's a lot of yard work that needs to be done around here. . . .

Travis: Uh, Dad? I was thinking more about joining a gym.

Mr. Underwood: A gym?

Travis: Yeah. So I could get a real, professional workout. There's this gym called Ultrabodies, and it's the best in town. They have summer memberships for the low, low price of three hundred dollars.

Mr. Underwood: Three hundred dollars?!

Narrator: I guess I should have been a bit more **subtle.**

Mr. Underwood: Out of the question, Travis. When I was your age, blah, blah, blah, blah . . .

Narrator: Whenever Dad started a sentence with, "When I was your age," I found it hard to listen.

Travis: I understand, Dad.

Narrator: Oh well. No gym. There went my dreams of shutting up Coach Willis. There went my fantasies of saying, "in your face" to Rocco.

Mr. Underwood: But if you'll help with the yard work I'll give you the money to join the gym at the YMCA.

Travis: You will? Thanks, Dad! I knew I could count on you!

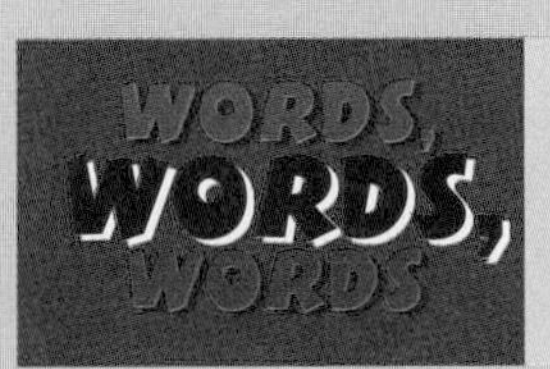

emotions: strong feelings of any kind
reasonable: fair
improve: to make better
subtle: fine or delicate in meaning

SCENE FIVE

Narrator: The YMCA had been around for years, but their equipment seemed pretty decent. Of course, I'd never actually used a workout machine. They sort of made me nervous. They looked like modern torture devices, not like bodybuilding equipment. It turned out they were both. On my first day, a guy on staff showed me how to use everything.

Al B.: Hi. I'm Al B. Is this your first time in a gym?

Travis: Does it show?

Al B.: Don't worry about it.

Narrator: Each machine **concentrated** on one muscle group: biceps, triceps, quadriceps, abdominals—we worked them all.

Al B.: Hey, don't strain so much, man! It's only your first day!

Travis: Don't they say, "No pain, no gain"?

Al B.: Yeah, they also say, "No gain if you injure yourself"! Listen to your body. Pay attention to what it tells you.

Travis: Okay. How often should I work out?

Al B.: That depends. What's your goal?

Narrator: The total destruction of Rocco.

Travis: Basic all-around fitness.

Al B.: Then you should work out at least three times a week. How's your diet?

Narrator: I told him that at that very moment I was craving a bacon cheeseburger and fries from Java Joe's. Al B. shook his head.

Al B.: Very bad, man. Very bad. Knock off foods with high fat or sugar. Think carbos—carbohydrates, like pasta. And think fresh fruit and vegetables.

Travis: No way!

Al B.: Hey, I don't make the rules. You want results or not?

Narrator: I wanted results. So I shut up. All of a sudden I had a little respect for how hard Rocco worked on his body. But of course, he had to work on his body since he didn't have a brain!

SCENE SIX

Narrator: The next morning, I really felt that workout.

Mr. Underwood: Hey, Travis, time to get up! You promised to help me today.

Travis: I'd be glad to, Dad. It's just that I can't seem to move.

Narrator: Every muscle in my body ached from working out. Does Arnold Schwarzenegger have days like this?

Mr. Underwood: Come on. I want to show you something.

Travis: Okay, ouch, Dad. I'll just put on my, ouch, T-shirt and, ouch, jeans. Or maybe I'll just put on a—ouch!—body cast.

Narrator: I looked in the mirror to check my progress. I looked exactly the same. Sigh. I limped out of my room.

Mr. Underwood: I thought that, well, maybe you could use this pull-up bar.

Narrator: He pointed to a shiny bar in the doorway.

Travis: A pull-up bar?

Mr. Underwood: Yes. Didn't you say you wanted to set a record or something?

Narrator: I didn't always think Dad listened to me, but I guess he heard the important things.

SCENE SEVEN

Narrator: The first few weeks were painful, but I kept up. Pretty soon my muscles didn't hurt quite as much. And I could already do six whole pull-ups! I complained to Al B. back at the gym.

Al B.: Hey, don't be **discouraged**, man. You've made great progress. This means it's time to move to the next level.

ASK YOURSELF

- Will Travis's hard work ever pay off?

Make your best prediction based on what you've read.

Travis: Yeah, thanks.

Ralph: As you wish, one fresh fruit plate.

Narrator: Actually, I was starting to like the fresh fruit plate.

Ralph: Don't look now, but here comes what's-her-name.

Narrator: Sure enough, Felicia had come in alone. She headed for the counter. I pretended not to notice her.

Felicia: Hi, Travis.

Narrator: I nearly choked on a grape.

Travis: Uh, hi, Felicia. What're you doing?

Felicia: Just getting something to go.

Travis: Felicia, this is my girlfriend, Sheryl.

Felicia: Hi, Sheryl.

Sheryl: Hi, Leslie.

Felicia: Uh, that's Felicia.

Sheryl: Oh, sorry.

Felicia: Well, I have to go now. Nice seeing you, Travis. Hey, what are you up to? You're looking pretty good these days.

Travis: You too, Felicia.

Narrator: I was not a fool, so I quickly turned to Sheryl.

SCENE EIGHT

Narrator: So I started doing laps in the pool at the YMCA. First I swam for ten minutes. Then I worked up to 30 minutes. At sunset I'd go for long bike rides. Sometimes Sheryl would join me if she wasn't too tired from working at her car wash which was making a lot of money. We'd always end up at Java Joe's.

Ralph: What'll you crazy kids have tonight? I recommend the pecan pie—only two sneezes.

Sheryl: Gross. I'll have a burger, hold the sneezes, Ralph.

Ralph: And the usual for you, Mr. Schwarzenegger?

concentrated: directed toward one point; focused
discouraged: caused to give up hope or confidence

Travis: But not as good as you, Sheryl.

Sheryl: Hmph! Nice save.

Narrator: Did Felicia really think I was "looking good"? Was Miss Popularity paying attention to me now merely because I'd been going to the gym? I guess she was shallow. Excellent!

SCENE NINE

Narrator: September again. But this time I was ready. This time I knew that I was in shape. This time I knew that I'd be respected!

Coach Willis: Welcome back, wimps!

Narrator: Maybe respect was a little too much to hope for.

Coach Willis: Let's see how all you wimps perform after sitting around all summer!

Narrator: The moment of truth. Thanks to Al B.'s coaching and my home pull-up bar, I had worked myself up to 22 pull-ups. With a little extra effort I thought I could equal Rocco's number. With a little luck, maybe I could do one or two more. It would be one small victory for the wimps of the world!

Coach Willis: You're next, Underwood. And remember, half a pull-up doesn't count!

Travis: Right. Don't worry, Coach.

Narrator: My mouth was dry. All the moisture had gone to my hands. This was it!

Coach Willis *(counting):* That's one, that's two, that's three . . .

Narrator: At least he could count. The first ten came easily.

Coach Willis: Ten, 11! Good, Underwood!

Narrator: What was this? Actual encouragement?

Coach Willis: Fourteen, 15!

Narrator: Now each one was getting harder. This was what would separate the men from the . . . well, wimps.

Travis: Uhh!

Coach Willis: Nineteen!

Narrator: My heart was pounding. My biceps were aching. Twenty! Twenty-one! I tried not to grunt too loudly.

Travis *(loudly):* Augh!

Coach Willis: Twenty-two! Go for it!

Narrator: How did my body get so heavy? My arms felt like they were made of spaghetti. I didn't know if I could do another one. Suddenly, the whole class started to count along!

The Class: Twenty-three!

Travis: UHH!

The Class: Twenty-four!

Travis: AAAAAAAAH!

The Class: Twenty-five!

Narrator: I did it! I dropped to the ground, hoping I wouldn't fall over. I tried to act as though it was no big deal.

Coach Willis: You've been working out, haven't you, Underwood?

Narrator: I tried not to gasp for breath.

Travis *(gasping):* Well . . . yeah . . . a little . . .

Coach Willis: Good going, big guy.

Narrator: Big guy?! This was a moment to enjoy!

Coach Willis: You're next, Rocco. Underwood is the one to beat.

Rocco: Watch me.

Narrator: Then Rocco wiped the floor with me, as they say. I guess he'd been working hard this summer, too. His final count was 36.

Rocco *(looking at Travis):* Top that, ladies!

Narrator: It didn't even make me feel better that he was sweating and gasping for air. I'd failed.

SCENE TEN

Narrator: Back at the gym I told Al B. what happened.

Al B.: Twenty-five pull-ups?? Man! That is awesome! That is outstanding!

Travis: What's the difference? I still didn't beat that jerk Rocco.

Al B.: So? Look at yourself, man. Since you started coming here you went from a guy who couldn't chin himself on a towel rack to a guy who can do 25 with no problem. Give yourself some credit!

Travis: I guess that is pretty good.

Al B.: No lie! And as long as you're giving out credit, it doesn't hurt to have a first-class trainer.

Travis: You said it. Thanks, Al B.

Al B.: Hey, no problem.

Travis: Can I ask you something?

Al B.: Shoot.

Travis: What's the "B" stand for?

Al B.: Promise you won't tell anyone?

Travis: I swear.

Al B.: Bookbinder.

Travis: That's your last name? So what's wrong with that?

Al B.: Nothing, if you're a librarian. But would you take orders from a fitness trainer named Bookbinder?

Narrator: I had to agree with him. He was right about Rocco, too. It didn't matter that he could beat me with one bicep. I'd made myself stronger and healthier that summer, and now when I looked in the mirror I approved of what I saw. Still, when it comes to beating Rocco, a guy could always dream. ●

ASK YOURSELF

- Did Travis solve his problem? Think about the conversation between Travis and Al B.

HEART-THUMPING WORKOUTS

Thirty minutes of aerobic exercise a day can help you feel great and live longer. Here's how.

By Bob Hugel

You're walking up the stairs at school on the way to class. By the time you reach the top of the second flight you're so out of breath you can barely talk.

What's going on? The last time you checked, you were young and healthy. How come you're gasping for air?

Chances are, you're out of shape. The U.S. Department of Health and Human Services reports that almost half of Americans between the ages of 12 and 21 do not perform vigorous activity on a regular basis. In fact, only 19 percent of U.S. high school students are physically active for more than 20 minutes a day.

That means many American teens are missing out on the benefits of aerobic exercise. This kind of exercise promotes long-term health, helps control your weight, relieves stress, and makes you sleep better.

The good news is that it's not hard to get an aerobic workout. You don't have to buy fancy equipment or be a jock. "You just have to be active," says one fitness expert. An aerobic exercise is anything that increases your heart rate and the amount of oxygen your muscles burn.

"Brisk walking or yard work are good examples," says the expert. "The activity doesn't have to be extremely rigorous as long as you do something that challenges your heart to work harder and get stronger."

What happens if you don't do any type of aerobic activity? Experts say that you're likely to set the tone of your physical health for life. "If teens are out of shape and overweight when they enter adulthood, studies show that they're going to continue to get heavier as they get older," says another fitness expert.

Lack of physical activity can also contribute to health problems like coronary heart disease, osteoporosis, and diabetes, many of which can show up later in life.

Fortunately, experts say that just 30 minutes of aerobic exercise a day is enough to promote good health. To get started, check out the following activities.

1 PLAY A GAME

A great way to get an aerobic workout is to play a game like basketball, soccer, or Frisbee. Start slowly, maybe once a week, then pick up the pace and play on a more regular basis. If you do a workout that's fun, you're more likely to stick with it.

RIDE A BIKE

Biking does a great job of raising your heart rate and also strengthening your leg muscles. Ride to school every day, or if that's impossible, explore your neighborhood on your bike during weekends. The nice thing about biking is that you can push yourself for a while and then take a break, coast, and enjoy the scenery.

3 TAKE A WALK

Walking is an easy and fun way to get a workout that doesn't put stress on your bones and joints. If you ride the school bus home, get off a stop or two early and walk the rest of the way. Or try taking a brisk, 30-minute walk before dinner. ●

THE HEART RATE CHART

For a good aerobic workout, you must raise your heart rate. But you don't want to overdo it. The following activity will help you estimate the right minimum and maximum training heart rates for your age. You'll want to keep your heart beating between these two rates next time you work out. Use a calculator and write down the answers to the following problems on a separate piece of paper.

1. First, you need to know your resting heart rate. To find it, sit quietly for 10 minutes. Place your index and middle fingers on your neck right underneath the corner bone of your jaw. Count the number of heartbeats you feel in 15 seconds. Multiply that number by 4. This tells you what your resting heart rate is for one minute. Write down, "My resting heart rate = (your number)."

2. Next, find your normal maximum heart rate. Subtract your age from 220 and write down, "My maximum heart rate = (your number)."

3. Now calculate your heart rate reserve. Subtract your resting heart rate from your maximum heart rate and write down, "My heart rate reserve = (your number)."

4. Use the following formula to determine your minimum heart rate: (heart rate reserve x .50) + (resting heart rate). Write down, "My minimum training heart rate = (your number)."

5. To find your maximum heart rate during training, calculate (heart rate reserve x .85) + (resting heart rate). Write down, "My maximum training heart rate = (your number) beats per minute."

Remember, during training keep your heart rate between the answers to numbers 4 and 5!

TALK ABOUT IT

Now that you've read *Confessions of a Gym-Class Dropout* and "Heart-Thumping Workouts," what do you have to say about these questions?

- Do you think teens are too obsessed with exercise and fitness? Or do you think they don't take it seriously enough? Explain.
- What's your favorite way to get exercise? Why?

COMPREHENSION CHECK

Write your answers to the questions below. Use information from the play and the article to support your answers.

1. Why did Travis decide to get in shape?
2. How can you tell that Coach Willis's opinion of Travis changed?
3. What qualities might describe someone who works hard to get in shape?
4. Which activities does the article recommend for getting a good workout?
5. Which activity recommended in the article does Travis do as part of his workout?

VOCABULARY CHECK

Answer each question below with a complete sentence. Before you answer, think about the meaning of the vocabulary word in bold.

1. What do you think is a **reasonable** amount of homework?
2. What could you do to **improve** your grades?
3. If you **concentrated** on getting in shape, what would you do?
4. When was the last time you felt **discouraged**?
5. What kind of **emotions** do you have when you win a contest?

WRITE ABOUT IT

Choose one of the writing prompts below.

- Write a journal entry by Travis the day he does 25 pull-ups. In the entry explain how Travis feels about his accomplishment and about losing to Rocco.
- Write a one day's menu of healthy foods. Include foods for breakfast, lunch, and dinner.
- Write a true story from your life about a time you accomplished a goal that was difficult to achieve.

Fact FILE

Exercise can definitely make you healthier. But if you're not careful, you can put yourself on the injured list. Read these fitness facts to make your workout work for you.

- **Always warm up.**
  Gently stretching your muscles before you start any kind of workout is the best way to prevent an injury. It's especially important to stretch out the big muscle groups in your legs.
- **Drink plenty of water.**
  Some people think that drinking water will give you cramps. Actually, the opposite is true. Being dehydrated (lacking in water) can cause cramps, headaches, and fatigue.
- **Eat healthy foods on a daily basis.**
  Don't bother grabbing an expensive protein bar before your workout. Your body is burning the foods you ate yesterday. To have the right fuel, you need to eat right every day.

Following a City Map

You're visiting a new city for the first time, and you're ready to go sightseeing. There's just one problem. How do you figure out where to go—and how to get there?

Check out this detail of a city map of Washington, D.C. Could you find your way around?

Detail of a Map of Washington, D.C.

These lines show the city's streets. Names of major streets are printed on the map.

City maps also show you where interesting sights are located.

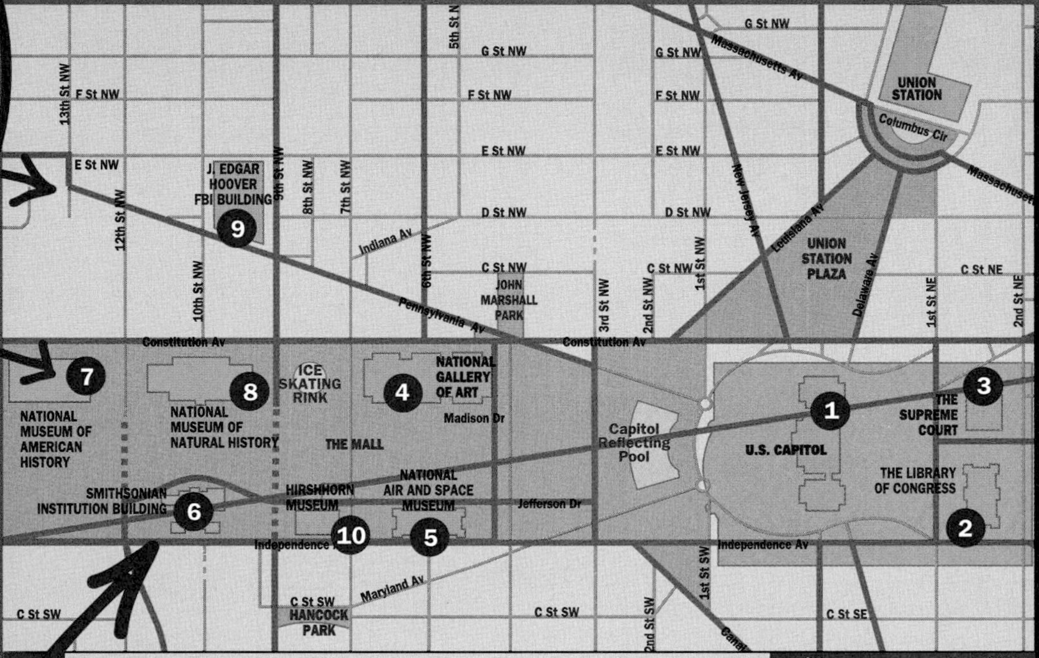

Each of these numbers in red circles stands for a different sight. Look at the key to find the name of the sight.

KEY

Miles 0 1/2

MAJOR POINTS OF INTEREST

1. U.S. Capitol
2. Library of Congress
3. Supreme Court
4. National Gallery of Art
5. National Air and Space Museum
6. Smithsonian Institution
7. National Museum of American History
8. National Museum of Natural History
9. FBI Building
10. Hirshhorn Museum.

"You'll probably do a lot of walking when you're sightseeing. If you want to find out how far it is from one sight to another, you can check the scale of miles. One inch on this map equals one-half mile."

Tour the City

Understanding how to read a city map will keep you from getting lost. Review the map on the left and the tips that go with it. Then use them to answer the questions below. Write your answers on your own paper.

1. What point of interest is located at number 5?
   a. National Museum of American History
   b. National Museum of Natural History
   c. National Gallery of Art
   d. National Air and Space Museum

2. You want to walk from the Smithsonian Institution to the Library of Congress. What street should you take?
   a. Louisiana Avenue
   b. Massachusetts Avenue
   c. Independence Avenue
   d. 10 St. NW

3. A friend has asked you to meet him at the intersection of 9th St. NW and Constitution Avenue. What sight is closest to that corner?
   a. Hancock Park
   b. National Museum of Natural History
   c. U.S. Capitol
   d. National Air and Space Museum

4. Look at the scale of miles. About how far is it from the U.S. Capitol to Union Station?
   a. less than a mile
   b. about 2 miles
   c. about 5 miles
   d. about 10 miles

5. Your friend just got off the train at Union Station and wants to go to the National Gallery of Art. What directions would you give him?

Plan a Trip

Plan a two-day visit to Washington, D.C. Make a list of the sights you will visit each day, in the order you will visit them. Plan your trip so that you will spend as little time as possible going from one place to the next.

Write About It

Write a postcard from Washington D.C. Tell the reader what you've seen since you arrived. Feel free to use your imagination.

"Some Internet search engines have a map link. Type in a street address, and you'll get a map of the area where it's located."

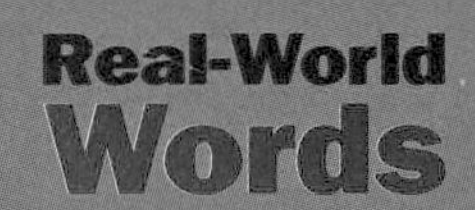

detail: a small part of a whole item
intersection: a point where two streets meet and cross each other
sight: a view or scene; an interesting place to see

Short story

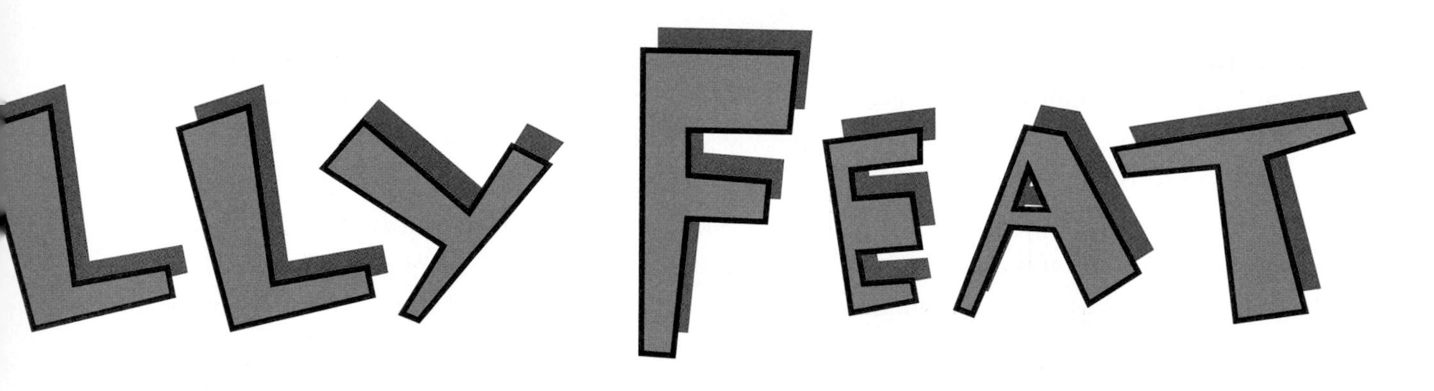

CAN BERIN'S BRAINS—AND FEET—SAVE A BELOVED SEA TURTLE FROM DISASTER?

BY PAUL JENNINGS

"No," screamed Dad. "Please don't. No, no, no. Have mercy. Please, Berin, don't do it." He dropped down on his knees and started begging.

"Very funny," I said as I pulled off one running shoe.

Dad rolled around on the floor. "I'm dying," he yelled. "I can't stand it." He held his nose and watched me untie the other shoe.

Talk about embarrassing. He was supposed to be a grown-up man. My father. And here he was acting like a little kid in grade three. He always carried on like this when I came back from tennis.

My feelings were hurt. "I can't smell anything," I said.

"You need a nose job then," he snorted.

My little sister Libby put her bit in. "The fox never smells its own," she said through a crinkled nose.

Talk about mean. I was sick of them picking on me every time I took off my shoes. I shoved my socks into my sneakers and stomped off to my bedroom. I threw myself down on the bed and looked around the room. Garlic was running around in her cage. I tapped the wire with my toe.

Garlic was my pet mouse. "At least you like me," I said.

The little mouse didn't say anything. Not so much as a squeak. In fact something strange happened. Garlic sniffed the air. Then she closed her eyes and fell fast asleep.

I jumped up and tapped the cage. Nothing. Not a movement. At first I thought she was dead, but then I noticed her ribs going in and out. She was breathing.

I ran across the room to fetch Dad. But just as I reached the door I noticed Garlic sit up and sniff. She was all right. I ran back over to her. She started to totter as if she was dizzy. Then she fell over and settled down into a deep sleep. I walked away and waited on the other side of the room. Garlic sat up and scampered around happily.

Something strange was going on. Every time I went near the cage, Garlic would fall asleep. When I left, she woke up. My mouse was **allergic** to me.

I looked down at my feet. It couldn't be. Could it? No. They weren't that bad. I put on my slippers and approached the cage. Garlic was happy. I slowly took off one slipper and held a bare foot in front of the wire.

Garlic dropped like a stone. She didn't even have time to wrinkle her nose. I put the slipper back on. Garlic sat up and sniffed happily.

This was crazy. My feet smelled so bad they could put a mouse to sleep. Just like chloroform. I had to face up to it. Even though I couldn't smell a thing, I had the strongest feet in the world.

I went out into the backyard to look for our cat. She was licking herself in the sun. "Here, Fluffer," I said. She looked up as I pushed a bare foot into her face.

Her eyes turned to glass and she fell to the ground. Fast asleep. I put the slipper back on my foot and Fluffer sprang to life. With a loud "meow," she hurtled off over the fence.

This was crazy. My feet worked on a cat.

A loud noise filled the air. Barking. It was that rotten dog down the street. Its name was Ohda and it barked all night. "Ruff, ruff, ruff." On and on and on. Most nights you couldn't get to sleep for it barking.

I smiled to myself. This was my big chance. I left my slippers on the porch and set off down the street. Ohda was a huge dog. An Alsatian. She growled and snapped and tore at the wire gate with her teeth. I was glad she couldn't get out. I approached the gate carefully and held out a foot. Ohda stopped barking and sniffed. Her eyes watered. She held her feet up to her nose and rubbed at it **furiously** with her paws. Then she rolled over on her back and whimpered.

The poor dog was suffering terribly. It was just like Dad rolling around on the floor and pretending he was dying. Suddenly Ohda yelped and squealed. The huge dog bolted off into the far corner of the yard and sat staring as me as if I were a monster. Ohda was terrified.

I walked home slowly and thoughtfully. My feet could put a mouse to sleep. And a cat. But not a dog. They weren't powerful enough for dogs. "Dogs must be too big," I said to myself.

Dad sat on the sofa watching the TV. As soon as I entered the room he screwed up his nose. "Oh,

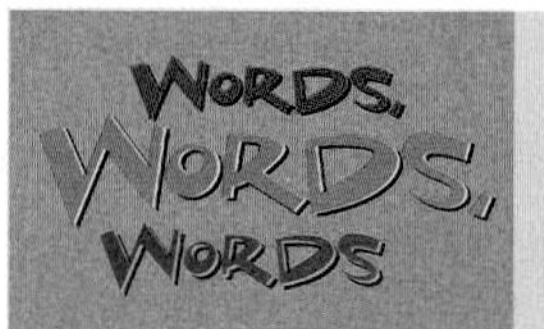

allergic: reacting to something by sneezing, coughing, or breaking out in a rash
furiously: intensely or fiercely
coma: a deep sleep that is very hard to wake up from

"IT WASN'T FAIR. I WAS BORN WITH SMELLY FEET. I COULDN'T HELP IT.... I HAD TO FACE UP TO IT."

Berin," he groaned. "Those feet are foul. Go and have a shower."

I couldn't take anymore. The world was against me. Dad was picking on me again. Garlic had fallen asleep. Fluffer had collapsed into a **coma.** Ohda had been reduced to a whimper. Even the animals didn't like me.

I rushed out of the house and slammed the door. I headed down the street without caring where I was going. Tears pricked behind my eyes. I loved animals. It wasn't fair. I was born with smelly feet. I couldn't help it.

After a bit I found myself at the beach. The tide was in, and a little river of seawater cut Turtle Island off from the shore. I felt a little better. Turtle Island. My favorite spot. And in three months' time, in November, my favorite thing was going to happen.

Old Shelly, one of the last of the South Pacific sea turtles, would haul herself up the beach to lay her eggs. If you were lucky and knew where to look you might be there when she arrived. Every year, on the twentieth of November, she came to lay her eggs.

Once there had been hundreds of turtles crawling up the beach every summer. But people caught them for soup. And stole the eggs. Now there were hardly any turtles left. I knew where she would come ashore. But I didn't tell anybody. Not a soul. Old Shelly was two hundred years old. I couldn't stand it if anything happened to her. Or her eggs.

Seagulls swooped down and formed a swarming flock on the sand. I walked toward them. As I went they started to collapse. One after another they fell over and littered the beach like feathery corpses.

Even the seagulls were passing out when they smelled my feet. The smile fell from my face. I had to clean my feet. I strode into the salty water and headed for Turtle Island. The sand swirled between my toes. The water was cold and fresh.

I looked behind me and saw the gulls waking. They flew and squawked, alive and wide awake. Some of them followed me to the other side. They scuttled along the sand and approached me as I left the water. Nothing happened. The gulls didn't fall asleep. The sea had washed away the smell. The animals of the world were safe again.

ASK YOURSELF

- What is wrong with Berin's feet?

Explain the problem in your own words.

I looked along the beach and frowned. Footsteps in the sand. They walked off along the shore into the distance. I always felt as if Turtle Island was my own special place. I didn't like anyone else going there. There are some cruel people in the world, and the fewer that knew about Old Shelly the better.

I followed the footsteps along for about a kilometer. They finally led into a huge sea cave. I silently made my way inside and edged around the deep pools that sank into the rocky floor. It was a favorite crashing spot.

Three kids were lowering a cray pot into the water. It was Horse and his gang. They didn't see me at first. "Empty," said Horse. "Not one rotten cray. I bet someone's been here and swiped 'em."

Horse was a real big kid. All the members of his gang were big. Greg Baker was his closest friend. "Just wait till November the twentieth," he said. "Turtle soup." They all laughed.

"And turtle omelet," said Horse.

I couldn't believe what I was hearing. They planned to catch Old Shelly. After two hundred years of swimming free in the sea, the grand old creature would end up as soup. It wasn't right. My head swam. I jumped out from behind the rock.

"You can't do it," I screamed. "There's hardly any turtles left. She might even be the last one."

They all turned and looked at me. "A spy," said Horse.

"Berin Jackson," said his friend Greg Baker. "The little turtle lover. What a loser."

The other kid there was nicknamed Thistle. I didn't notice him edging his way behind me. I was too mad to notice anything.

"You can't hurt that turtle," I screamed. "It's protected."

"Who's going to stop us?" sneered Greg Baker.

"Me," I yelled. "I'll tell my dad."

They thought about that for a bit. "We wouldn't hurt the turtle, would we?" sneered Horse.

"Nah," said the other two.

I knew they were lying. And they knew that I knew they were lying. But there was nothing I could do. You can't turn someone in for something they might do.

"Get him," yelled Horse.

Thistle grabbed me from behind. The other two held one leg each. They lifted me into the air.

"Let me go, you ratbags," I shouted. There were tears in my eyes. I tried to blink them back as they swung me higher and higher. I struggled and kicked, but they were too strong for me.

Suddenly they let go. I flew through the air and splashed into the deep water. I sank down, down, down, and then spluttered up to the surface. I spat out salt water and headed for the rocky shore. The gang were already leaving. They laughed and shouted smart comments back at me.

It was the worst day of my life. Animals fainting at my feet. Tossed into the water by a bunch of bullies. And now Horse's gang was going to try to catch Old Shelly.

I walked home along the beach, shivering and wet. I thought about that turtle. Two hundred years ago she hatched out on this very beach. Her mother would have laid scores of eggs. When the tide was right the babies would have hatched and struggled toward the water. Seagulls would have pounced and eaten most of them. In the sea, fish would have gobbled others.

Old Shelly might have been the only one to live. And for the last two hundred years she had swum and survived. And now Horse and his rotten gang were going to catch her.

There was nothing I could do. If I told Dad about the gang they would just lie and say I made it up. I knew those kids. They were in my class at school. I had tangled with them before. They were too strong for me. I couldn't handle them on my own.

Or could I?

I suddenly had an idea. Three months. I had three months to get ready before Old Shelly began to lumber ashore and dig a hole for her eggs. Three months should be enough. It might work. It just might work. I might just be able to save the turtle if I used my brains.

And my feet.

That night I emptied out my sock drawer. I had six pairs of blue socks. Mum bought them at a sale. I slipped one pair on my feet. Then I put on my running shoes. After that I struggled into my pajamas. I could just get my feet through the legs without taking off my shoes.

I hopped into bed. But I felt guilty. I pulled back the blankets and looked at the sheets. The sneakers were making the sheets dirty. I jumped out of bed and crept down to the kitchen. I found two clear plastic bags. Just right. I pulled them over my shoes and fastened them around my ankles with rubber bands. Terrific. I pulled up the covers and fell asleep.

I had a wonderful dream.

In the morning I faced my next problem. The shower. As soon as the coast was clear, I nipped into the bathroom and locked the door. I didn't want my little sister Libby to see me. She would tell for sure.

The shower was on the wall over the bath. I put in the plug and turned on the shower. When the bath was full I took off my pajamas and lowered myself in. But I left my feet hanging out over the edge. I couldn't let my running shoes get wet. And I couldn't take them off. Otherwise my plan would fail.

That night before bed I took a pair of clean blue

ASK YOURSELF

- How do you think Berin will use his feet to save Old Shelly?

Think about what you've read so far, and make your best prediction.

socks out of the dresser. I went outside and rubbed them in the dirt. Then I threw them in the wash basket. That way Mum would think I had worn the socks that day and she wouldn't get **suspicious.**

Every morning and every night I did the same thing. I wondered if it would work. I planned to go for three months without taking off my shoes.

It was a **diabolical** plan. I wouldn't have done it normally. Not for anything. But this was different. I had to save Old Shelly from the gang. And smelly feet were my only weapon.

If my feet could send a cat to sleep after only one day, imagine what they could do after three months. Three months in the same socks and the same shoes. Three months without taking off my running shoes. What an idea. It was magnificent. I smiled to myself. I really hoped it would work.

Well, it was difficult. You can imagine what Mum would have said if she'd known I was wearing my shoes to bed. And I had to stop Libby from finding out too.

Every night for three months I went to bed with my sneakers on. And every night I dirtied a pair of socks outside and put them in the wash. Mum and Dad didn't suspect anything. Although I did have a couple of close calls.

One day Mum said, "Your socks don't smell like they used to, Berin. You must be washing your feet a lot more." I just smiled politely and didn't say anything.

I also had problems at school with the phys ed teacher. I had to forge a note to get out of football and gym. "These corns are taking a long time to heal," he said to me one day. I just smiled and limped off slowly.

Three months passed and still I hadn't taken off my shoes or socks once. I hoped and hoped that my plan would work. I knew that Horse's gang was planning to catch Old Shelly. They sniggered every time I walked past them at school.

Finally the day came. November the twentieth. High tide was at half past four. After school. Old Shelly wouldn't arrive until high tide. And the gang wouldn't be able to do anything while they were in school.

All went well in the morning. But after lunch it was different. I walked into the class and sat down in my seat. The day was hot. Blowflies buzzed in the sticky air. Mr. Lovell sat at his desk and wiped his brow. I looked around. There were three empty seats.

Horse and his friends weren't there.

They were skipping school. And I knew where they were. Down at the beach. Waiting for Old Shelly.

I went cold all over. What if Old Shelly came in early? What if I was wrong about the tides? Turtle soup. I couldn't bear to think about it.

"Mr. Lovell," I yelled. "I have to go home. I forgot something. Horse is after Old Shelly."

All the kids looked at me. They thought I was crazy. Mr. Lovell frowned. He didn't like anyone calling out without putting up their hand.

"Don't be silly, Berin," he growled. "We aren't allowed to let students go home without their parents' permission."

"But I have to go," I yelled. "Old Shelly is . . ."

Mr. Lovell interrupted. He was angry. "Sit down, boy, and behave yourself."

"You don't understand . . . ," I began.

"I understand that you'll be waiting outside the principal's office if you don't be quiet," he said.

I sat down. It was useless. Kids don't have any power. They just have to do what they're told.

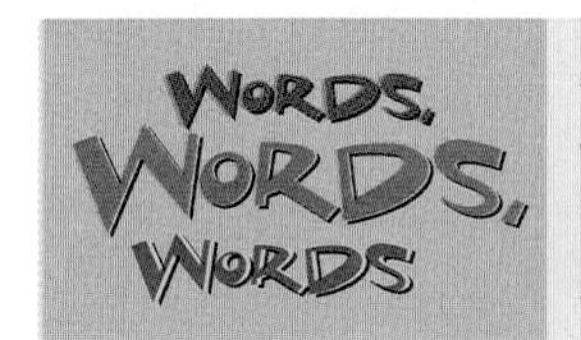

suspicious: feeling as if something is wrong with little or no proof
diabolical: extremely wicked
rancid: spoiled
stench: a strong, unpleasant smell

"MY THREE-MONTH SMELL WAS POWERFUL.... HORSE AND HIS GANG WOULDN'T HAVE A CHANCE."

Or do they?

I looked at my feet. I looked at the running shoes and socks that hadn't been changed for three months. I bent down and undid the laces. Then I pulled off my shoes and socks.

I stepped out into the aisle. In bare feet.

The room suddenly grew silent. The hairs stood up on the back of my neck. I looked at my feet. Long black nails curled out of my putrid toes. Slimy, furry skin was coated with blue sock fuzz. Swollen veins ran like choked rivers under the **rancid** flesh. The air seemed to ripple and shimmer with an invisible **stench.**

I sniffed. Nothing. I couldn't smell a thing. But the others could.

The blowflies were the first to go. They fell from the ceiling like rain. They dropped to the floor without so much as a buzz.

Mr. Lovell jumped as if a pin had been stuck into him. Then he slumped on his desk. Asleep. A crumpled heap of dreams. The class collapsed together. They just keeled over as if they had breathed a deadly gas.

They were alive. But they slept and snored. Victims of my fetid feet.

I wish I could say that there were smiles on their lips. But there weren't. Their faces were screwed up like sour cabbages.

I ran out of the room and across the schoolyard. The caretaker was emptying a trash can into the incinerator. He dropped the can and flopped unconscious to the ground as I passed.

My three-month smell was powerful. It could work in the open at a distance of ten meters. Horse and his gang wouldn't have a chance. They wouldn't even get near me.

But I had to hurry. If Old Shelly came early . . . I couldn't bear to think about it.

The beach bus was pulling up at the curb. I had one dollar with me. Just enough. I jumped onto the bus steps. "Turtle Island please," I said to the driver.

He didn't answer. He was fast asleep in his seat with the engine still running. I looked along the row of seats. All the passengers were snoring their heads off. I had gassed the whole bus.

"Oh no," I said. I jumped off the bus and headed for the beach. The quickest way was straight through the shopping mall.

I didn't really want to run barefoot through the town, but this was an emergency. I passed a lady on a bike. She fell straight asleep, still rolling along the road. The bike tottered, and then crashed into a bush.

This was terrible. No one could come near me without falling asleep. I ran over to help her but her eyes were firmly closed. The best thing I could do was to get away from her as quickly as possible.

I jogged into the shopping mall. People fell to the ground in slumbering waves as I approached. I stopped and stared around.

ASK YOURSELF

- How does Berin manage to get out of school early?

Think about how Berin turns his "problem" feet into a solution.

The street was silent. Hundreds of people slept on the sidewalks and in the shops. A policeman snored in the middle of the road. I felt as if I was the only person in the world who was awake.

Suddenly I felt lonely. And sad.

But then I thought of Old Shelly. That poor, helpless turtle dragging its ancient shell up the beach. To the waiting Horse and his cooking pot.

I ran on. My heart hammered. My knees knocked. My feet fumed. "Old Shelly," I said. "I'm coming, I'm coming, I'm coming."

I pounded on and on, not stopping for the people around me as they fell to the ground like leaves tumbling in autumn.

At last I reached the beach. The tide was in. A strong current cut me off from Turtle Island. A flock of seagulls flew overhead. They plummeted to the ground, reminding me of planes that had lost their pilots.

My feet still worked. They were as powerful as ever.

I gazed at the swiftly running water. I peered along the beach for a boat. There was none. I looked at my foul feet. If only I could fly. On the wind I thought I heard wicked laughter. "Old Shelly," I mumbled. "I'm coming." I plunged into the sea and waded toward the island.

My toes sank into the sand. I could feel the grains scouring my skin. Washing away at three months of muck. The water was clear and cold and salty. On and on I struggled through the cleansing stream. Splashing. Jumping. Crying. Until I reached the other side.

The seagulls scampered around my feet. They were awake. They didn't even yawn.

I looked down at my lily-white toes. They were spotless. The water had stolen their strength. Three months of saving my smell. Gone. Scrubbed away by the salt and the sand.

There was no sign of the three bullies. But I knew where to find them. I staggered up to the top of a huge sand dune and stared along the beach. There they were. And there in the clear blue water was a moving shadow. Old Shelly.

Horse and his friends hadn't seen her. There was still a chance. I plunged down the dune toward them, yelling and screaming. Trying to **distract** them from their search.

It worked. They turned around and watched me approach. I had to draw them off. Once they saw the turtle they would know which part of the beach she was on. Even if old Shelly escaped they would dig around and find the eggs.

I knew it was no use arguing with them. They wouldn't listen. I had to say something mean.

"Birdbrain," I said weakly to Horse. I felt silly. It didn't come out right. It wasn't tough. I bunched up my fists. "Get off this island," I ordered.

"Who's going to make us?" **jeered** Horse.

"Me," I said.

I felt very small. They were really big kids. They walked toward me with snarling faces.

I turned and ran.

"Get him." They raced after me. I scrambled up the sand dune and along the top. I felt them panting behind me. The sandy ground turned to rock. It cut my bare feet. They hurt like crazy. I slowed down to a hobble. My toes were bleeding. It was no use. The gang had me trapped.

I turned and faced the gang. Behind them, way below, I could see Old Shelly hauling herself over the sand. They hadn't seen her. Yet.

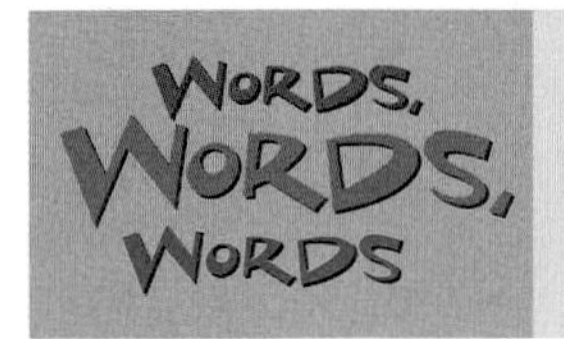

distract: to weaken a person's concentration
jeered: shouted in a rude way
desperate: willing to do anything to change your situation

Thistle circled around me. They closed in. I tried to find something to defend myself. There was nothing. I put my hands in my pockets in a **desperate** search. My fingers found something useful.

"Get back," I yelled. "Or I'll use these."

Horse laughed out loud. "We're not scared of a pair of . . ."

He never finished. He crashed to the ground like a tree falling. The others followed. They were fast asleep on the sand. I held my putrid socks in the air. Boy, were they powerful.

I put the socks near the sleeping bullies. Then I walked down to the beach.

Old Shelly was digging a hole with her flippers. Slowly, painfully, she dug and dug and dug. She was helpless. "Don't worry, girl," I said. "I won't hurt you."

I sat a little way off and watched the miracle. I watched the eggs drop like beads from a broken necklace. The sun sank into the sea, lighting the old turtle with gold.

I watched as Old Shelly covered the eggs and then crawled back toward the shore. Just as she reached the edge she turned. And nodded her head as if to thank me.

"Think nothing of it," I said. "Your eggs are safe now. I'll see you next year."

I have to admit there was a tear in my eye as I watched her sink under the water and swim out beneath the silvery arms of the rippling moonbeams.

I went back and fetched the socks. I threw them in the sea and waited. In no time at all, Horse and his friends started to stir. They sat up and peered into the darkness. They couldn't work it out. It was light when they had fallen asleep. They didn't know where the sun had gone.

Suddenly Horse gave an enormous scream. He ran for it. The others followed him, streaking along the sand as if a demon was after them. They thought I had strange powers. I guess if you think about it, they were right in a funny sort of way.

I walked slowly home.

A nasty thought entered my mind. What if Horse found more members for his gang? What if they came back to wait for Old Shelly next November?

I was worried. Then I chuckled and spoke to myself. "If I start going to bed with my shoes on tonight," I said, "my feet ought to be pretty strong by this time next year." ●

Helping Sea Turtles Cope With Birth, Sickness, and Storms

by EMILY YELLIN for *The New York Times*

TOPSAIL BEACH, North Carolina, Aug. 31, 1999—Today at the Topsail Beach Shop and Grill, most people were checking to see how their neighbors weathered Hurricane Dennis. But anyone who walked up to Jean Beasley's table first asked how well the sea turtles survived the hurricane.

For Ms. Beasley and the six people at her table, sea turtles are like family. Everyone at the table spends much of the summer helping turtles through birth, sickness, and even death.

They are among more than 100 volunteers in the Topsail Turtle Project. They patrol the beaches of Topsail Island every day, all summer, to protect the more than 180 sea turtle nests dug this season.

Each of them also volunteers at the Karen Beasley Sea Turtle Rescue and Rehabilitation Center here. The center is named in memory of Ms. Beasley's daughter, who founded the Topsail Turtle Project. The hospital is caring for nine injured or ill sea turtles, found on the beaches of North Carolina, South Carolina, and Georgia.

Ms. Beasley, 63, a retired teacher, is the director of the turtle project and of the turtle hospital. The volunteers share a love of the big, prehistoric creatures who lumber from the sea every year to burrow nests in the sand.

The female turtles, which are often 200 to 300 pounds, lay a clutch of about 125 eggs. They then cover them with mounds of sand before returning back into the ocean.

"I first saw a mother turtle come up and nest at the steps of my house 30 years ago," Ms. Beasley said. "It was such an awesome sight. I have been committed to the sea turtles ever since. They are such gentle, magnificent creatures."

The turtle eggs hatch about two months after the nest is dug. The hatchlings then join together in the night to push up the sand covering them. Guided by the light of the moon, they make their way into the ocean. They go into a "swimming frenzy" for a few days until they reach warmer waters, where they live for their first year or more.

That is, if everything goes well.

About 90 percent of the hatchlings make it to water, said Terry Meyer, a volunteer who works with Ms. Beasley. "About 1 in 1,000 of those will survive the first year. And about 1 in 5,000 to 10,000 will reach adulthood, which is anywhere from 20 to 30 years old."

"It was such an awesome sight. . . . They are such gentle, magnificent creatures."

Turtles have always had many natural enemies, like sharks, in the sea. In addition, hurricanes threaten the nests of the turtles, who have a life span of more than 100 years. But in the past few decades, humans are what have threatened the turtles most.

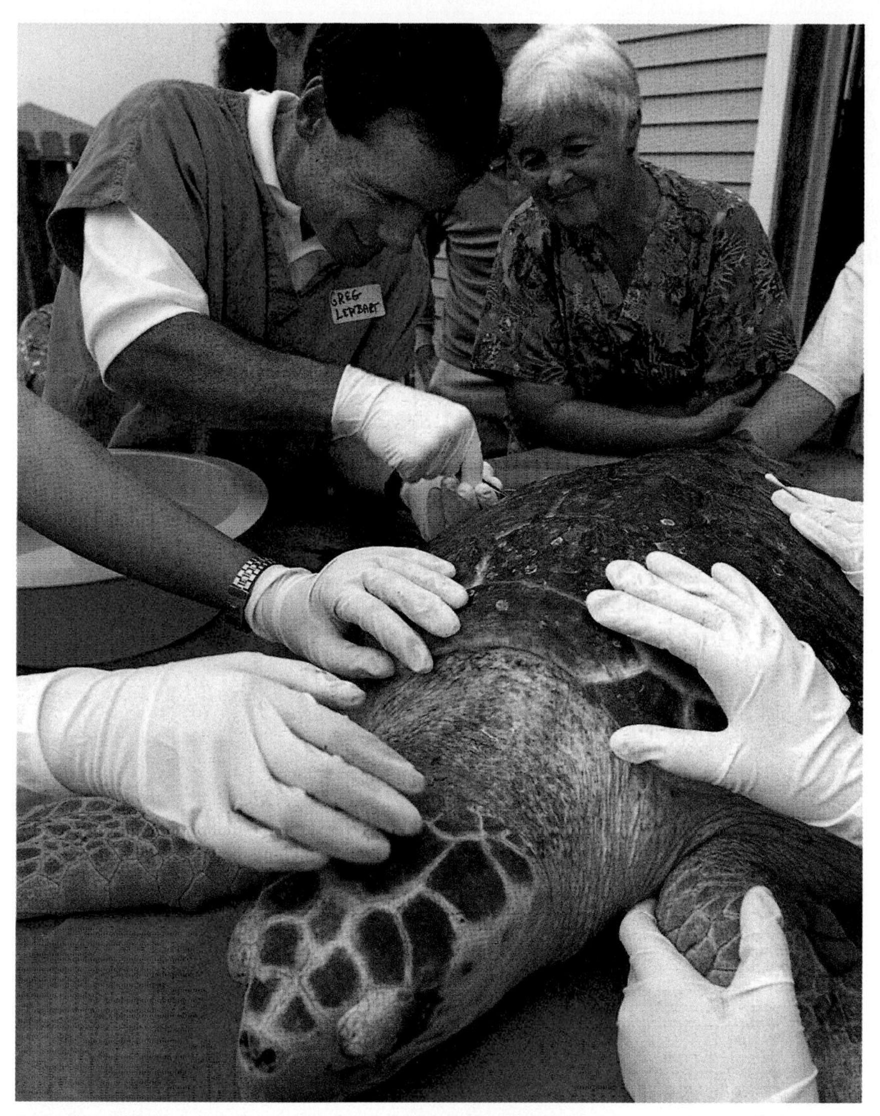

Jean Beasley watches as Dr. Greg Lewbart tries to remove a piece of dead bone from the shell of a turtle at the turtle hospital.

People building along the beachfront have thrown off the turtles' nesting instincts. Lights from houses and businesses sometimes trick the baby turtles into heading onto land instead of into the sea. If they do not get to the water soon after hatching, they die. And motorboat propellers and the nets and hooks of commercial fishers have killed many turtles.

In fact, all five species of sea turtles found on the shores of this country are in danger of dying out and disappearing forever. They are on the endangered or threatened species lists of the United States Fish and Wildlife Service.

Ms. Beasley, Ms. Meyer, and thousands of other volunteers along the Southeastern coast are determined to make sure the turtles do not become extinct. In North Carolina, 21 volunteer groups totaling about 500 people patrol about 320 miles of beaches.

The volunteers sit with the turtles' nests at night when they look ready to hatch. They protect the hatchlings from natural enemies like ghost crabs. They patrol the beaches at dawn looking for new nests. Then they block off the nests so people will not accidentally disturb them. Finally, they teach people about sea turtles, which are especially of interest to children.

"Turtles and kids always go together," said Ruth Boettcher, a North Carolina official who oversees sea turtle protection groups. "If somebody's curiosity about them is sparked when they are young, it stays with them."

Today Ms. Beasley is getting things back to normal at the turtle hospital. Meanwhile, Ms. Meyer and the other volunteers began checking on each of the nests.

"The turtles teach us that we are just specks in a great big world," Ms. Meyer said. "Through these turtles, we learn how important it is to take care of other things in the world besides ourselves." ●

TALK ABOUT IT

Now that you've read "Smelly Feat" and "Helping Sea Turtles Cope," what do you have to say about these questions?

- What do you think is the best way to deal with a bully?
- Should people try to protect animals who are in danger? Explain your point of view to someone who might disagree.

COMPREHENSION CHECK

Write your answers to the questions below. Use information from the story and the article to support your answers.

1. How does Berin use his feet to save Old Shelly?
2. How do you think Berin feels about his foot problem?
3. How else might Berin have saved the turtle?
4. Name two things that threaten the survival of sea turtles.
5. Do you think Berin would make a good volunteer for Topsail Turtle Project? Why or why not?

VOCABULARY CHECK

Complete the sentences below. Be sure that each complete sentence expresses the meaning of the vocabulary word in bold.

1. I'd know I was **allergic** to chocolate if . . .
2. I would **furiously** defend . . .
3. An easy way to **distract** someone is . . .
4. A **suspicious** person might . . .
5. I could tell the milk was **rancid** because . . .

WRITE ABOUT IT

Choose one of the writing prompts below.

- Write an article for the school paper about bullies from Berin's point of view. Give two or three ideas about what should be done about this problem.
- Write a short paragraph explaining how to save the sea turtles. Then write another short paragraph telling why people should care.
- Write an ad for a product that would create (or cure) smelly feet. Explain why and how this product would be used.

Take ACTION

Now that you've learned about the sea turtle, you might want to help an endangered species, too. Here are places to contact for three things you can do.

Adopt an Animal:

The Nature Conservancy
International Headquarters
4245 North Fairfax Drive, Suite 160
Arlington, Virginia 22203-1606
(703) 841-5300
www.tnc.org

Volunteer at an Organization:

U.S. Fish & Wildlife Service
1-800-344-WILD
www.fws.gov

Write and Publish a Report:

SchoolWorld Endangered Species Project
www.schoolworld.asn.au/species/reports.html

Reading Editorial Cartoons

Editorial cartoons are meant to make you think. You won't find them with the comics. They're on the editorial page of a newspaper because they express a point of view. Check out the one below. Read all about it. Do you get the point?

First, look at the picture. What's going on? What is the man in this cartoon reading about?

Editorial cartoons usually have a punchline. Sometimes it's printed beneath the cartoon. In this case, it's in the thought bubble.

An Editorial Cartoon

Source: Bennett/Christian Science Monitor

The cartoonist made these words look like an Internet address. He's making a point about what's important to this man.

Do You Get It?

All editorial cartoons express a point of view. What was this cartoonist trying to say? Reread the cartoon and the tips. Then use them to answer the questions. Write your answers on your own paper.

1. The newspaper in the cartoon is reporting that
  a. people use the Internet to study for school.
  b. some people are "hooked" on the Internet.
  c. some people spend too much money on software.
  d. not enough people spend time on the Internet.

2. How often do you think the guy in the cartoon uses the Internet?
  a. never **c.** only on Saturday
  b. a lot **d.** only when he can't buy a newspaper

3. Explain how you figured out question 2. How does the cartoonist let you know the answer?

4. What's the cartoonist's point of view?
  a. You should get your news from the Net, not a paper.
  b. Studies that say that people who are addicted to the Internet are silly.
  c. Lots of people use the Internet too much and don't even realize it.
  d. No one should ever use the Internet.

Readers Respond!

Do you agree with this cartoonist? Is it possible to be addicted to the Net? Is it bad to spend a lot of time surfing the Web? Write a letter to the cartoonist explaining your point of view.

Analyze It

Find an editorial cartoon in a newspaper. Read it closely. What do you think the cartoonist is saying? Write a few sentences describing the message of the cartoon.

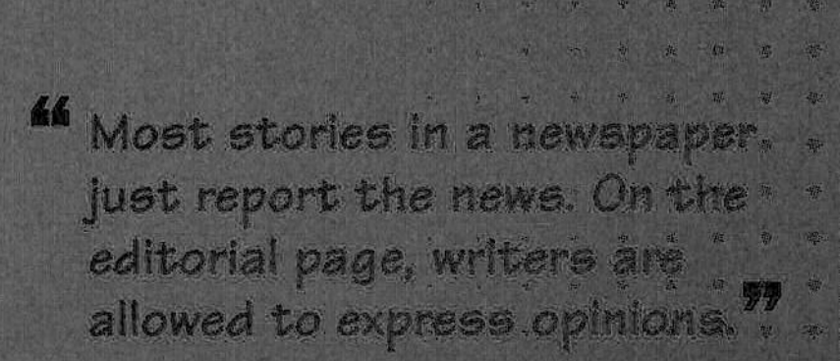

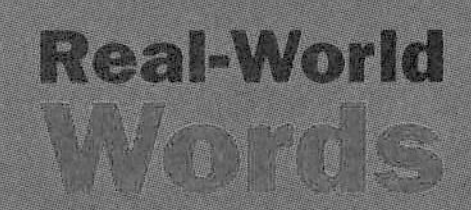

cartoonist: a person who creates a cartoon
editorial: expressing an opinion or a point of view
express: to communicate or say

profile

Iqbal Masih

Crusader for Children

Iqbal Masih was just 12 years old when he died. But he did more to inspire the world to fight against child labor than most people could do in a lifetime.

When Iqbal Masih started to work, he was too young to ride a bike. At age four, he'd wake up before dawn. He'd leave the small hut he shared with his mother and sister in Pakistan.

Iqbal would walk to a dusty carpet factory. Once there, he would sit for the next 12 hours. He would tie knots into carpets until his fingers felt like they were falling off. Sometimes the factory owner would chain Iqbal down to make sure he wouldn't run away.

Each carpet Iqbal made would be sent to Europe or America. There it would sell for hundreds of dollars. Iqbal was paid 20 cents per week for his work. If he was lucky, he'd get maybe 50 cents.

Iqbal's courage inspired hundreds of formerly enslaved children to fight child labor.

Living in Slavery

Iqbal Masih wasn't alone. Millions of children worked instead of going to school all over the world. In Pakistan alone, eight million kids under the age of 15 lived in near slavery. They worked 12 hours a day, six days a week. They stitched soccer balls and sneakers. They molded bricks. They made carpets. In most cases, the parents needed the money badly. The children didn't ask any questions.

Iqbal was different. He refused to accept his fate. He found a way out. Then he worked to free the kids who were still stuck behind the looms.

An Evil Debt

Iqbal never liked working. He wanted to play sports or practice the kung-fu moves he'd seen in a movie once. But, at first, he didn't have a choice.

His parents had needed 600 rupees—about $12—to pay for their older son's wedding. So they did what many poor Pakistani parents did. They sold their son's childhood for a small sum of money. They borrowed it from a factory owner. Iqbal would work at a loom until the debt was paid.

Iqbal's parents didn't realize that the debt would *never* be paid. Each month, the factory owner added more money in fines or interest. Iqbal couldn't possibly work hard enough to keep up. The system was totally unfair.

Iqbal's Escape

Iqbal began to fight back however he could. Some days he would run away at lunchtime. But each time the factory owner caught him. The punishments got worse and worse. Iqbal was beaten. He was hung upside down. He was burned with hot oil. When he told the local police about the abuse they just took him back to the factory.

When he was ten, Iqbal got away for good. He made his way to a nearby city. There, he discovered

"I used to be afraid of the carpet masters. Now they are afraid of me."

the Bonded Labor Liberation Front (BLLF). The group had freed thousands of child workers in Pakistan. It also ran dozens of schools around the country. Child workers could learn to read and work their way toward better jobs at their schools.

Through the BLLF, Iqbal learned that selling children to pay off debts was **illegal.** But the law was often ignored. By law, Iqbal was free and his parents didn't owe any more money. Iqbal promised he would never return to the factory.

Fighting for Justice

In 1992, Iqbal went to school for the first time. At ten years old, he was under four feet tall and weighed less than 50 pounds. Six years in the factory had left Iqbal underfed and in poor health. But his physical hunger had not dimmed his hunger for knowledge—or for **justice.**

Iqbal finished his classes in less than half the normal time. Then he went on the road to share the most important lesson of all. He wanted everyone to know that no one has the right to enslave another human being.

Iqbal hiked from factory to factory for the next two years. He told child workers like himself that they had the right to be free. Iqbal helped to free 3,000 kids by the time he was 12.

Iqbal during his visit to Broad Meadows Middle School

ASK YOURSELF

- How was Iqbal's life different once he escaped from the factory?

Compare the details of his life before and after his escape.

The World Takes Notice

Suddenly, the world noticed Iqbal. In December 1994, he traveled to Boston, Massachusetts. There, he accepted a human rights award for youth. Iqbal stood before a crowd of celebrities and journalists. He held a pen in one hand and a carpet weaving tool in another. "This," he said, pointing to the pen, "should be the tool of children everywhere, not this knife."

Iqbal returned home a different person. He'd seen carpets on sale in the United States for more money than he'd made in six years of labor. He had spoken to kids his age who didn't work all the time. They had free time to go to places like the mall or the beach. Iqbal had been promised a full scholarship to college. He decided he would become a lawyer.

A Sudden, Tragic End

Iqbal's dreams exploded with a single shotgun blast. He was gunned down and killed four months after he came home from the U.S. He was riding his bike near his grandmother's house. Many believe that Iqbal was killed by factory owners who wanted to silence his **campaign** against child labor.

"I used to be afraid of the carpet masters," Iqbal liked to tell reporters. "Now they are afraid of me."

Even after his death, Iqbal gave factory owners something to fear. Stories about child labor appeared in magazines and newspapers everywhere. Millions of people stopped buying products made by children. Pakistan lost $10 million in carpet orders from Europe and America. Iqbal may be gone, but his fight for justice continues to this day.

Keeping the Dream Alive

Iqbal touched many lives while he was in the U.S. One school he visited was Broad Meadows Middle School in Quincy, Massachusetts. Students there were so moved by Iqbal that they started their own campaign against child labor. They've raised more than $146,000 since Iqbal died.

Broad Meadows' students also formed a partnership with a local Pakistani group called Sudhaar (which means "improving"). Sudhaar has used the money to help **convert** an office building into the School for Iqbal in Pakistan. Former child workers can now receive an education at the school.

Craig Kielburger started a group called Free the Children after he heard about Iqbal. He was only 12 years old at the time. The Canadian teen later went to Asia and helped a pair of Indian children escape from a fireworks factory. He wrote to companies and asked them not to use child labor. He spoke to children all over and asked them to join his campaign.

Today, Free the Children has grown to more than 5,000 members in 20 countries. And Craig is one of North America's most vocal and well-known **opponents** of sweatshops and child labor.

"The most important thing I've learned," he says, "is that kids can make a difference." ●

GOALS
- to put an end to child labor worldwide
- to promote education for all children

WORK HISTORY
- six years in a Pakistani carpet factory
- two years fighting child enslavement

EDUCATION
- began school at age ten, after escaping factory enslavement
- finished studies in less than half the usual time

MAJOR ACHIEVEMENTS
- helped free 3,000 child laborers
- awarded Reebok's Human Rights Youth in Action Award, 1994
- inspired millions to fight child labor

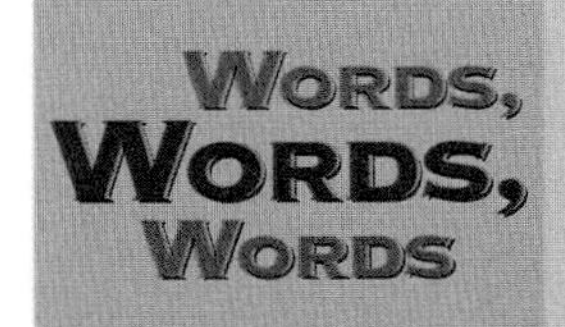

illegal: against the law
justice: fair treatment
campaign: actions that lead to something important
convert: to make something into something else
opponents: people who fight against a cause or person

The HIGH COST of CHEAP LABOR

Things have improved since Iqbal died. But there's a long way to go before the world's children stop paying the price of child labor.

You probably went shopping for new clothes before school started this fall. Did you get a great bargain? If you did, you might want to ask yourself this: Why was the price so low?

The answer *might* be that your bargain outfit was made by a kid like Wendy Diaz. Wendy was 13 years old when she went to work at a clothing factory in Honduras. She worked 12- to 16-hour days and was paid 31 cents per hour. She got only two bathroom breaks a day. She didn't go to school. If you knew Wendy had made your outfit, would you still want to wear it? Or would you feel guilty for enjoying something that another person suffered to make?

Wendy Goes to Washington

Eventually, Wendy's story made national news. Here's what happened:

The factory where Wendy worked manufactured a line of clothing for popular TV talk-show host Kathie Lee Gifford. An American organization that fights to end child labor learned that Gifford's clothes were made by child workers. They decided to bring it to the attention of Gifford—and of everyone else in the country. The organization, the National Labor Committee (NLC), held a press conference in Washington, D.C. They flew Wendy in from Honduras to describe her experiences.

"I want to talk to Kathie Lee to ask her to help us put an end to all this," Wendy told dozens of

More than 250 million children worldwide still work full-time.

newspaper and TV reporters. "We want better working conditions and a just wage."

Gifford did take action. After meeting with Wendy, she launched a campaign against child labor and sweatshops. Sweatshops are factories where workers are not paid well or treated fairly. She promised to closely watch over the factories that make her clothes.

Wendy's story put a human face on the issue of child labor. Since then, many people in the United States have expressed concern about the working conditions in factories throughout the world. "This is a national issue now," says Charles Kernaghan, executive director of the NLC. "We've had more success than anyone could have imagined."

The Good News

There has been progress. Many U.S. schools now refuse to purchase anything made under sweatshop conditions. Students at more than 100 colleges have protested the conditions under which university sweatshirts, caps, and athletic uniforms have been produced. One company has raised the salary of its workers in the country of Indonesia by 25 percent. They've also promised not to employ anyone under the age of 16 at the factory.

Some celebrities have embraced the cause, too. Soccer star Julie Foudy was offered a contract to endorse soccer balls. Before agreeing, she asked for a tour of the plant where the balls were made.

All of that is encouraging. But it doesn't mean the problem has disappeared.

Looking for Solutions

Despite everyone's efforts to fight child labor, there are still about 250 million children under the age of 15 who are working worldwide, according to the United Nations. Their backbreaking labor produces clothing, sneakers, sporting goods, carpets, sugar, and dozens of other items.

Why do people in the United States continue to buy products made by child laborers? Partly because products made in sweatshops cost less, and people want to save money. But also because it's not always easy to tell which products have been made by children. The NLC wants, among other things, to put a label that says "no sweat" on products made outside of the U.S. The label would guarantee that workers were treated well and child labor wasn't used.

"You can buy a can of tuna fish and know that it hasn't led to the slaughter of dolphins," says Charles Kernaghan of the NLC. "You ought to be able to buy a product and know it hasn't been made by children." ●

Talk About It

Now that you've read "Iqbal Masih" and "The High Cost of Cheap Labor," what do you have to say about these questions?

- ▶ Do you think that people should be willing to pay more for products to make sure that they haven't been made by child laborers? Explain why or why not.
- ▶ Should celebrities be able to guarantee that the products they endorse are not made with child labor? Explain your point of view.

Comprehension Check

Write your answers to the questions below. Use information from the hero profile and the article to support your answers.

1. What did Iqbal Masih do to fight against child labor?
2. Why did Iqbal receive a human rights award for his effort?
3. Why didn't Iqbal's death put an end to the fight against child labor?
4. Why did Wendy Diaz want to talk to Kathie Lee Gifford?
5. What do Wendy Diaz and Iqbal Masih have in common?

Vocabulary Check

Complete each sentence with the correct vocabulary word.

illegal **justice** **campaign**
opponents **convert**

1. I began a long _______ to convince my parents to give me an allowance.
2. Many young people feel strongly about ideas such as world peace and social _______.
3. My little brother has a toy robot that he can _______ into a toy car.
4. Our _______ played a great game, but we still won.
5. On our block, cars parked in _______ spots get towed away.

Write About It

Choose one of the writing prompts below.

- Using Iqbal's voice, write about the experience of working in the carpet factory.
- Write a letter to your school paper explaining your views about child labor.
- Write a song or poem about freeing child laborers.

Take ACTION

Would you like to help in the campaign to end child labor? Contact these organizations to see what you can do:

UNICEF (United Nations Children's Fund)
333 East 38th Street
New York, NY 10016
http://www.unicefusa.org

This United Nations organization deals with the problems children face all over the world, including the problem of child labor.

Free the Children
1750 Steeles Ave. W.
Suite 218
Concord, ON L4K 2L7
(905) 760-9382
http://www.freethechildren.org

This organization, founded by 12-year-old Canadian Craig Kielburger, works to create awareness about child labor and to free child laborers worldwide.

Writing a Letter to the Editor

You just read an article that you really liked. Or maybe you just read one that you really *disliked*! You decide to write a letter to the editor, saying what you think.

Most magazines and newspapers print a page of letters from their readers in every issue. Check out these letters about an article on women's soccer. Then get ready to write your own letter to an editor.

Letters to the Editor

Tell which article you're writing about. Also, include the date of the issue in which the article appeared.

Did something in the magazine bug you? Suggest a solution.

Why should the editors do what you say? Give them a reason that backs up your opinion.

I enjoyed reading the article on Mia Hamm (9/16). But I find it very aggravating that soccer is the only women's sport that gets a lot of publicity. I'd like to see an article about female lacrosse players. I am a lacrosse player, and lacrosse happens to be the fastest-growing sport for women in college.

Trya Genn
Sticktown, New Jersey

appens to be the fastest-growing sport for women in college.
Trya Genn
Sticktown, New Jersey

More than Mia

Thanks for your article on Mia Hamm (9/16). I am a big fan of women's soccer and love to read about the players.

Ima Fan
Grass Stain, Georgia

Write Us

Send your letters to *XL Magazine*, 1234 Speedy Street, Rapid City, Alaska 00012-3999, or send e-mail to rewind@xl.com. In order to be considered for publication, letters must include the writer's name, address, and phone number. We reserve the right to edit letters for length. We regret that we cannot personally answer every letter we receive.

"The 'Write Us' box tells where to send your letter. It also gives rules for getting your letter published. You can find this information on most 'Letters to the Editor' pages."

Speak Your Mind!

Got something to say to the editors of a favorite magazine or newspaper? Find an article or story you like—or one that you really dislike. Then get ready to write a letter about it.

1. What is the article about? Write down the title and date. Then write a few sentences that sum up the article. Think about these questions:
   a. Who or what was the story about?
   b. What was the main idea?

2. Make a list of the things you liked about the article. Make a list of the things you did not like. Think about these questions:
   a. Why was the article so good?
   b. How could the article have been better?

3. Review your list. Pick one or two things you feel strongly about. These are the things you will write about in your letter.

4. Write a rough draft of your letter. Did you state your opinion clearly? Did you give a reason to support it?

5. Is your letter ready to send? Or does it need a little more work? Follow these steps to create your final letter.
   a. Revise your letter to make your message clear.
   b. Proofread your letter. Correct any mistakes. Make sure you have followed the magazine's guidelines for writing a letter to the editor.
   c. Write a final draft. Then send it to the editor!

Getting Into Print

Turn to the "Letters to the Editor" page in a magazine. Find a positive letter about an article. Find a negative one about the same article. What are the main ideas of each letter? Do you agree or disagree with the writers?

Writing Back

Find a partner and trade articles and letters from "Getting Into Print." Read your partner's article and letter. Now imagine you're the editor. Write a short letter back to your partner saying why you agree or disagree.

"Save yourself the price of a stamp. Most magazines and newspapers have e-mail addresses."

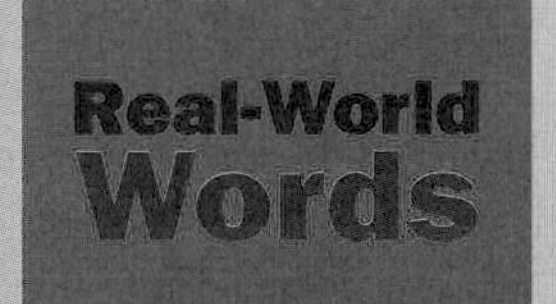

article: a piece of writing published in a newspaper or magazine
editor: a person in charge of a newspaper or magazine
issue: an edition of a newspaper or magazine

photo essay

THE MAN WHO CHANGED AMERICA

Jackie Robinson was much more than an outstanding ball-player. To many, he was the most important athlete of the 20th century.

Jackie Robinson was the grandson of a slave. He was born in 1919, near Cairo, Georgia. When he was 16 months old, his family moved to Pasadena, California, near Los Angeles.

In Pasadena, Jackie first learned the ugliness of racial hatred. When his family moved into a white neighborhood, neighbors tried to force them to move away. Racial slurs were hurled at Jackie. One man threw rocks at him! These were troubled times for America. But Jackie was destined to change that.

On April 15, 1947, Jackie Robinson took the field for the Brooklyn Dodgers. No African-American man had played for a major league baseball team since 1884. Jackie's courage helped show that blacks and whites could live, work, and play together.

To celebrate Jackie's courage, here is his story. It is written in his voice. It is based on his published quotes, interviews, and writings.

BIG STICK: Jackie had a .311 lifetime batting average. Despite the obstacles he faced, he played in the World Series six times!

A Four-Sport Star

I was a good athlete, and I loved sports. In grade school, some of my classmates begged me to play on their pickup teams. In high school I lettered in football, basketball, baseball, and track. I did the same thing at the University of California at Los Angeles (UCLA).

After the United States entered World War II, in 1941, I joined the Army. I was sent to Texas, where I trained soldiers to drive tanks.

In 1945, after the war was over, I decided to play pro baseball. Blacks were not allowed to play in the major leagues. The Negro leagues were started in the 1920s to give black people a place to play. I became a shortstop for the Kansas City Monarchs.

It was a hard life. We took long trips by bus. Many restaurants didn't serve food to blacks. We had to eat outside or on the road.

That August, a scout told me that Branch Rickey wanted to meet me. Mr. Rickey ran the major league Brooklyn Dodgers.

On the train to New York City, I wondered: Is this my big chance?

Mr. Rickey's Plan

When I walked into Mr. Rickey's office, he rose from his

MAKING HISTORY: Dodger president Branch Rickey (far right) believed Jackie could stand up to racists and bullies. Mr. Rickey was right! Here, Jackie signs his 1948 contract.

HE'S SAFE! Jackie brought a hustling, aggressive style of play to the Dodgers. He would do anything to get on base, and his baserunning drove pitchers crazy. He loved to steal third base!

MICHAEL TALKS ABOUT JACKIE

"It took a man of courage, determination, and talent to break the color barrier. Jackie Robinson was that special person. Black athletes owe him a lot."

—Michael Jordan

leather swivel chair and shook my hand.

Mr. Rickey got right to the point. "I think you can play in the major leagues," he said.

I was batting over .300, and I had stolen a lot of bases. But there were plenty of older, more **established** Negro league stars. Why me?

Mr. Rickey had been looking for a black player who could stand up to **taunts** from bullies and racists. He thought I was that man.

Mr. Rickey warned that I would face beanballs and fists. He said I would be called dirty names. He told me I'd have to permit all those things to happen and not lose my temper.

MO TALKS ABOUT JACKIE

"I think kids should find out as much as they can about Jackie Robinson, no matter what color they are. That's why I wear his number, 42. I want to keep his memory alive."

—Mo Vaughn, former Boston Red Sox

A GOOD SIGN: Many white fans supported Jackie too.

"Mr. Rickey," I asked, "are you looking for a Negro who is afraid to fight back?"

"Robinson," he rumbled, "I'm looking for a ballplayer with guts enough *not* to fight back."

Brooklyn Bound!

In 1946, I joined the Dodgers' top farm team, in Montreal, Canada. It seemed as if the whole world were watching me. Reporters and photographers were buzzing around, and huge crowds came to see me play. I batted .349, with 40 stolen bases. I was ready.

In April 1947, I was promoted to the Brooklyn Dodgers. I was the first black player in the major leagues since 1884!

I played first base. At first, I was very nervous. But gradually I began to relax and play my game.

Sadly, Mr. Rickey's predictions all came true. I was called names by fans and other players—and even by some of my teammates.

There were **snubs** and insults. There were balls pitched at my head. There were players who deliberately cut me with their spikes. There were death threats.

At times, I felt deeply sorry for myself. At times I wondered if

ASK YOURSELF

- Why did Mr. Rickey choose Jackie Robinson?

Think about the kind of player Mr. Rickey wanted.

WATCH OUT! **Many players slid into Jackie with their sharp spikes high.**

being the first Negro in the majors was worth it.

And at times I wanted to fight back. But I had promised Mr. Rickey that I wouldn't.

I Had to Be Great

My wife, Rachel, helped me through the bad times. Black fans supported me loyally. After a while, my fellow Dodgers did too. Southern-born shortstop Pee Wee Reese became my good friend.

I knew I couldn't be **mediocre** or just good. I had to be great.

In 1947, I batted .297, hit 12 home runs, and led the National League with 29 stolen bases. I was named Rookie of the Year!

Two years later, as a second baseman, I led the league in hitting (.342) and steals (37). I was the National League MVP!

My breakthrough helped many Americans change their thinking. And it paved the way for many fine athletes to come after me.

A firm step forward had been taken. But baseball—and the nation—still had a long way to go.

Jackie Robinson retired after the 1956 season. By that time, nearly every team in baseball had black players. Most pro teams in other sports had black players too.

After he retired, Jackie went on to become a successful businessman. Jackie also continued to speak out against racial injustice. He met with civil rights leaders including Dr. Martin Luther King Jr.

Jackie's life was very stressful. His hair turned gray when he was still a young man, so he looked much older than he was. When he died of heart failure, in 1973, he was only 53 years old. But in a way, Jackie is still helping others. His wife Rachel heads the Jackie Robinson Foundation, which offers college scholarships to minority students.

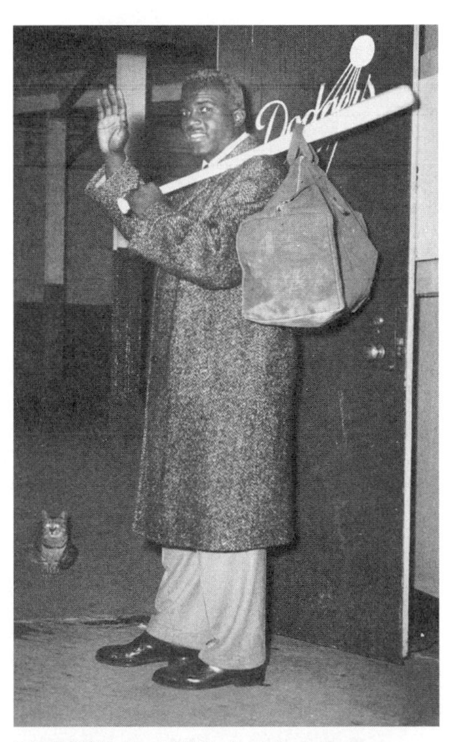

SO LONG: In 1956, Jackie left the Dodger clubhouse for the last time.

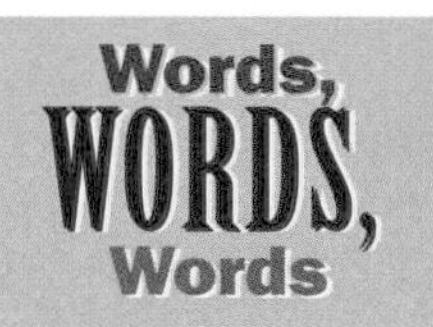

established: experienced
taunts: mean and insulting remarks
snubs: attempts to ignore and reject a person
mediocre: less than average quality

HARD TIMES: In the 1940s, some African Americans had to use separate fountains.

BAD LAWS

In 1947, when Jackie Robinson became the only African-American player in major league baseball, African Americans were treated unfairly in some parts of the United States.

Many communities were segregated. In those areas, African Americans and whites could not live, work, or play together.

Many states, mostly in the South, had laws that **restricted** what African Americans were allowed to do. For example:

- African-American kids were not allowed to attend schools with white kids.
- Many areas required two sets of public water fountains and bathrooms—one for whites and one for African Americans.
- Marriages between whites and African Americans were illegal.
- African Americans were often required to sit in the back of a bus. When the bus filled up, they had to give up their seats to white people.
- Many bus and train stations had separate waiting rooms for African Americans.
- Some restaurants refused to serve African Americans.

In the 1960s and 1970s, Congress passed laws to stop discrimination. The laws **ensured** all U.S. citizens would be treated alike, regardless of their race. The Civil Rights Act of 1964 ordered businesses to serve all people. It also banned discrimination at work. ●

TERESA TALKS ABOUT JACKIE

"I am very proud to share the same hometown as Jackie Robinson. We're both from Cairo, Georgia. Jackie stood firm in his beliefs, knowing that he could make a difference. His life speaks to every human. He showed that people should respect one another on the basis of character, not color."

—Teresa Edwards, U.S. women's basketball

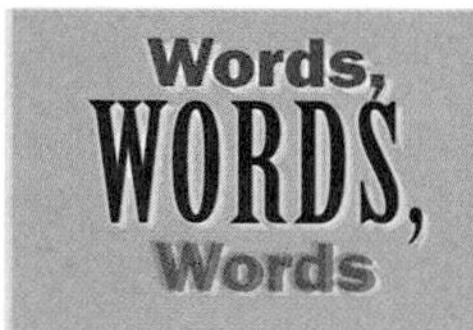

restricted: stopped from doing something
ensured: made sure

It's no secret that kids look up to famous athletes. Lots of young fans want to be just like the stars they admire. In Jackie Robinson's case, that was a good thing. Robinson was a great role model. But not every athlete sets the fine example that Robinson did. Some people think that's OK. They say that athletes are people like anyone else. You can't expect them to lead perfect lives. Others disagree. They feel it's a star's duty to be a good role model to fans.

What do you think? Read this debate and decide for yourself.

yes

Like it or not, star athletes should be positive role models. It's the price they pay for fame. Pro athletes live their lives in the spotlight. Thousands of kids look up to them and want to follow in their footsteps. When a star breaks the law, or just acts like a jerk, it's as though he or she is telling all those kids it's okay. That's not cool. And just look at how much top athletes are paid. For that much money, the least they can do is behave well. It's a star's duty to set a good example for his or her fans.

If you said yes:

- Should other famous people like rock stars and movie stars be role models as well? Where do you draw the line?

no

It's true that kids need role models. But that duty should be left up to parents, teachers, and other adults who've *chosen* to take on the job. Athletes get paid to play sports—not to show people how to live. It's not fair to expect them to be role models. Top athletes may be rich and famous, but they're still human. They make mistakes just like anyone else. What's more, it's not their fault that the whole world gets to hear about their mistakes. The media should stick to athletes' careers and stop reporting on their personal lives.

If you said no:

- What do you think should happen to athletes who misbehave in public or during a game?

What's your point of view?

Talk About It

Now that you've read "The Man Who Changed America" and "Should Athletes Be Role Models?" what do you have to say about these questions?

- Why do you think people love sports and professional athletes so much? Do you? Explain.
- Who is your favorite athlete? Why?

Comprehension Check

Write your answers to the questions below. Use information from the photo essay and debate to support your answers.

1. What hardships did Jackie Robinson endure when he joined the Brooklyn Dodgers?
2. Why does Jackie say that he couldn't just be good, he had to be great?
3. What do today's professional athletes owe to Jackie Robinson?
4. Why do some people think that athletes should not have to be role models?
5. If he were alive today, what do you think Jackie Robinson would say about athletes as role models?

Vocabulary Check

Complete each sentence with the correct vocabulary word.

taunts **established** **restricted**
mediocre **ensured**

1. I tried out for the soccer team even though I was only a _______ player.
2. The other students' _______ hurt my feelings.
3. The teacher was hired because she was an _______ expert in math.
4. The coach noticed my improvement and _______ that I would have a place on the team.
5. Now I am no longer _______ to sitting on the bench during a game.

Write About It

Choose one of the writing prompts below.

- Write the copy that might appear on a "Jackie Robinson Award" certificate. What kind of person might win such an award?
- Write a letter to all the people who gave Jackie Robinson a hard time. In the letter, tell them what they would be missing if they succeeded in keeping African Americans out of major league sports.
- Write down your best argument why an athlete should or should not be expected to be a role model for young people. Give at least three reasons to support your argument.

More to READ

If you want to find out more about Jackie Robinson, or just more about life in Brooklyn in the late 1940s, check out:

Stealing Home: The Story of Jackie Robinson
By Barry Denenberg

This biography gives you a lot more details about Jackie Robinson's life and his historic career with the Brooklyn Dodgers. Learn more about the hardships and triumphs of Jackie's first few seasons.

In the Year of the Boar and Jackie Robinson
By Bette Bao Lord

It's 1947, and Shirley Temple Wong has just moved from China to Brooklyn. At first, life in this strange new city is difficult and lonely. Then Shirley discovers the Brooklyn Dodgers and their controversial star, Jackie Robinson.

Evaluating Sports Statistics

You and your friends love pro basketball. You always argue about which players are the best. What you need are some stats to back you up. The box scores below are from an imaginary final game of a championship series.

Look at the stats. Can you figure out what they mean?

Box Scores: Chicago Bulls and Utah Jazz

"RB" is short for "rebound." A rebound is when a player grabs the ball after a missed shot.

"FG" stands for "field goal." A field goal is a 2-point shot. "3P" is a basket made from behind the 3-point line.

Chicago Bulls

PLAYER	MINUTES PLAYED	FG MADE OR	FG ATTEMPTED	3P MADE OR	3P ATTEMPTED	FT MADE OR	FT ATTEMPTED	RB	TOTAL POINTS
PIPPEN	43	5	17	1	4	10	12	9	23
RODMAN	33	0	4	0	1	1	2	11	1
LONGLEY	14	0	4	0	0	0	0	3	0
HARPER	18	1	4	0	1	0	0	3	2
JORDAN	44	14	35	1	4	8	10	11	39
WILLIAMS	23	2	5	0	0	0	0	7	4
KUKOC	25	2	6	1	1	2	4	4	9
KERR	25	2	5	1	2	2	2	1	9
CAFFEY	2	0	0	0	0	0	0	0	0
BUECHLER	8	0	1	1	1	0	0	1	3
BROWN	5	0	0	0	0	0	0	0	0
TOTALS	240	26	81	5	14	23	30	50	90

Utah Jazz

PLAYER	MINUTES PLAYED	FG MADE OR	FG ATTEMPTED	3P MADE OR	3P ATTEMPTED	FT MADE OR	FT ATTEMPTED	RB	TOTAL POINTS
RUSSELL	43	3	10	3	8	2	2	3	17
MALONE	44	7	15	0	0	7	15	7	21
OSTERTAG	21	0	2	0	0	1	2	8	1
STOCKTON	37	5	9	0	1	3	3	6	13
HORNACEK	36	2	9	2	4	8	9	4	18
EISLEY	11	2	5	0	0	2	2	0	6
FOSTER	5	0	1	0	0	0	0	2	0
CARR	6	1	2	0	0	0	0	0	2
ANDERSON	26	2	10	0	1	4	6	3	8
MORRIS	11	0	2	0	1	0	0	3	0
TOTALS	240	22	65	5	15	27	39	36	86

"FT" stands for "free throw," a shot worth one point. Players get to take free throws when they are fouled while shooting.

Keeping Score

Who's leading the league? Review the box scores on the left and reread the tips that go with them. Then use the scores to answer the questions below.

1. Who won the final game and locked up the championship? What was the final score of the game?

2. Take a look at how Scottie Pippen did in this game. How many points did he score? How many rebounds did he make? How much time did he spend on the court?

3. Which player made the most three-point shots in this game? What team did he play for?

4. Which two players scored the most points in the game?
   a. Jordan and Malone
   b. Jordan and Pippen
   c. Pippen and Malone

5. **Write about it.** Dennis Rodman scored only one point in this game. Does that mean that he didn't help his team very much? (Hint: Check his rebounds.)

Create a Team

Choose five players from this lesson. Make a box score chart for their first game. Use the same stats for the players as those in this lesson. What is your team's total score? What is their rebound total?

Do the Stats

Watch a basketball game. Track one player's field goals, free throws, three-pointers, and rebounds. Check your records against the official box scores in the newspaper. How did you do?

"The National Basketball Association has a great Web site at www.nba.com. You can find stats there for all the NBA teams. Other pro sports leagues have Web sites, too."

Real-World Words

attempted: tried
league: a group of sports teams
stats: short for statistics, facts expressed as numbers or percentages

nonfiction article

Ricky-mania: Over 3,000 fans waited outside a California record store in 1999 for pop idol Ricky Martin to appear.

THE LATINO NEW WAVE

By Mireya Navarro, Peter Vilbig, and Susan Brenna

HISPANIC CULTURE HAS ARRIVED IN AMERICA IN A BIG WAY. FIND OUT HOW.

It was Saturday night in Tampa, Florida. Rosana Estevez sneaked away from her high school dance. She made a beeline for Casa Blanca, the hot Latin teen club. All she wanted to do was dance. The Dominican-born Estevez pushed her way onto the dance floor. Hundreds of Peruvian, Puerto Rican, and Cuban kids were moving together under a huge disco ball.

Estevez explained why she left her own high school dance. "People were just standing around there," she said. "Only five people were dancing. Here, people will dance and they don't care about what other people think."

But Estevez and her Casa Blanca pals are only one small part of a huge cultural change. More people are dancing. But that may be the least of it. Latinos—the word that is most often used for people whose families come from Spanish-speaking countries—are changing the face of the United States.

In Las Cruces, New Mexico, high school student-artist Hector Hernandez views the mural he painted with other students.

A Growing Presence

There's no doubt about it. Latino influence is growing in America. Just look at the facts:

- Spanish words have entered the language faster than you can say *que pasa.*
- Novelists such as Gary Soto and Sandra Cisneros are on most middle school, high school and college reading lists.
- Dominican-born Sammy Sosa has hit hundreds of homers out of U.S. ballparks.
- Colorful murals, inspired by Mexican painters like Diego Rivera, are appearing on buildings in U.S. cities.
- Musicians from many Latin-American countries are making their voices heard in the U.S.
- Salsa outsells ketchup as our number-one condiment.

It's happening from food to music to art. Latinos are adding more than flavor to the mix. They're **redefining** what's uniquely American.

Latinos are no newcomers to America. They've been here since the 1500s.

The Power of Numbers

So what's causing this explosion of Latino influence? Part of the answer lies in sheer numbers. Latinos are the fastest-growing ethnic group in the U.S. By 2005, they will overtake African Americans as the nation's largest minority group. By 2050, one in four Americans will be Latino.

"We're having a tremendous impact on all parts of culture," says Larry Gonzalez. Gonzalez is a member of the National Association of Latino Elected Officials. "We've got our foot in the door. We're opening it wider and wider every day."

Latinos are no newcomers to America. They've been here since the 1500s. They arrived way before English-speaking pilgrims did on the *Mayflower*. But Latino communities were always small. They lived far away from the Anglos (non-Hispanic whites). Today, Latinos have **merged** with the mainstream.

The Latin trend is most visible in the world of pop music. Gloria Estefan has always been popular with Latino and Anglo audiences. Now, Latin singers like Ricky Martin, Marc Anthony, and Shakira are hot. Teens are going

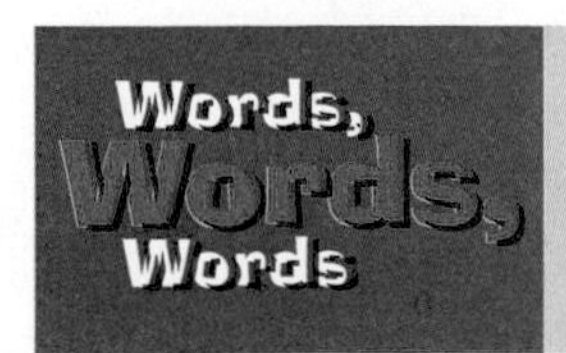

redefining: giving new meaning to
merged: joined together
strides: gains or improvements

crazy over these stars. Their popularity has reached a level not seen since the Beatles in the 1960s.

Beyond Pop

But many Americans hope the rise of Latin pop won't go down as the Latino revolution's main achievement. "I'd be prouder to see a Latino president than to see Ricky Martin win another Grammy," said Marilyn Aguila, a Florida high school student.

That dream may become reality someday soon. Latinos have made huge **strides** in U.S. politics. Every national politician goes after the Latino vote. Why? It's because of where Latinos live. The five states with the largest Latino populations are California, Texas, New York, Florida, and Illinois. Those same states deliver almost two-thirds of the electoral votes needed to win the U.S. presidency.

Candidates during the 2000 presidential campaign took these numbers seriously. Some even took lessons in order to address Latino crowds in Spanish.

ASK YOURSELF

- Why do politicians care about the Latino vote?

Think about the states where most Latinos live and what their size means.

▶ America's Future

The U.S. population projected for 2000 and 2050, broken down by race and ethnic origin:

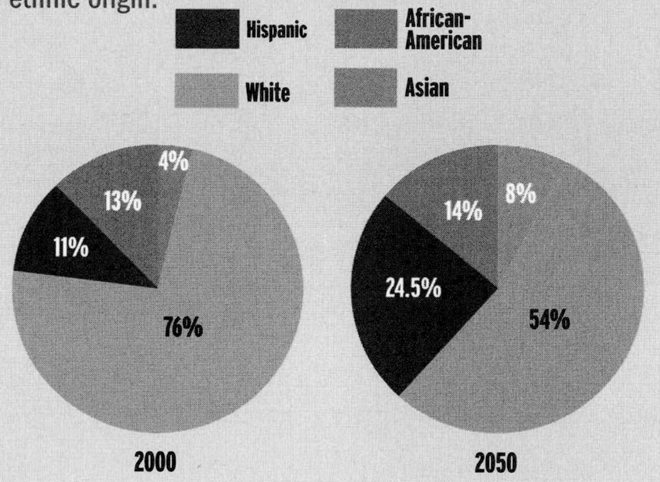

▶ Where U.S. Latinos Live

The percentage of the Latino population of the ten states with the highest Latino population:

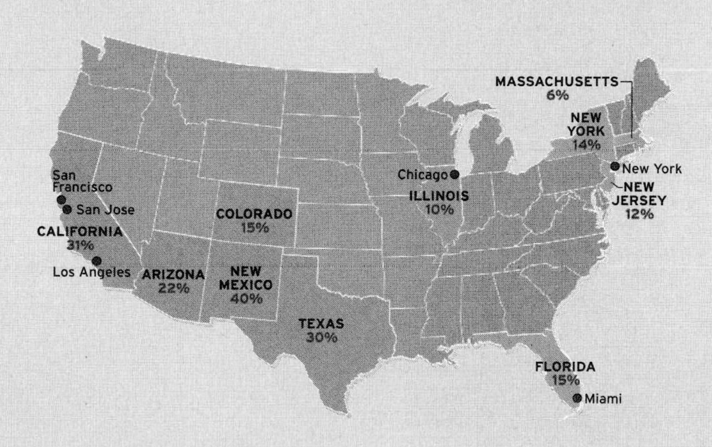

▶ Where They Come From

The U.S. Latino population broken down according to country of origin:

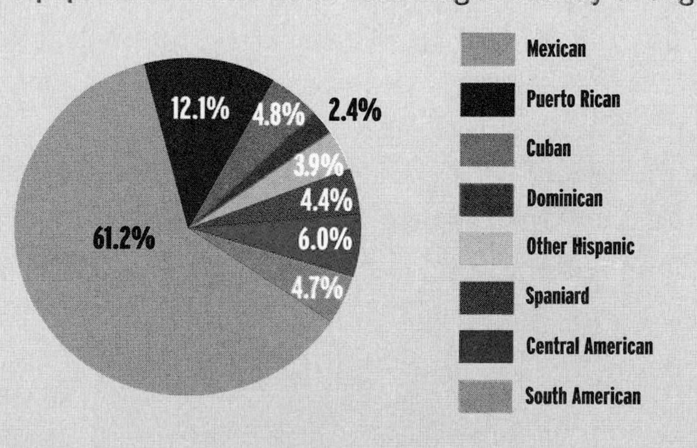

A celebration of pride: the Puerto Rican Day parade in New York City

Outside the Voting Booth

Latinos are making an **impact** outside politics, too. More and more, they're using the power of the pocketbook. By 2020, Latinos are expected to spend about $520 billion per year. And they are making inroads in the business world. A dozen Latinos have risen to the top of Fortune 1000 companies. These companies are the biggest in the U.S.

Latinos are also entering the world of technology. Carlos Cardona founded Yupi.com, a Spanish-language Web site. He wanted to help his father understand computers. Yupi has become a huge success. It is one of the most-visited Spanish-language sites on the Web.

Then there are the words we speak. Spanish phrases like *que bueno* (awesome) and *que pasa* (what's up) are used more and more by English speakers. They've joined other Spanish words, like *patio* and *cafeteria,* that have been used by English speakers for years.

Javier Deligne, a Florida teen, works part-time in a Burger King. There, he's seen the growing acceptance of Spanish firsthand. His manager, who is Anglo, used to ignore Latino employees when they spoke in Spanish. But now the manager has begun to say things like, *"Pollo con queso,"*

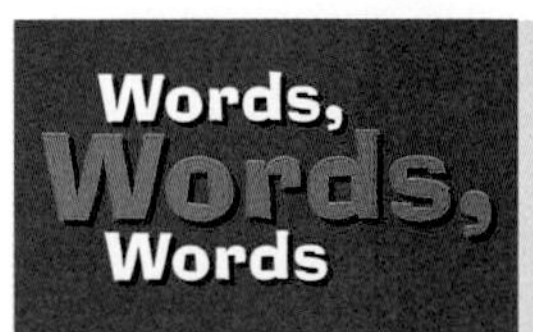

impact: a strong effect
acceptance: feeling like you belong
preserve: to protect something so that it stays in its original state

when he wants a chicken sandwich with cheese. "He wants to fit in around us," says Deligne.

Latino Teens Struggle

Many Latino teens care about what happens in Hollywood or the White House. But that is less important than what goes down on the home front. That's where the true struggles for identity and **acceptance** take place. For some teens, the choice is a tough one. Should they become a part of American culture or **preserve** the heritage of their families?

Sofia Angela Lopez of Houston, Texas, passed up the traditional Mexican 15th birthday party to have a Sweet 16 party instead. "I don't really know how Mexico is," says Lopez. "I'm more like, 'This is America now.' "

But other teens struggle to hold on to their Latino culture. "It's something we should be proud of," says Bridget Mendez, 16, of North Hollywood, California. "It's something beautiful." ●

ASK YOURSELF

- Why do some Latino teens struggle with their identity?

Put what these teens have said into your own words.

What's Your Latin IQ?

Think you know your quesadillas from your nachos? Your samba from your salsa? Test your Latino culture IQ here. Answers given below.

1. The poncho is:
a. A tent used for camping
b. A cloak that looks like a blanket with a hole in the center for the head

2. A guayabera is:
a. A grilled pork sandwich
b. A pleated men's shirt

3. "Conga" was:
a. Gloria Estefan's breakthrough recording in 1985
b. Elvis Crespo's MTV launchpad

4. A pupusa is:
a. A Salvadoran stuffed pancake
b. A Dominican leather pouch

5. A traditional Mexican wedding song that's still a hit on oldies radio is:
a. Carlos Santana's "Oye Como Va"
b. Ritchie Valens's "La Bamba"

6. What young Latino singer has a father who crooned to your parents' generation?
a. Marc Anthony
b. Enrique Iglesias

7. What group was Ricky Martin a part of as a child?
a. Menudo
b. New Kids on the Block

8. Gloria Estefan helped this Colombian-born singer adapt her album into English:
a. Esmerelda Santiago
b. Shakira

9. Christy Haubegger is:
a. The publisher of *Latina* magazine
b. The talk show host called the "Spanish Oprah"

10. What is the birth country of Chicago Cubs slugger Sammy Sosa?
a. Brazil
b. Dominican Republic

11. Gary Soto is a
a. Politician
b. Novelist

12. Which of the following states has the larger Latino population?
a. Florida
b. Massachusetts

ANSWERS

1) b 2) b 3) a 4) a 5) b 6) b
7) a 8) b 9) a 10) b 11) b 12) a

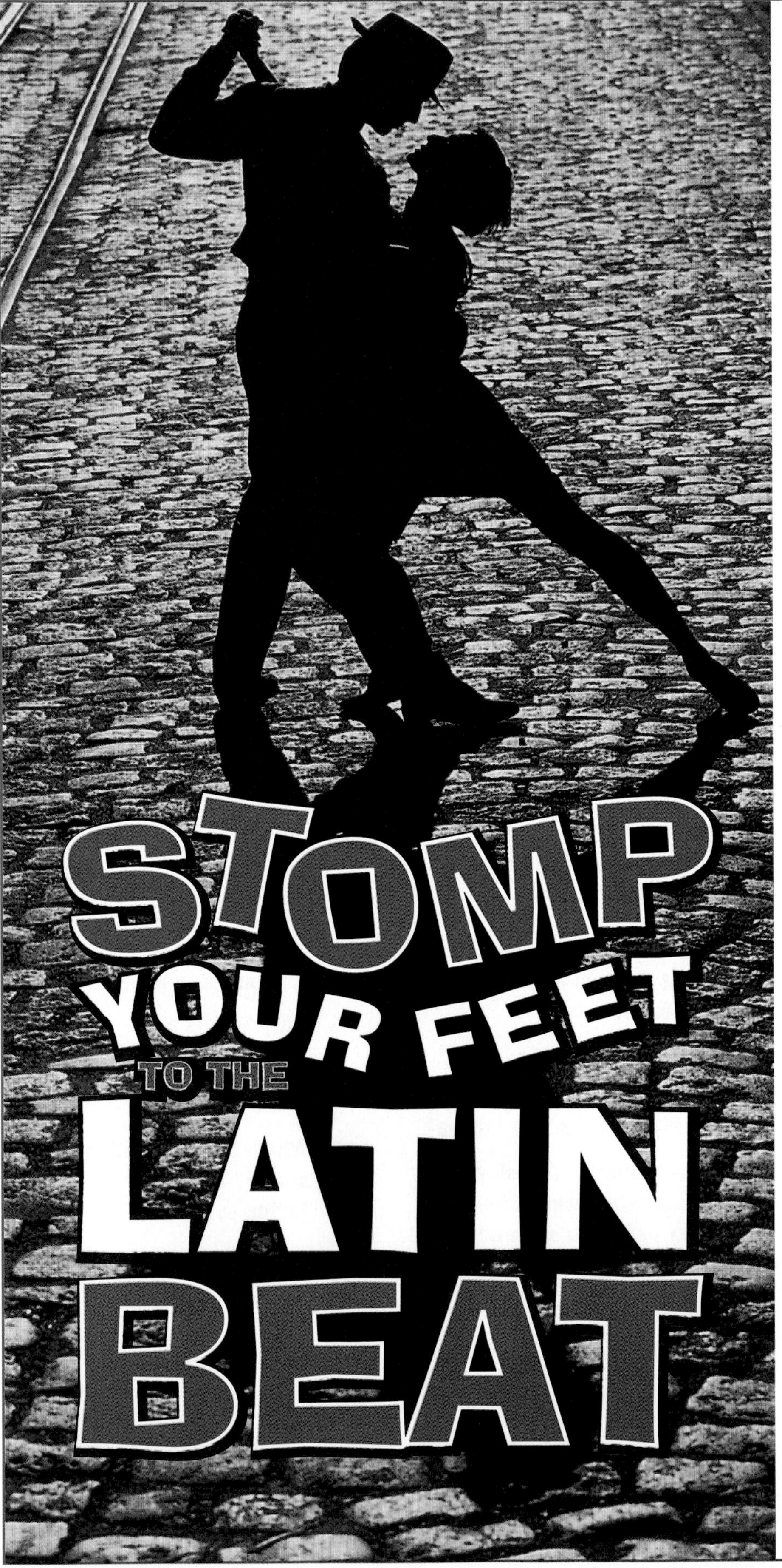

Latin music is sweeping the country. But there's more to it than just Ricky Martin.

by Jennifer Smith

One minute, the mood is low-key. A group of friends hang out on couches and munch on snacks. Then somebody plugs in a boom box—and suddenly, everyone's in motion. For Latino kids nationwide, a party's just not a party without dancing. Not head-bopping. Not foot-tapping. Real dancing—salsa, merengue, bachata, and cumbia to be exact.

Maybe you've never heard of these dances before, but unless you've been on another planet for the past few years, you know Latin music is hot, hot, hot. Pop acts like Ricky Martin, Shakira, and Marc Anthony have been bringing new flavor to the music scene.

Nobody takes more pride in these success stories than Latino teens in America. "It helps people realize that Hispanics are talented," says Maurice Corchado of New York.

Latino music stars also inspire Latino teens. Armando Alderete of Houston, Texas, is putting together a band that will sing in Spanish and English. He says Ricky Martin is a role model: "He's good at what he does and he makes people happy." Armando even admits to copying a few dance steps from his idol.

But Martin and Shakira are just the tip of the iceberg. There's a lot more to the sounds of Latino culture. Traditional music, sung in Spanish, is common ground for family members of all ages. Grandparents, parents, and kids pick up dance steps from each other. "My brothers and sisters would put on a show for me while they were cleaning the house," says Jovel Roman of New York City.

It's About Having Fun!

Latin dance may start in the home. But by the time kids hit the teen years, it's all about having fun with your friends. Having a dance partner is important. But having a boyfriend or girlfriend isn't. When a couple is on the floor, it's not always about love, but it's always fun. "When you dance the cumbia, it just makes you feel good," says Bonnie Mesquita of Pasadena, Texas.

Today's Latino teens may also update the moves they were raised on. Stephanie Vasquez of Miami, Florida, likes to go clubbing on teen nights. The DJs create a whole new style by mixing both Latin and hip-hop rhythms, and Spanish lyrics and rap vocals. "I drag a friend onto the dance floor and we just move," says Vasquez.

But dancing goes beyond the fun factor. It's also a way for Hispanic teens to celebrate their heritage and self-esteem. "When you dance, you're representing where you're from," says Michelle Fermin of New York City. "It's a way of saying, 'Look, we're Hispanic, this is how we dance, and we're good at it.' "●

Say it en español

Heard the terms but don't know what they mean? Here's a guide to the language that leads the Latin dance scene.

bailamos: You might know this as the title of an Enrique Iglesias hit. But in Spanish, this word is an invitation to the dance floor. It means "Would you like to dance?"

bongos: These percussion instruments are the little cousins to the conga drums.

chevere: As in hip and cool. Pronounced "CHAY-veh-ray," it's another way for saying something's "the bomb."

congas and timbales: Congas are tall and deep and get played with the palms of your hands. Timbales are short and loud and get played with sticks. Both produce the beats that make Latin music unique. They go together like beans and rice.

guayabera: Many Latin *abuelos* (grandfathers) wore these loose-fitting cotton shirts, made cool for the tropics. Now they're back and hot again—in a spectrum of colors.

maracas: You're likely to find these handheld rattles or shakers at many Latin parties.

merengue: This Dominican music dates back to the 19th century. But there's nothing old-fashioned about this lively rhythm that is danced like a very fast walk, with plenty of turns and spins.

salsa: You can eat it. But better still, you can dance it, as a couple, fast or medium-paced. Loud trumpets and Latin percussion lead the way.

suave: Used to describe music, it's the rating you'd give to a really good song. Instead of the English pronunciation, say "SUAV-ay" and you'll sound like a native speaker.

Talk About It

Now that you've read "The Latino New Wave" and "Stomp Your Feet to the Latin Beat," what do you have to say about these questions?

- What would you say is the most important or interesting contribution that your ancestors' culture has made to the United States?
- Some people have called the United States a "melting pot" because people from so many backgrounds have come here to live. What are the advantages of this?

Comprehension Check

Write your answers to the questions below. Use information from the two articles to support your answers.

1. How long have Latinos been in the United States?
2. Why does Marilyn Aguila say that she'd rather see a Latino become president than see a pop star win more Grammy awards?
3. How has the "Latino explosion" affected your life? If it hasn't, why do you think that is?
4. Why has Ricky Martin been compared to the Beatles?
5. Why do you think Latino music is becoming so popular?

Vocabulary Check

Complete each sentence starter below. Before you answer, think about the meaning of the vocabulary word in bold.

1. The store is **redefining** itself by . . .
2. Our team made great **strides** after . . .
3. The two bands **merged** after . . .
4. She had great **impact** on . . .
5. His **acceptance** in the school was proven by . . .

Write About It

Choose one of the writing prompts below.

- ▶ Write a review of your favorite book or record by a Latino writer or musician.
- ▶ Write a brief biography or career profile of one of the famous Latinos mentioned in the reading.
- ▶ Write a paragraph describing your feelings about the importance of holding on to traditions.

Do you have what it takes to salsa with the best? If not, here are some basic moves to get you out on the dance floor.

The Right Moves

- ▶ **Keep your feet and knees close together.**
- ▶ **Using small steps, shuffle your feet back and forth in place.**
- ▶ **As you dance, let your hips rock from side to side. You can move your shoulders to the beat if you like.**

Keep the Beat

- ▶ **Salsa music has four beats to a measure. That means you can count the beat out like this: 1, 2, 3, 4 (repeat).**
- ▶ **When you dance to salsa, you move on three beats, and pause on the fourth: 1, 2, 3 (pause on 4), 1, 2, 3 (pause on 4).**

Reading a Pie Chart

You're a boss in the music business. Your assistant took a useful survey. He asked kids to name their favorite kind of music. He presented the results on a pie chart, but you're not sure how to read it.

Look at the chart. Read all about it. Can you figure it out?

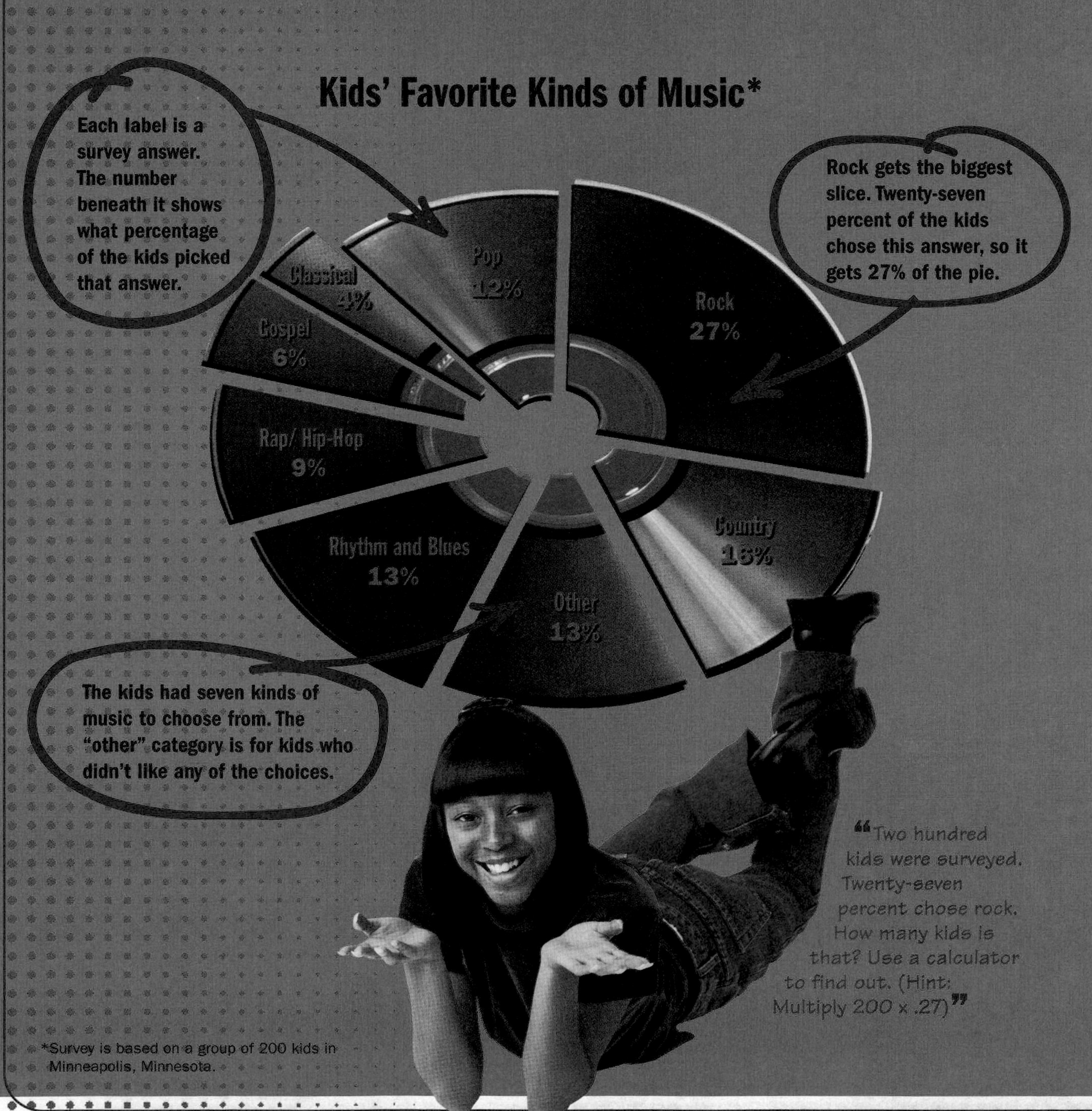

*Survey is based on a group of 200 kids in Minneapolis, Minnesota.

Have a Slice

Do you know whose discs will sell? Reading this chart is the first step toward finding the next big hit. Use the chart and the tips to answer the questions below. Write your answers on your own paper.

1. What is the most popular type of music? The second most popular? What is the least popular type?

2. Which two statements are true?
a. More people like rock than country.
b. More people like pop than gospel.
c. More people like pop than country.

3. Two kids said that jazz was their favorite kind of music. In which slice of pie is their answer shown?

4. Nine percent of the kids said that rap/hip-hop was their favorite kind of music. Out of 200 kids, how many kids is that? (Hint: See the tip below the chart.)

5. What is the total percentage of kids who like each of these combinations of music?
a. rock and pop
b. gospel and country
c. rap/hip-hop and rhythm and blues

Take a Survey

Survey 10 kids in your class. Ask them what their favorite type of music is. Give them the same choices that appear on this chart. Make a list of their answers.

Chart It Out

Make a pie chart that shows your results. (Hint: Your survey is based on 10 kids. So if two kids like rock best, then rock will be 20% of your pie, and so on.)

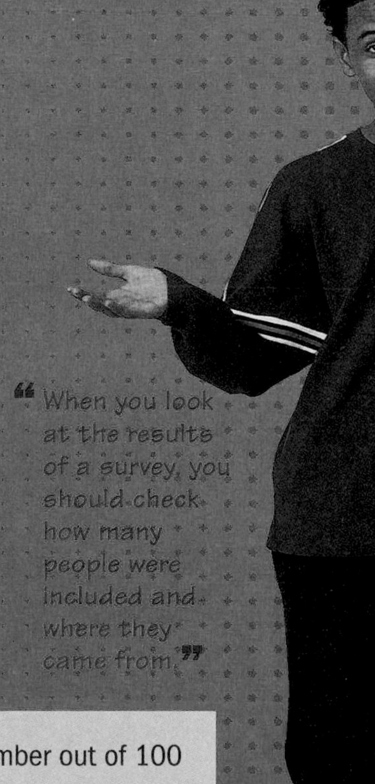

Real-World Words

percentage: a fraction of something, stated as a number out of 100
results: responses to a survey
survey: a report or study of people's opinions about something

play

by R. L. Stine

R. L. Stine is best known for his humorous and exaggerated tales. Here, once again, he uses fantasy and wacky twists in his writing. The events in Stine's stories are never possible . . . but always entertaining!

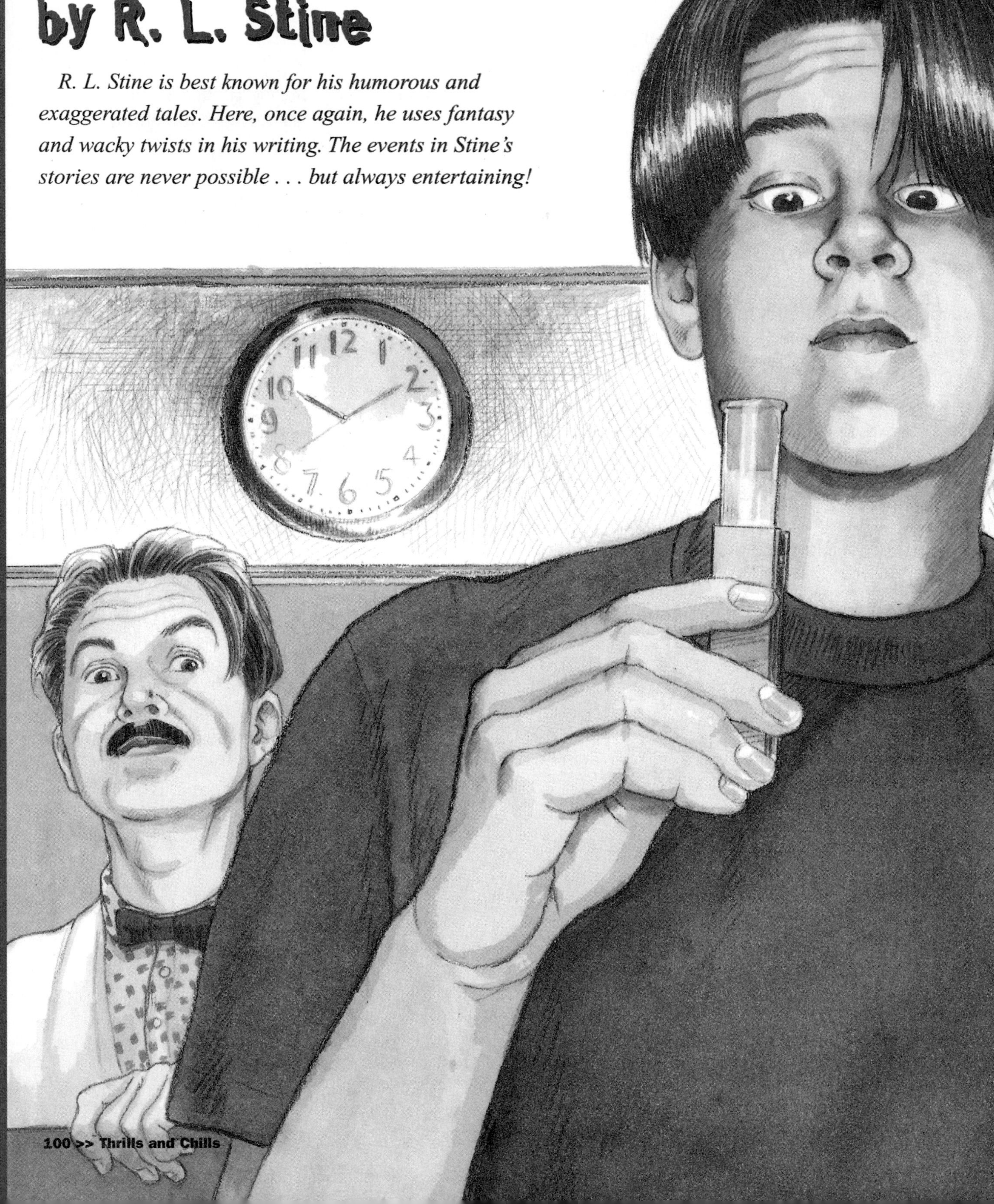

Jordie's Revenge

Will Jordie's unusual science project scare his classmates to death?

CHARACTERS

Narrator 1 *

Narrator 2 *

Jordie Barron, a high-school boy *

Mr. Harwood, a chemistry teacher *

Gene Polk, a football player

Norm Spring, Jordie's uncle *

Marvin, Norm's assistant

Krystal, a high-school girl

* Starred parts are major roles.

SCENE ONE

Narrator 1: Jordie is having a bad day in chemistry class. He has to identify a chemical compound in a test tube. He can't figure it out—no matter how hard he tries.

Narrator 2: Jordie's teacher, Mr. Harwood, sees Jordie struggling. Mr. Harwood has a reputation for being a tough teacher. He doesn't always have patience with his students. He's usually very hard on Jordie in this class.

Harwood: Your lab work is incredibly sloppy. How do you expect to pass this course?

Narrator 1: Jordie stares hard at the floor—as usual.

Harwood: My goldfish does better compound analysis than you do. Are you listening to me?

Jordie *(embarrassed):* Yes, sir.

Harwood: Focus on the compound in the test tube. Have you even sniffed it yet? That's the most basic test.

> "What's wrong, Jordie? You look like something the cat dragged in."

Narrator 2: A few people laugh. Jordie looks angrily around at the smirking faces. He wishes he could disappear.

Harwood: Go ahead! Sniff it! Are you waiting for a formal invitation?

Narrator 1: Jordie wants to walk out of the classroom. But he needs a good grade. So he picks up the test tube. He sniffs. Suddenly, a burning sensation grips his nose. He drops the test tube. It shatters. Tears pour from his eyes. His nose runs.

Harwood: Reckless. That was very reckless! You must sniff cautiously when you don't know what's in a test tube. Would you care to make a guess right now?

Jordie *(whispering):* The chemical compound is ammonia.

Harwood: You're right. And you may have learned something about doing a sniff test.

Jordie: Yes, sir.

Narrator 2: Everyone is laughing at him again. Jordie feels humiliated. He sinks down low in his chair.

Krystal *(whispering):* Would you like a tissue?

Jordie: Thanks.

Narrator 1: He takes the tissue from her. Jordie thinks Krystal is the only **decent** person in the whole class. Everyone else is mean. The way they laugh makes Mr. Harwood focus on Jordie even more. It **encourages** him.

Narrator 2: Mr. Harwood turns away from Jordie. He starts to talk to the rest of the class.

Harwood: Just a reminder. As you all should know, the science fair will be held in this lab on Saturday morning. You should have your projects here by seven-thirty.

Narrator 1: Jordie gasps. He had completely forgotten about the fair.

Harwood: I will judge the science projects again this year. And I expect . . .

Narrator 2: Before Mr. Harwood can finish talking, the bell rings. As Jordie escapes into the hall, he feels a hand on his shoulder. It's Gene Polk, a popular football player. Gene pushes a dirty gym sock into Jordie's face.

Gene: How about giving this the sniff test? Sniff it, boy. Sniff it!

Jordie *(breaking away):* No! You sniff it!

Narrator 1: Everyone around Jordie laughs.

SCENE TWO

Narrator 2: Jordie is angry about what happened in chemistry class. And he's worried about the science fair. So he goes to see his Uncle Norm. Norm likes to listen and tells good jokes.

Narrator 1: Norm is only in his twenties. But he has his own business. He owns the **Eternal** Rest Funeral Home.

Norm: Come in, kid. What's wrong, Jordie? You look like something the cat dragged in. What's the matter?

Jordie: Rough day at school. So how's business?

Norm *(laughing):* Business is

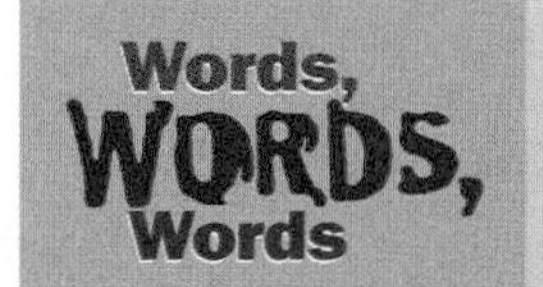

decent: thoughtful or kind
encourages: shows approval for one's actions
eternal: lasting forever
dissect: to cut apart a human body in order to examine it

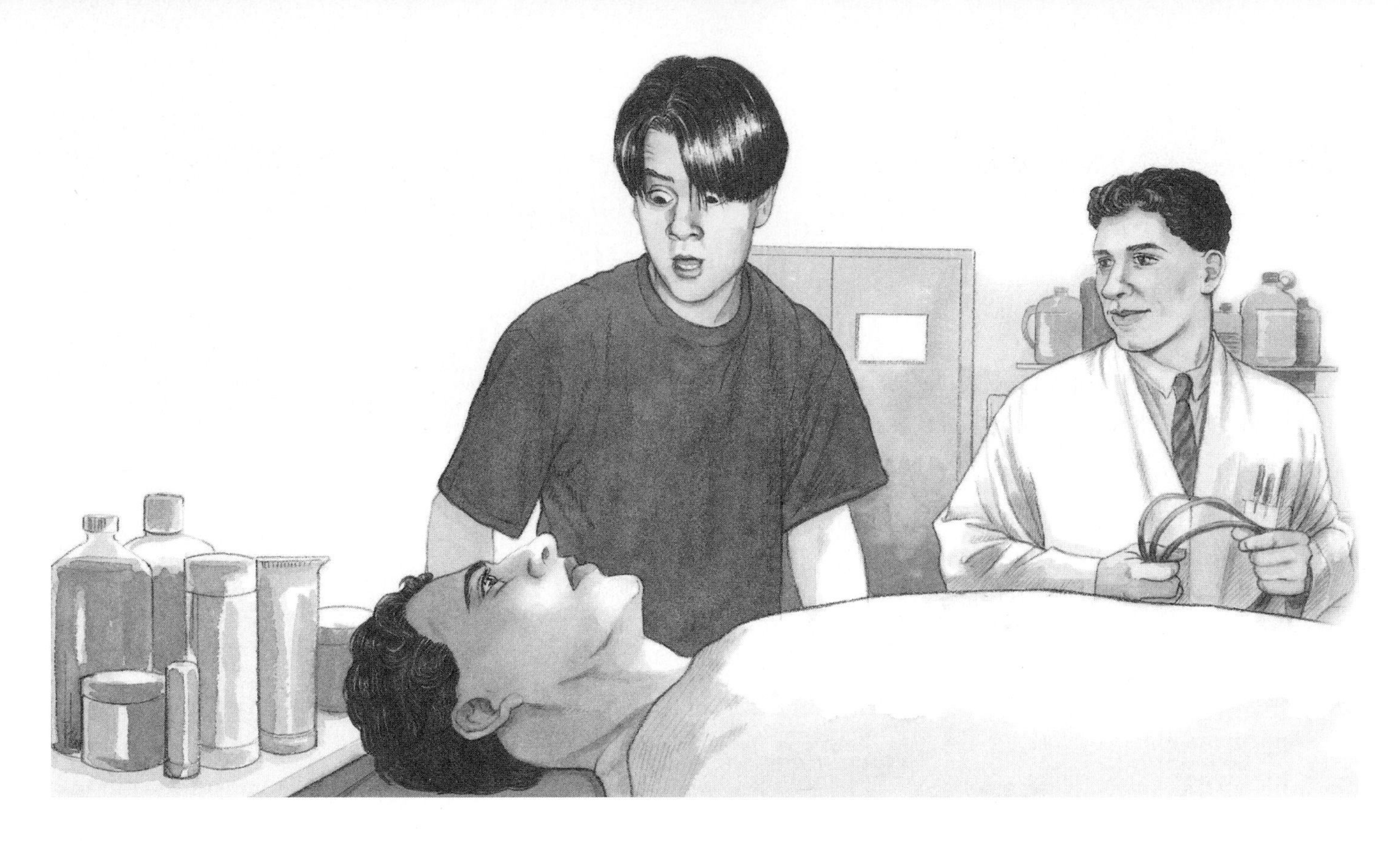

dead—as usual.

Jordie *(cheering up):* I thought people were dying to get in here!

Norm: Well, they are. Let me show you my latest client. His funeral isn't until Sunday.

Narrator 2: Norm takes Jordie over to his work table. When Jordie sees the corpse, he is shocked.

Jordie: Norm! He looks exactly like you!

Norm: He's just my age too.

Jordie: This is so weird! You don't have a twin brother, do you?

Norm: Not that I know of.

Narrator 1: Jordie stares at the corpse. Suddenly he has an idea. He can't believe how great it is.

SCENE THREE

Narrator 2: Jordie stands for a moment thinking about his idea. But he can't keep it a secret.

Jordie: Norm, I have the craziest idea.

Norm: That's normal for you, kid.

Jordie: Could you help me out with my science-fair project? And maybe play a joke on my class?

Norm: The joke part sounds interesting. Spill.

Narrator 1: Jordie tells Norm everything that happened at school. He really wants to get back at Mr. Harwood and the whole class. Norm understands how he feels.

Norm: So what's your crazy idea?

Jordie: You might not want to do it. It's kind of . . . uh . . . unprofessional.

Norm: I love it already.

Jordie: I'd like to bring the corpse in for my science project.

Norm: Whoa! What do you plan to do with him?

Jordie: Nothing. It's just a joke. But I'll tell Harwood that I'm going to **dissect** it.

ASK Yourself

- Why does Jordie want to play a joke on his science class?

Sum up what has happened to Jordie in chemistry class.

Norm (*hesitating*): I don't know, Jordie.

Jordie: He'll want to inspect the corpse first. So I'll wheel in the casket and show it to him.

Norm (*concerned*): I can't let you cut this guy up. That wouldn't be right.

Jordie: There won't be any cutting. After Harwood inspects the corpse, I'll wheel it back to the parking lot. Are you with me?

Norm: I guess.

Jordie: In the parking lot, we'll make the switch.

Norm: Switch? What switch?

Jordie: We'll take the corpse out of the casket. Then you'll climb in there instead.

Norm (*getting it*): I'm beginning to like this idea. I'll be dressed just like the corpse, right? And I'll be wearing makeup to make me look dead.

Jordie: Right. Then I'll wheel the casket back into the classroom. I'll get out my dissecting tools.

Norm: I think I get it. Harwood will ask you to **proceed.** You'll open the casket.

Jordie: Right. Everyone will be watching. They'll probably hold their noses and make bad jokes. They'll think you're a stiff. But when I move toward you, you'll raise your arms. You'll jump right out of the casket. You'll chase everyone. They'll be scared for the rest of their lives!

Norm: I love it! It's a great joke!

Jordie: But will you do it?

Norm (*laughing*): It's too good. I can't say no!

"Our plan's perfect. It's foolproof! After this, people will think twice before they pick on me again."

SCENE FOUR

Narrator 2: The next day, Jordie tells Mr. Harwood about his project.

Harwood (*turning pale*): You're dissecting a corpse? That's an unusual project. Are you sure you have the stomach for it?

Jordie: I hope so, sir.

Harwood (*skeptically*): Well, just don't give it the sniff test.

Jordie: No, sir.

Harwood: Of course, I'll want to inspect the corpse first. I'll need to make sure it's in good condition. Otherwise, it might upset everyone. We wouldn't want that, would we?

Jordie (*trying to keep from laughing*): No, sir. We certainly wouldn't want that.

Narrator 1: Later in the day, Jordie and Norm talk. Norm suggests a few changes in the plan.

Norm: I'll have my assistant, Marvin, drive the hearse to school. That way I can hide in the back of it.

Jordie: And then?

Norm: Marvin will be with you when Mr. Harwood inspects the corpse. Then Marvin will say he forgot something back in the hearse.

Jordie: Why?

Norm: It will give him a chance to take the casket back outside with him. When he does, we'll take the corpse out. Then I'll climb in. When we're ready, Marvin will wheel me into the classroom.

Jordie: Our plan's perfect! It's **foolproof!** After this, people will think twice before they pick on me again.

SCENE FIVE

Narrator 2: Jordie gets up early Saturday morning. He is so excited he can hardly stand it. He goes to meet the hearse at school. But Marvin is late getting there. Finally, he arrives fifteen minutes late.

Jordie: Good morning, Marvin.

Narrator 1: Marvin starts to take the casket out of the hearse. He turns to Jordie.

Marvin: Listen. There's something I've got to tell you.

Jordie: There's no time. Tell me later. We've got to hurry. We're late for the science fair!

Marvin: But I've got to tell you one thing. It's important!

Narrator 2: Jordie is too excited to listen. He hurries off before Marvin can finish. He can't wait to take the casket in to show Mr. Harwood.

Harwood: So this is the famous corpse. I hope it's fresh enough to display.

Jordie *(smiling):* Oh, it's fresh. Very fresh.

Narrator 1: Mr. Harwood opens the lid. He looks inside.

Harwood: Your uncle does very nice work.

Jordie: Thanks.

Narrator 2: Mr. Harwood finishes inspecting the corpse. Marvin just stands there. For a second, Jordie is afraid that Marvin has forgotten the plan. He gives him a quick kick.

Marvin: Oh, yeah. There's just one thing. I forgot something outside. I'll have this corpse back in a jiffy.

Narrator 1: As they planned, Marvin starts to wheel the casket back to the hearse. Marvin whispers to Jordie as they leave.

Marvin *(whispering):* Jordie, come with me. I have to talk to you.

Narrator 2: Jordie tries to go with Marvin. But Mr. Harwood stops him at the door.

Harwood: Just a minute, young man! You haven't filled out your entry form. You have to do it right now. I insist.

Jordie: OK, sir.

Narrator 1: Jordie watches **anxiously** as Marvin pushes the casket out the door.

Narrator 2: A bit later, Marvin comes back with the casket. He tries to talk to Jordie one last time.

Marvin: Listen. I've got to tell you one thing.

ASK Yourself

- What do you think Marvin needs to tell Jordie?

Make your best prediction based on what you know about these kinds of stories.

SCENE SIX

Narrator 1: Just then Mr. Harwood begins to shout.

Harwood: Silence! Silence, everyone! We must have silence so we can start. Today we'll begin with Krystal.

Narrator 2: Marvin gives up and leaves. Krystal brings her project to the front of the room.

Harwood (*tapping his foot as he speaks):* What have you got there? A fruit market of some kind?

Krystal: No, sir. It's a model of the solar system. I've made the planets out of different fruits.

Harwood *(sarcastically):* How clever. Do you plan to eat the solar system after the fair?

Narrator 1: The room fills with laughter.

Krystal *(shakily):* As you can see, Mars is a grapefruit. Earth is a lemon.

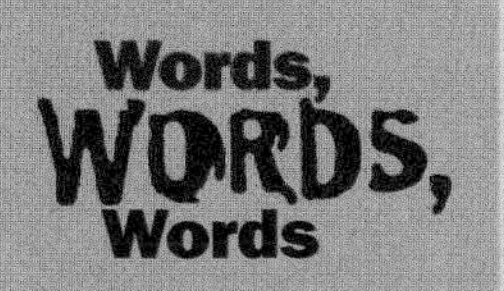

proceed: to begin and continue an activity
foolproof: something that cannot fail
anxiously: with worry

Harwood *(impatiently):* You can say that again! Enough of this. Let's see what delightful package Jordie has brought us.

Narrator 2: There is more scattered laughter. Jordie pays no attention. All he can think about is the great joke he is playing on everyone.

Jordie: I hope nobody is squeamish. And I hope nobody ate a big breakfast. I brought a corpse as my project.

Narrator 1: Everyone groans.

Harwood: People, let's be mature. Even though this is Jordie's project, it may prove to be educational.

Jordie: I'm going to remove the lid now. The corpse is a young man in his twenties.

Narrator 2: Grinning, Jordie opens the casket.

Gene: Yuck!

Harwood: Can everyone see? That blue tie doesn't go very well with his green skin. *(turning to Jordie)* So what do you plan to show us?

Jordie: I'm going to dissect the corpse's left arm.

Narrator 1: Looking sick, Krystal gets up. She leaves the room.

Narrator 2: Nervously, Jordie puts the scalpel on the corpse's arm. As he lowers it, the corpse sits up and starts to moan: "No! No! Help me!" Several kids scream. Then the corpse gets up. It jumps out of the coffin. It staggers forward.

Narrator 1: Terrified, everyone runs as fast as they can. Jordie watches as Mr. Harwood trips, and the corpse moves towards him. Mr. Harwood gets up and lurches out the door. The corpse is only a few feet behind him.

Harwood: Save me! He's after me! Someone help me!

Narrator 2: Jordie runs after them, laughing. All around him, kids are stampeding. Jordie finally stops in the parking lot and watches happily. His joke has been a complete success.

Narrator 1: Then something strange happens. A horn honks. A familiar car pulls up. Jordie's Uncle Norm gets out of it.

Norm: Hi, Jordie. I'm sorry I'm late. Did Marvin tell you that I got hung up at work? I hope I didn't ruin your joke or anything! ●

ASK Yourself

- Why did Jordie think that his joke was a complete success?

Summarize Jordie's plan for this joke and who ends up being surprised.

Meet the Skull Ma

Frank Bender uses his artistic talents to help solve crimes. How does he do that? Read this interview to find out.

Q: Your job is difficult to describe. Can you tell us what you do?

A: Sure. One of my jobs is to help put faces on the skulls of crime victims. Sometimes, the police find a body and they don't know who it is. I take the skull. I try to figure out what the face looked like. Then I make a sculpture of the face. That way, the police can show people the sculpture so hopefully somebody can identify the victim.

Q: You actually handle the skulls?

A: Oh, yeah. I have one here now that I'm working on for the police.

Q: What are you doing with that skull?

A: To start, I've been studying it. I try to see the differences from one side to another. What makes this person different from all the other skulls I've worked with? Then I'll put the clay on my sculpture and shape the face. I sculpt the hair too, in most cases.

Q: What else do you do to help solve crimes?

A: I "age" criminals for the police and the FBI. Let's say that the police are looking for someone who disappeared many years ago. This person has gotten older. He or she looks different. I look at a picture of what that person looked like back then. Then I create a sculpture of what that person probably looks like today.

Q: Does it work?

A: Yes. I've helped police catch seven criminals so far.

Q: You started as an artist. How did you get into crime solving?

A: I was taking art courses in Philadelphia. I wanted to learn more about the human body so I could be a better artist.

Q: So what did you do?

A: A friend worked at the morgue. That's where they keep dead bodies. He showed me all

n : Frank Bender

these bodies. Some had died violently. This one woman only had a number. My friend said, "We don't know her name or what she looks like." I said, "I could show you what she looks like."

Q: What happened next?

A: I came in the following night. I got the body out of the freezer. I took some measurements. Then I did a sculpture of her face. Five months later, the police found out who she was. Twenty years later—just last year—they caught the man who killed her. The victim's family came over and thanked me. What a good feeling that was!

Q: Most of the people you work with are dead. How do you deal with that?

A: When you have a purpose, like I do, you get used to it. But the first day at the morgue was difficult. It was a very emotional experience. Death is usually kept away from us. In the morgue you see how fragile we are. You see how quickly life can be taken away. ●

Frank Bender with three of his creations.

Talk About It

Now that you've read *Jordie's Revenge* and "Meet the Skull Man," what do you have to say about these questions?

- ▶ What kinds of things do you find scary? Why?
- ▶ Why do you think people are fascinated by "gross" things?

Comprehension Check

Write your answers to the questions below. Use information from the play and the interview to support your answers.

1. Why does Jordie decide to play a trick on Mr. Harwood?
2. Why does Jordie like Uncle Norm?
3. Were you scared by the play's ending? Why or why not?
4. What two things does Frank Bender do to help police solve crimes?
5. Do you think Frank Bender would have been scared by Jordie's corpse? Explain.

Vocabulary Check

Answer each question below with a complete sentence. Before you answer, think about the meaning of the vocabulary word in bold.

1. When a teacher **encourages** you, how does she do it?
2. When might you wait **anxiously?**
3. Why would someone **dissect** a corpse?
4. How would you describe a **decent** person?
5. If a plan is **foolproof**, what does that mean?

Write About It

Choose one of the writing prompts below.

- Write copy for a poster advertising *Jordie's Revenge—The Movie.* Give a description of the story and make up some movie review quotes, too.
- Who was that guy? Write a short paragraph explaining who the corpse is, how it got there, and what happens to it next.
- Are you curious to learn more about the Skull Man's job? Write him a letter asking what you'd like to know.

More to READ

Want to learn more about the master of fright himself, R. L. Stine? Want to learn more about the "real-life" monsters that have inspired many a scary story? If so, then you'll be interested in checking out these books.

It Came From Ohio
by R. L. Stine and Joe Arthur

This best-selling author tells you everything you ever wanted to know about him—and *Goosebumps!* Was R. L. Stine a scary kid? Did he have a weird family? How did he start writing books? Where does he get all his scary ideas? These and many more questions are answered in this humorous autobiography.

Beastly Tales: Yeti, Bigfoot, and the Loch Ness Monster
by Malcolm Yorke

All around the world people tell stories about seeing mysterious monsters in faraway places. The storytellers are often accused of making things up. But sometimes a discovery is made that proves them right. Do you think these monsters really exist? Read this collection of amazing eye-witness stories and make up your own mind.

Scheduling Your Time

Does it ever seem that there aren't enough hours in the day? You have homework, after-school stuff, chores at home—and more! How can you get it all done?

It helps if you make a schedule. Look at the one below. Are you ready to organize your time?

This schedule is only for school days. If you like, you can make a schedule for your weekends, too.

See where it says "report"? That shows that Lisa will start working on her report at 3 P.M. The arrow shows that she'll stop at 5 P.M.

Lisa's Weekly Schedule

	Monday	Tuesday	Wednesday	Thursday	Friday
8:00	school →				
3:00	social studies report	social studies report	social studies report	mall	science project
4:00	↓	↓	↓	↓	skating
5:00	basketball practice	dinner	basketball practice	dinner	dinner
6:00	↓	work	↓	work	babysitting
7:00	dinner	↓	dinner	↓	↓
8:00	reading homework	↓	reading homework	↓	↓
9:00	↓	social studies report	math homework	math homework	TV
10:00	read →				
10:30	bed →				

"When you're scheduling time for a big project like a report, estimate how many hours you'll need to complete it. Set aside an hour or two each day to work on it until it's done."

When you make your schedule, first write in the activities that you *must* do. Then see how much time is left over for your other activities.

Looking at Schedules

You've got a busy week ahead of you, and you're really feeling pressured. How will you ever get everything done? Reread Lisa's schedule and the tips that go with it. Then answer the questions below. Write your answers on your own paper.

1. Answer these questions about Lisa's schedule.
  a. What does Lisa do from 8 A.M. to about 3 P.M. every day?
  b. What does she do every day from 10 P.M. to 10:30 P.M.?
  c. What time does Lisa go to bed every day?

2. How many hours of math homework does Lisa have this week? What days will she do it?
  a. 2 hours; Wednesday and Thursday
  b. 4 hours; Tuesday, Wednesday, and Thursday
  c. 4 hours every day
  d. 3 hours; Tuesday, Wednesday, and Thursday

3. Lisa just bought new skates. She'd really like to skate for two hours on Friday. That means she'll have to find an extra hour Thursday or Friday for her science project. Which activities could she spend less time on or skip to make time for her science project?

4. This Wednesday, basketball practice was canceled. What do you think Lisa should do instead? Tell why.

5. Lisa wasn't happy with her last report card. She thinks she needs more time to study. What activities do you think she should cut back on or cut out? Explain.

Make a List

Make a list of everything you plan to do next week. Start with your top priorities—such as homework, sports practice, and chores. Then list everything you'd *like* to do—such as shopping and hanging out with your friends.

Plan a Schedule

Use your list from above. Organize your activities into a schedule like Lisa's. First write in the things you have to do. Then use the remaining time to schedule the things you do for fun.

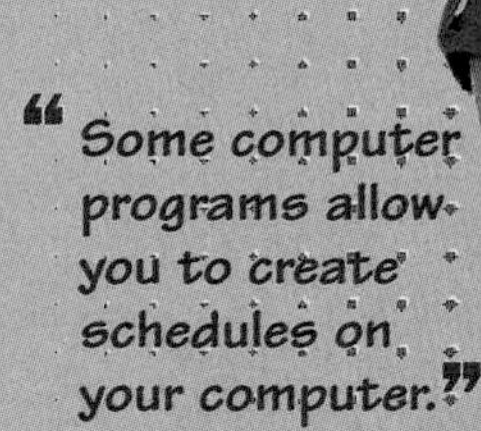

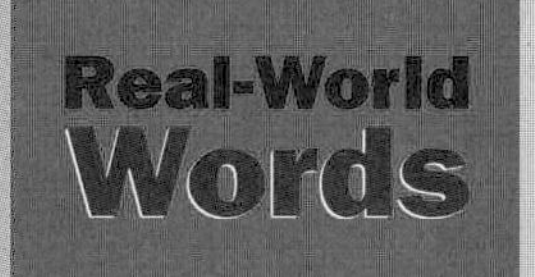

estimate: to make an informed guess about an amount
organize: to put things in order
priority: something that is more important than something else

nonfiction selection

PASSAGE TO FREE

The Sugihara Story

If he helped, his family would be in danger. If he didn't, thousands of people would die. What would Hiroki Sugihara decide?

by Ken Mochizuki
Illustrated by Dom Lee

DOM

There is a saying that the eyes tell everything about a person.

At a store, my father saw a young Jewish boy who didn't have enough money to buy what he wanted. So my father gave the boy some of his. That boy looked into my father's eyes and, to thank him, invited my father to his home.

That is when my family and I went to a Hanukkah celebration for the first time. I was five years old.

In 1940, my father was a **diplomat,** representing the country of Japan. Our family lived in a small town in the small country called Lithuania. There was my father and mother, my Auntie Setsuko, my younger brother Chiaki, and my three-month-old baby brother, Haruki. My father worked in his office downstairs.

In the mornings, birds sang in the trees. We played with girls and boys from the neighborhood at a huge park near our home. Houses and churches around us were hundreds of years old. In our room, Chiaki and I played with toy German soldiers, tanks, and planes. Little did we know that the real soldiers were coming our way.

Then one early morning in late July, my life changed forever.

My mother and Auntie Setsuko woke Chiaki and me up, telling us to get dressed quickly. My father ran upstairs from his office.

"There are a lot of people outside," my mother said. "We don't know what is going to happen."

In the living room, my parents told my brother and me not to let anybody see us looking through the window. So, I parted the curtains a tiny bit. Outside, I saw hundreds of people crowded around the gate in front of our house.

The grown-ups shouted in Polish, a language I did not understand. Then I saw the children. They stared at our house through the iron bars of the gate. Some of them were my age. Like the grown-ups, their eyes were red from not having slept for days. They wore heavy winter coats—some wore more than one coat, even though it was warm outside. These children looked as though they had dressed in a hurry. But if they came from somewhere else, where were their suitcases?

"What do they want?" I asked my mother.

"They have come to ask for your father's help," she replied. "Unless we help, they may be killed or taken away by some bad men."

Some of the children held on tightly to the hands of their fathers, some clung to their mothers. One little girl sat on the ground, crying.

I felt like crying, too. "Father," I said, "please help them." My father stood quietly next to me, but I knew he saw the children.

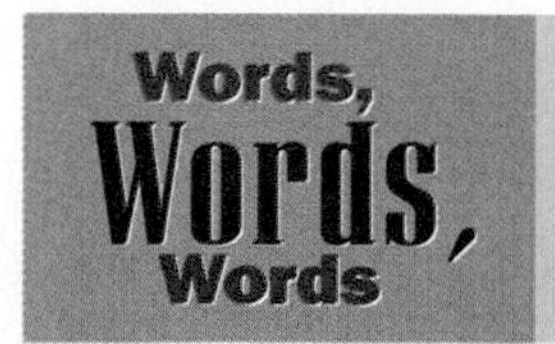

diplomat: a person who represents his or her country's government in a foreign country

peering: looking at something that is difficult to see

Then some of the men in the crowd began climbing over the fence. Borislav and Gudje, two young men who worked for my father, tried to keep the crowd calm.

My father walked outside. **Peering** through the curtains, I saw him standing on the steps. Borislav translated what my father said: He asked the crowd to choose five people to come inside and talk.

My father met downstairs with the five men. My father could speak Japanese, Chinese, Russian, German, French, and English. At this meeting, everyone spoke Russian.

I couldn't help but stare out the window and watch the crowd, while downstairs, for two hours, my father listened to frightening stories. These people were refugees—people who ran away from their homes because, if they

ASK YOURSELF

- Why does the Sugihara family consider helping the Jewish refugees?

Think about what might happen to the refugees if they don't.

stayed, they would be killed. They were Jews from Poland, escaping from the Nazi soldiers who had taken over their country.

The five men had heard my father could give them visas—official written permission to travel through another country. The hundreds of Jewish refugees outside hoped to travel east through the Soviet Union and end up in Japan. Once in Japan, they could go to another country. Was it true? the men asked. Could my father issue these visas? If he did not, the Nazis would soon catch up with them.

My father answered that he could issue a few, but not hundreds. To do that, he would have to ask for permission from his government in Japan.

That night, the crowd stayed outside our house. **Exhausted** from the day's excitement, I slept soundly. But it was one of the worst nights of my father's life. He had to make a decision. If he helped these people, would he put our family in danger? If the Nazis found out, what would they do?

But if he did not help these people, they could all die.

My mother listened to the bed squeak as my father tossed and turned all night.

The next day, my father said he was going to ask his government about the visas. My mother agreed it was the right thing to do. My father sent his message by cable. Gudje took my father's written message down to the telegraph office.

I watched the crowd as they waited for the Japanese government's reply. The five representatives came into our house several times that day to ask if an answer had been received. Any time the gate opened, the crowd tried to charge inside.

Finally, the answer came from the Japanese government. It was "no." My father could not issue that many visas to Japan. For the next two days, he thought about what to do.

Hundreds more Jewish refugees joined the crowd. My father sent a second message to his government, and again the answer was "no." We still couldn't go outside. My little brother Haruki cried often because we were running out of milk.

I grew tired of staying indoors. I asked my father constantly, "Why are these people here? What do they want? Why do they have to be here? Who are they?"

My father always took the time to explain everything to me. He said the refugees needed his help, that they needed permission from him to go to another part of the world where they would be safe.

"I cannot help these people yet," he calmly told me. "But when the time comes, I will help them all that I can."

My father cabled his superiors yet a third time, and I knew the answer by the look in his eyes. That night, he said to my mother, "I have to do something. I may have to **disobey** my government, but if I don't, I will be disobeying God."

The next morning, he brought the family together and asked what he should do. This was the first time he ever asked all of us to help him with anything.

My mother and Auntie Setsuko had already made up their minds. They said we had to think about the people outside before we thought about ourselves. And that is what my parents had always told me—that I must think as if I were in

ASK YOURSELF

- What happened when Mr. Sugihara wrote to the Japanese government?

Reread the page to find out what happened.

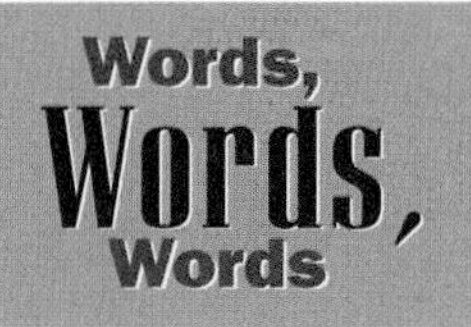

exhausted: very tired
disobey: to go against the rules or someone's wishes

someone else's place. If I were one of those children out there, what would I want someone to do for me?

I said to my father, "If we don't help them, won't they die?"

With the entire family in agreement, I could tell a huge weight was lifted off my father's shoulders. His voice was firm as he told us, "I will start helping these people."

Outside, the crowd went quiet as my father spoke, with Borislav translating.

"I will issue visas to each and every one of you to the last. So, please wait patiently."

The crowd stood frozen for a second. Then the refugees burst into cheers. Grown-ups **embraced** each other, and some reached to the sky. Fathers and mothers hugged their children. I was especially glad for the children.

My father opened the garage door and the crowd tried to rush in. To keep order, Borislav handed out cards with numbers. My father wrote out each visa by hand. After he finished each one, he looked into the eyes of the person receiving the visa and said, "Good luck."

Refugees camped out at our favorite park, waiting to see my father. I was finally able to go outside.

Chiaki and I played with the other children in our toy car. They pushed as we rode, and they rode as we pushed. We chased each other around the big trees. We did not speak the same language, but that didn't stop us.

For about a month, there was always a line leading to the garage. Every day, from early in the morning till late at night, my father tried to write three hundred visas. He watered down the ink to make it last. Gudje and a young Jewish man helped out by stamping my father's name on the visas.

My mother offered to help write the visas, but my father insisted he be the only one, so no one else could get into trouble. So my mother watched the crowd and told my father how many were still in line.

One day, my father pressed down so hard on his fountain pen, the tip broke off. During that month, I only saw him late at night. His eyes were always red and he could hardly talk. While he slept, my mother massaged his arm, stiff and cramped from writing all day.

Soon my father grew so tired, he wanted to quit writing the visas. But my mother encouraged him to continue. "Many people are still waiting," she said. "Let's issue some more visas and save as many lives as we can."

While the Germans approached from the west, the Soviets came from the east and took over Lithuania. They ordered my father to leave. So did the Japanese government, which reassigned him to Germany. Still, my father wrote the visas until we absolutely had to move out of our home. We stayed at a hotel for two days, where my father still wrote visas for the many refugees who followed him there.

Then it was time to leave Lithuania. Refugees who had slept

at the train station crowded around my father. Some refugee men surrounded my father to protect him. He now just issued permission papers—blank pieces of paper with his **signature.**

As the train pulled away, refugees ran alongside. My father still handed permission papers out the window. As the train picked up speed, he threw them out to waiting hands. The people in the front of the crowd looked into my father's eyes and cried, "We will never forget you! We will see you again!"

I **gazed** out the train window, watching Lithuania and the crowd of refugees fade away. I wondered if we would ever see them again.

"Where are we going?" I asked my father.

"We are going to Berlin," he replied.

Chiaki and I became very excited about going to the big city. I had so many questions for my father. But he fell asleep as soon as he **settled** into his seat. My mother and Auntie Setsuko looked really tired, too.

Back then, I did not fully understand what the three of them had done, or why it was so important.

I do now. ●

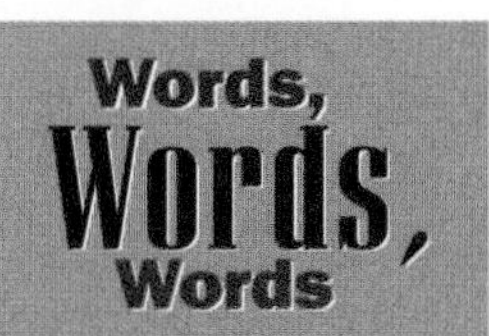

embraced: hugged
signature: your full name written in script
gazed: looked at something for a long time
settled: made one's self comfortable

Hero

lyrics by Mariah Carey

There's a hero
If you look inside your heart
You don't have to be afraid
Of what you are
There's an answer
If you reach into your soul
And the sorrow that you know
Will melt away

And then a hero comes along
With the strength to carry on
And you cast your fears aside
And you know you can survive
So when you feel like hope is gone
Look inside you and be strong
And you'll finally see the truth
That a hero lies in you

It's a long road
When you face the world alone
No one reaches out a hand
For you to hold
You can find love
If you reach within yourself
And the emptiness you felt
Will disappear

And then a hero comes along
With the strength to carry on
And you cast your fears aside
And you know you can survive
So when you feel like hope is gone
Look inside you and be strong
And you'll finally see the truth
That a hero lies in you

Lord knows
Dreams are hard to follow
But don't let anyone
Tear them away
Hold on
There will be tomorrow
In time
You'll find the way

And then a hero comes along
With the strength to carry on
And you cast your fears aside
And you know you can survive
So when you feel like hope is gone
Look inside you and be strong
And you'll finally see the truth
That a hero lies in you ●

Talk About It

Now that you've read "Passage to Freedom" and "Hero," what do you have to say about these questions?

- What do you think makes someone a hero?
- Would you put your family at risk to help others? Explain your opinion.

Comprehension Check

Write your answers to the questions below. Use information from the reading to support your answers.

1. Why do the Jewish families want Mr. Sugihara to give them visas?
2. What do you think would have happened to the Jewish refugees if Mr. Sugihara had not given them visas?
3. Why is the decision to issue the visas so hard to make?
4. Who is the hero in Mariah Carey's song?
5. According to the song's definition, is Mr. Sugihara a hero? Explain.

Vocabulary Check

Complete each sentence starter below. Before you answer, think about the meaning of the vocabulary word in bold.

1. I **gazed** at the floor because . . .
2. I was asked for my **signature** on . . .
3. The only kind of rule I might **disobey** would be . . .
4. I was **exhausted** after . . .
5. Our family **settled** in for an evening of . . .

Write About It

Choose one of the writing prompts below.

- Write a formal letter from Mr. Sugihara to Japan requesting permission to issue visas for the Jewish refugees. Make sure to include the reasons why the visas should be issued.
- If Mr. Sugihara was given an award for his heroism, what do you think he would have said in his acceptance speech?
- Write a thank-you note from one of the refugee families to the Sugiharas. Make up a story about the family's journey to include in the note.

Take ACTION

One way to get involved is to get and share information. Here are two ways you can learn more about refugees around the world today.

- Visit the U.S. Committee for Refugees Web site at *www.refugees.org/field/listen.htm*, and listen to audio recordings of refugees talking about their experiences.
- Visit the UN High Committee on Refugees Web site at *www.unhcr.ch*, or write to them at UNHCR, Public Information Section, CP 2500, 1211 Geneva 2 Depot, Switzerland. They will send your class the following things for free:

  Refugee Children (1993, updated) A color brochure with personal stories of three refugee children.

  Passages (1995) A game that helps you understand the problems of refugees.

Browsing a Newspaper

Reading the newspaper is a great way to start the day. You can find out about the weather, check sports scores, or even keep up with politics.

Check out the newspaper index below. It's a listing of the major stories in the paper and the pages you'll find them on. Read all about it!

A Newspaper Index

Every newspaper is divided into sections. Each section is given a letter.

The "international" section contains world news. "National" has news about the nation. "Local" has state and city news.

The Daily News

National, A3-8

Hurricane Mindy Strikes High winds destroy hundreds of homes in southern Florida. Damage is estimated at $870 million. A1

Girls Gain in Math and Science A new study found that test scores for girls in math and science are on the rise. They have traditionally done worse than boys, the study said, but they are closing the gap. A6

International A9-13

Famine Worsens in East Africa Nearly 2 million face starvation, says the Red Cross. Rainfall is still at an all-time low for the region. A9

Swiss Ski Resorts Booming Record snowfalls in the Alps are drawing American skiers away from Colorado and Vermont. A11

Local, B1-8

Schools Going On-Line All area students now have access to the Internet, says the district superintendent. The new computing centers were built with federal funds. B2

Business, C1-12

General Widget to Build New Plant The company announced that the new facility will provide 400 to 500 new jobs. C1

Sports, D1-8

Heisman Up for Grabs College football's highest prize could go to any one of four stars. D1

Jim Spafford's Eye on Sports: Are NBA salaries out of control? D5

Living, E1-10

Winter Hiking All the Rage More and more people are refusing to let the cold keep them cooped up. Plus: Good deals on fleece outerwear. E1

***Lightning Bolt VII* Fizzles** Latest movie in the popular series can't get into warp speed at the box office. E6

Crossword E9
Editorial A14
TV Listings E8
Movie Schedule E7
Obituaries B7
Stocks C6-11
Weather B8

The index includes a sentence or two to sum up each big story in the paper. The summaries can help you decide what you want to read.

"All of the day's biggest stories start on the front page. The bigger the headline, the more important the story is. If you need to skim the news really quickly, just check out the headlines."

Hot Off the Presses

Your favorite team played last night, and you want to find the score. The index will direct you to the sports section. Reread the index and the tips. Then use them to answer the questions below. Write your answers on your own paper.

1. Look at the index for this issue of *The Daily News*. Where will you find stories about natural disasters?
   a. pages A11 and E1
   b. pages A1 and C1
   c. pages A1 and A9

2. Which one of these headlines might appear on page C10 of *The Daily News*?
   a. Italy Edges Austria in World Cup Soccer Semifinal
   b. U.S. Stock Market Gains 2% in a Single Day
   c. French President Re-elected to Third Term

3. Which pages of the *The Daily News* will give you answers to the following questions: What time is the evening news on TV? Should you bring an umbrella to school? Who might win the Heisman trophy?

4. According to today's *The Daily News*, which of the following statements is true?
   a. Girls' scores on math and science tests are improving.
   b. Heavy rains fall in East Africa.
   c. The Heisman trophy was awarded to four people.

Top Stories

List the three stories in *The Daily News* that you would want to read first.

Editor for a Day

You are the editor of *The Daily News*. Create an index listing the section and page for these stories: "Montreal Canadiens to Make Stanley Cup Play-Offs," "Another Bad Day for U.S. Stocks," "President to Visit Kenya," and "Mayor Wins Re-election in Close Race."

"Most newspapers have Web sites that are updated throughout the day. Check the Web for up-to-the-minute news."

Real-World Words

editorial: an article that reflects an opinion
national: relating to the nation
obituary: a notice of a person's death

poetry

My Friend's Got This Problem, Mr. Candler

Mr. Candler—or Mr. C. as many of his students call him—is a guidance counselor. Through the door of his office come Gloria, Rodney, Henry, Virginia, and many others. Five days a week, eight periods a day, students—and some parents as well—seek out Mr. Candler with their questions. On the following pages you'll hear them tell Mr. C. about their problems, sorrows, joys, and dreams through a series of poems. As you travel with Mr. C. on a typical day you may recognize some of these people as friends, as classmates . . . or as the person you see in the mirror.

by Mel Glenn

Period 1

It is Monday, Period 1. Patrick DeShannon knocks gently on Mr. Candler's office door. He walks in and sits down.

Patrick DeShannon

My little brother, Brendan, is a pain.
He never leaves me alone.
He always messes up my room,
Looking for my magazines, he says.
He makes horrible bird noises,
Which embarrasses me in front of my friends.
And when I scream at him,
Calling him all sorts of names,
He goes running to my mother,
Who says, "Stop teasing him, you're older."
I tell him to get lost,
But he follows me everywhere.
"He wants to be like you," my mother says.
Last week, in order to get Brendan off my back,
I taught him how to ride my bike.
It took the little pain three days to learn.
Now he rides everywhere with his friends.
I miss him.

Patrick thanks Mr. Candler for listening as he gets up to leave. Anthony slips past Patrick and sits down in Mr. C's office. It is now Period 2.

Anthony Ricci

My father dreamed of football
While he worked on the boats in the bay.
My mother said when I was born
He put a football in my crib instead of
  a teddy bear.
And when he wasn't workin'
He was tossin' me a football,
  over and over again.
His love was measured in yards thrown and
  catches received.
All his life on the boats,
And what's he got to show for it?
A bad back and scarred hands
And a son who plays football for the varsity.
Well, last week I got hurt in a game.
It was a cheap shot.
The ref had blown the play dead
And then this huge Number 58 piled on me.
I heard something in my knee snap.
That linebacker ended my pro dreams,
  Mr. Candler.
He also broke my father's heart.
I'd like to go out on the boat with
  my old man, soon,
Put my arm around him and tell him
The years we spent together were not in vain.

Mr. Candler is talking on the telephone when Lizette walks into his office. It is Period 3 and Lizette looks frustrated.

Lizette Ramirez

I wouldn't know love
If it stood up and smacked me in the face.
Every day in my fourth period class
A paper heart, red with scalloped edges,
Appeared taped to the corner of my desk,
With "I love you, guess who?" written in
the middle.
No one knew who put it there,
But, boy, did I take abuse for it.
"Lizzy, you need a transplant?"
"Lizzy, how many boyfriends you got?"
"Lizzy, you tearing up another heart?"
I couldn't take it no more, so
One day I stood up and screamed:
"Will the jerk who's sendin' me hearts
Step up like a man or just shut up!"
Subtle, huh.
Well, that was the last heart I ever seen.
I must have scared him away.
You know, it's probably the best love
I ever found and lost.
I guess he didn't have the heart to stick around.

Period 3

ASK yourself

- What kind of person do you think Mr. Candler is?

Think about why all these students come to see him.

Mr. Candler is walking into the library when he spots a new student, Ramona, sitting alone. He asks her to come to his office so they can talk during Period 4.

Period 4

Ramona Castillo

When the soldiers came in the middle of the night
There was no moon watching over
Our little house in Central America.
My parents hid me under the bed
And gave me a towel to chew on
So that I would not cry out.
It was the last time I saw them.
The next morning relatives found me
Still under the bed, still **clutching** the towel.
We waited for days, but there was no word.
Finally my relatives sent me to an uncle here,
To start a new life, to outrun the **tragedy.**
I did not like my new land or language.
I felt embarrassed by my own accent.
Then, about a year ago, a nice teacher,
Mr. Loomis,
Showed me how to take photographs,
Showed me how to speak with film and f-stops.
I try to shoot many pictures of children smiling,
To capture in their bright, glowing faces
A childhood stolen from me
In the middle of a moonless night,
Five years ago in time, but
Yesterday in my heart and in my memory.

Just after the Period 5 bell rings Mr. Candler bumps into Gloria in a stairwell. She's breathless and looks anxious.

Gloria Simonetti

Mr. Candler, where are you going?
You can't go to lunch now.
You gotta help me find it.
I've looked everywhere,
My last period class, my locker, the stairs,
Even the sink in the bathroom.
I can't calm down
Until I find my "number one" charm.
It was just on my neck,
On a gold chain.
Yes, I've checked the lost and found.
They never find anything.
My grandfather gave me that charm
When I was six years old.
I've always worn it.
I never take it off.
It was the last present I got
from my grandfather
Before he died.
Please, Mr. Candler, you just gotta help me
find that charm.

ASK yourself

- Which of these students can you relate to most?

Think about things you've dealt with in your own life.

Virginia and Tamara are about to walk into their Period 6 class when they suddenly start to shout angrily at each other in the hallway. Virginia is sent to Mr. Candler's office first.

Virginia Pilgrim

There isn't going to be any fight, Mr. C.
But she started it.
What's she yellin' at me for,
Calling me names?
I don't even know the girl.
I hear she's been spreading lies 'bout me.
If you ask me, there's too many of them in this school,
Acting like they own the place.
Me?
I get along with everybody.
Yeah, yeah, get her in here.
No fight, I promise.
We can work it out.
She better watch her step, though.
Nobody starts with me.
I'll talk to her, OK?

During their talk, Mr. Candler offers Virginia some ideas on how to work things out with Tamara. He offers Tamara the same advice when she walks into his office during Period 7.

Tamara Jackson

There ain't gonna be no fight, Mr. C.
But she started it.
What's she comin' in my face for,
Callin' me all kinds of dirt?
I don't even know the girl.
I hear she's been tellin' stories about me.
If you ask me, there's too many of them in this school,
Actin' like they own the place.
Me?
I get along with everybody.
Yeah, yeah, get her in here.
No fight, I promise.
We can work it out.
She better watch her step, though.
Hey, nobody messes with me.
I'll talk to her, OK?

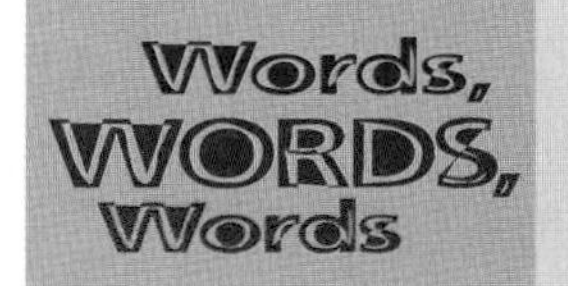

clutching: holding on tightly
tragedy: a very sad event
anxious: worried

Hank is late for his Period 8 appointment. Mr. Candler is catching up with phone calls and paperwork when Hank walks in and takes a seat.

Henry (Hank) Grendell

Mr. Candler, would you say I'm too fat?
Hefty? Well, that's one way of putting it.
Occupational hazard, I guess.
I work the snack counter, fries and stuff,
Down at Bowlmore Lanes.
When my uncle Harry got me the job
I thought I was the luckiest guy alive.
I love to bowl; I love to eat.
What could be better?
I also thought I'd make some new friends.
In the beginning the job was great.
I met some terrific new people.
Then I realized they just wanted
Free food instead of free friendship.
Now the guys don't hang around the snack bar much.
They prefer to strike up conversations
With the girls hangin' around the video games.
I know now I will have plenty of time to spend
Eating—fry by fry,
Bowling—frame by frame,
Alone.

Mr. Candler doesn't rush Hank even though the Period 8 bell has sounded. As Hank walks out, Mr. Candler starts to collect his things. Then the office phone rings.

(Henry's uncle)—Telephone conversation

You don't know me, sir,
But I know all about you.
I want to thank you
For spending so much time with my nephew, Henry.
He talks about you a lot,
How you always have time for him, how you always
listen.
Please don't say it's only your job,
I know better.
You don't get paid extra for being nice,
For helping him with his problems.
You know my brother and sister-in-law died
last year,
In a plane crash; it was terrible.
Henry's living with me now,
But I'm afraid I'm too old to deal with
teenagers.
Yes, I did get him a job,
But it isn't enough.
At night I still hear him crying in his room.
There are no words to comfort his loss
And mine.
But I did want to thank you
For making his pain a little less painful.
You're a good man, sir.

occupational: having to do with a job
hazard: a danger or a risk
muffler: something that reduces the noise made by a car engine

Mr. Candler sets down the phone and takes a deep breath. He starts to think about what he still has to do after school.

Mr. Mark Candler

Counselor

I'm beat, can't even move.
Got to get home,
Maybe catch a few winks
Before I have to
        take the car in for a **muffler**,
        go to the dentist at five,
        pick up supper, Chinese maybe,
        pick up Jamie from Mrs. Brenner.
My desk?
The mess can keep till Monday.
Where'd I put my keys?
They were here a second ago.

final bell

It's OK, Randy, you can come in.
You look upset.
That bad?
You better sit down.
No, I wasn't leaving,
Not just yet, that is.
So what's up?
Just tell me about it—slowly.
I'm here,
Like always. ●

ASK yourself

- Why is Mr. Candler a good person to go to with a problem?

Think about what Mr. Candler is willing to do for his students.

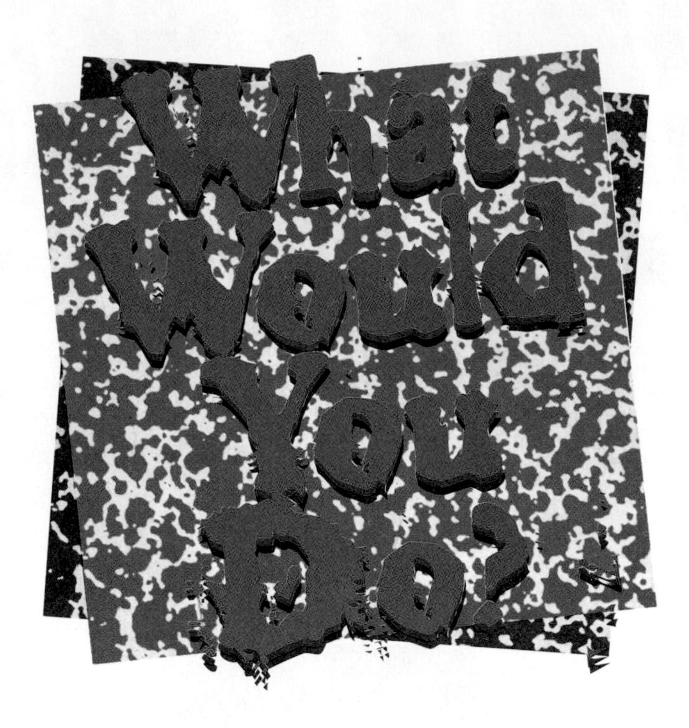

Part of Mr. Candler's job is to help kids figure out what they should do when trouble strikes. Below are some sticky situations. What would you do if these situations happened to you? Record your answers on a separate piece of paper.

1. The coolest girl in your school has invited you to a party. You'd be psyched, except for one thing. She said not to bring your "really strange" best friend. What would you do?

A. Tell your friend you're going to your aunt's—then go to the party anyway.

B. Tell the cool girl you can't make it, and hang out with your friend instead.

C. Explain to the cool girl that your friend is not so strange, and then ask if she would reconsider inviting her too.

D. Explain the situation to your friend, and hope your friend will understand.

E. Another solution of my own would be . . .

2. Your brother has been acting weird lately. He's dropped most of his friends, and stays in his room with the door locked. Your parents don't seem to notice, but you're sure something's up—maybe something serious. What should you do?

A. Explain your concerns to your parents, asking them not to tell your brother that you tipped them off.

B. Ask your brother if anything's wrong and offer to help him.

C. Talk to a counselor at school or another adult you trust.

D. Keep your mouth shut and ignore him.

E. Another solution of my own would be . . .

3. Your new lab partner is from a different country. His customs sometimes seem strange to you. You're not sure how to act. What would you do?

A. Learn all you can about his culture so you'll understand him better.

B. Just be yourself, and get to know him as a friend.

C. Try to teach him how to do everything the American way.

D. Just do your work and be polite.

E. Another solution of my own would be . . .

4. Your sister is a total Miss Perfect. She's brainy, athletic, and popular—all the things that you're not. People always compare you to her, which makes you feel like a loser. What would you do?

A. Tell these people that all the comparisons just aren't fair.

B. Remind yourself that everybody has their own strengths and weaknesses, including you and your sister.

C. Ignore the comparisons and pretend that they don't bother you—even though they really do.

D. Tell everyone the reasons why your sister isn't so great.

E. Another solution of my own would be . . .

5. Now that you've got an after-school job, a good friend seems to think you're the First National Bank. She borrows money nearly every week. Even though she always pays you back, you're getting sick of handing out cash. What would you do?

A. Tell your friend that you won't lend her money anymore.

B. Agree to an occasional loan—but only if it's an emergency.

C. Suggest that your friend look for her own after-school job.

D. Get over it—as long as your friend pays you back, what's the big deal, right?

E. Another solution of my own would be . . .

6. You're in the middle of a tough math test. You look up and see Kyle, a school football star, cheating off your paper. You're mad because you spent the weekend studying. But if you get on Kyle's bad side, you're in for trouble for the rest of the year. What would you do?

A. Let Kyle cheat and not say anything.

B. Cover your answers with your arm.

C. After class, tell Kyle that he owes you a favor.

D. Ask Kyle if he'd like to study with you sometime.

E. Another solution of my own would be . . .

7. There's a new kid in school. Some of your friends like to pick on him. You went along with the teasing once. But afterward, you felt terrible. Your friends still expect you to join in when they tease the kid. They think it's hysterical. What would you do?

A. Tell your friends you feel it's wrong to pick on the kid.

B. Just walk away when your friends start teasing.

C. Try to laugh along with your friends—and be happy it's not you they're teasing.

D. Talk to the new kid and maybe become his friend.

E. Another solution of my own would be . . .

Discuss your answers with your class. Why did your classmates make the choices they did? Why did you? ●

Talk About It

Now that you've read *My Friend's Got This Problem, Mr. Candler* and "What Would You Do?" what do you have to say about these questions?

- What do you think are the biggest problems students your age face?
- Who would you talk to if you had a problem? Why?

Comprehension Check

Write your answers to the questions below. Use information from the poems and the questionnaire to support your answers.

1. What are some of the problems students come to Mr. Candler with? Name at least two.
2. How do you think Mr. Candler feels about the students who come to see him?
3. How can you help someone by saying nothing at all?
4. Which of the sticky situations in the questionnaire do you think would be the hardest to handle? Why?
5. If you went to talk to Mr. Candler about any of the problems on the questionnaire, what do you think he would do?

Vocabulary Check

Complete each sentence starter below. Before you answer, think about the meaning of the vocabulary word in bold.

1. Dad got a new **muffler** because . . .
2. I was **anxious** about . . .
3. A real driving **hazard** is . . .
4. I was **clutching** my friend's arm because . . .
5. It was a **tragedy** when . . .

Write About It

Choose one of the writing prompts below.

- Working with a partner, write a letter you might send to an advice column. Each of you can ask for advice about an imaginary problem. Next, trade letters with your partner. Then, write an answer that gives your partner advice for solving his or her problem.
- Write a thank-you letter from one of the students to Mr. Candler. In the letter explain how he was able to help and how his help made you feel.
- Write a poem about one of the situations in "What Would You Do?" Use the poems in *My Friend's Got This Problem, Mr. Candler* as models.

About the AUTHOR

Mel Glenn may not be a guidance counselor like Mr. Candler, but he sure does have a lot of experience with teenage students. He has been teaching English for over twenty-five years at Lincoln High School in Brooklyn, New York. Before that, he worked as a Peace Corps volunteer in Africa. His seven books of poetry and three novels have won many awards, including an American Library Association award for *My Friend's Got This Problem, Mr. Candler.*

Taking a Business Message

You just got a job answering phones for a small company. That should be no problem for you—you spend hours on the phone every day! But wait a minute, this is business.

Take a look at the message below. Are you ready to grab that call?

Standard Business Message Form

This line tells who called and left this message. The "M" is the first letter of Mr., Mrs., Ms., or Miss.

Phone Call

For Bailey Flynn Date 5/12/01 Time 4:20 A.M. (P.M.)
Ms. Goldie Silver
Of XL Films
Phone ☐ Fax ☐ Cell 917-555-5555
Area code Number Extension
Message
Loved your screenplay. Wants to meet with you right away. Please call her ASAP.
Signed Michael Waters

X	Phoned
	Returned your call
X	Please call
	Will call again
	Came to see you
X	Wants to see you

If the caller leaves a fax or cell phone number, check the correct box.

Check the appropriate boxes to sum up the main points of the message.

"This may be obvious, but it's important. Write legibly. If you mess up, start over on a fresh message slip."

Take a Message

Even a short call can contain lots of information. It's important to get it all down. Reread the message and the tips. Then use them to answer the questions below. Write your answers on your own paper.

1. Who is the message for? Who called? Who took the message?

2. What is the name of Goldie Silver's company?
   - **a.** Silver Co.
   - **b.** Michael Waters Ltd.
   - **c.** XL Films

3. Reread the message. What do you think ASAP stands for?
   - **a.** as soon as possible
   - **b.** and send a postcard
   - **c.** additional services are provided

4. Which two statements are true of Goldie Silver?
   - **a.** She visited Bailey Flynn's office in the afternoon.
   - **b.** She called Bailey Flynn on 5/12/01.
   - **c.** She loved the screenplay.

5. Which of the following is true about this message?
   - **a.** Goldie Silver called in the afternoon.
   - **b.** Ms. Silver wants to speak with Michael Waters.
   - **c.** Goldie Silver has a great screenplay that she wants Mr. Flynn to read.

Phone Tag

Bailey Flynn just returned Goldie Silver's call. Her assistant, Beth Scott, answered and said Ms. Silver was out to lunch. Bailey left his cell phone number so that Goldie could reach him anytime. Use the form to the left as a model and create the message that Ms. Silver's assistant took.

Get a Job

Michael Waters just quit. You want his job. Write a list of the skills you'd need to do the job.

"If you have sloppy handwriting, you might want to take messages on the computer."

Real-World Words

area code: a three-digit number needed to call other areas
extension: a private phone line linked to a company's main line
legibly: clearly; in a way that can be read easily

short story

Young Blue Eyes

On the planet Zyglot everyone has a bald head, three eyes, and three arms. How's an Earth kid supposed to fit in?

by Susan Beth Pfeffer

It's tough enough when you're the new person in school. But imagine you're the new person at a school on a planet millions of miles from home. Not only do your friends speak a different language, but they look and do things in an entirely different way. In the story you're about to read, the experience for one Earth kid is eye-opening. Can you relate?

Of course I was homesick. They'd warned me about that lots of times. Be prepared to be homesick, and don't be surprised if you have trouble opening the doors.

You would think such an advanced civilization would have automated all its doors. But it hasn't, and I walked into a dozen doors the first dozen rooms I entered. All the doorknobs were in the center of the doors, and my hand would automatically reach to the left, which is where doorknobs are on Earth. Not that Earth's doorknobs are better. The guidebooks all told me not to assume just because I was used to things being one way on Earth, it meant they were better that way. But I sure did get tired of walking into those doors.

I guess I was expecting more on Zyglot because all my life grown-ups have been telling me how perfect it is there. Or more to the point, how perfect the children there are. "Why can't you be more like Zyglot

"You may be asking yourself how it was I ended up on Zyglot? A good question, and one I've asked myself plenty of times . . ."

children?" teachers used to shout at us. "Zyglot children are always so well behaved." Once we had an entire school assembly telling us about the children of Zyglot, and they made this really big point of showing us all those little Zyglotians doing their homework and being polite.

I speak for all Earth kids when I say Zyglot kids were our teachers' dreams and our own worst nightmares.

You may be asking yourself how it was I ended up on Zyglot? A good question, and one I've asked myself plenty of times, especially each time I walked into a Zyglot door.

It was my mother's idea. "Travel is so broadening," she said. You have to understand, Mom's never been farther away from home than the supermarket. But I guess she figured I should do the traveling for both of us. So when I came home from school and told her about the Zyglot Student Exchange Program, she made me sign up for it right away.

Frankly, I never thought they'd pick me. The school I'd be going to had never had an Earth student there before, and I don't think of myself as exactly representative of all that's best in my species. Even my principal was surprised when she heard I'd been selected.

"Well, you're typical enough," she said. "I guess they're looking for someone kind of average."

That's me all right. Your kind-of-average high-school student with a mother who wants to travel through the galaxy, and is counting on me to get her the frequent flier miles to do it with.

After I was picked, they gave me all these orientation lectures, so I'd feel at home right away on Zyglot. Of course there was no way I was going to feel right at home on a planet that insists on putting its doorknobs dead center, but we all had to pretend the orientation sessions were working. One good thing about them. I picked up Zyglotian pretty easily, and except for an accent that cries out EARTH, language hasn't been a problem. And it turns out "Ow!" is the same on any planet. At least everyone on Zyglot knows what I'm saying each time the doorknob and I make contact.

I guess if I'd been born with three arms, I'd find a doorknob in the center perfectly sensible too. They gave me my third arm (robotic, of course; cheaper than the surgically attached kind and almost as useful) about a month before I left home and told me to wear it every day until I was used to it. That's great advice, but if your clothes only have two sleeves, a third arm smack in the middle can be a real nuisance.

Tell you the truth, I would have dumped the arm altogether except that schools on Zyglot all insist on uniforms, and I would have felt pretty silly with that empty sleeve flapping around all day.

So the first few days I was homesick and black and blue, but they put me with a nice family, and that helped.

Anyway, my Zyglotian family **consisted** of a mother and daughter. I was told to call my Zyglotian mother Em, which is their **equivalent** of Mom. I would have felt funny calling some stranger Mom, but Em had a nice sound to it. And Em's daughter, my "sister," was named Grudnick. Grudnick's my age, and she couldn't be nicer.

Every time I bumped into a door, she'd say how she was sure if she were on Earth, she'd be bumping into doors all the time herself.

I got to Zyglot about a week before school started. During that week, all the Earth kids had a big orientation session at Bruzchok University. I made a lot of good friends that week since we were all bumping into doors and trying to get our arms to work, and it was comforting being with kids just like myself.

But then the school year began, and we had to say good-bye. Lots of crying and swearing we'd stay in touch, but of course the whole idea of being an exchange student is you don't hang out with other Earth kids. So we each started at the schools we'd been selected for. And if you think I'd felt homesick before, you should have seen me carrying on as we Earth kids said good-bye to each other.

But I'm a resilient kind of person (which may be why they picked me), and the first day of school is exciting and scary and fun no matter where you go. Em helped me on with my uniform, and Grudnick swore she'd stick around and make sure I didn't get too lost.

"Be sure to use your arms," Em cried out to me as we began the long walk to school. "The middle one comes in so handy!"

She laughed, so I guess that's like a Zyglot joke. I tried not to hold it against her.

"See those girls up ahead," Grudnick whispered to me as we entered the schoolyard. "That's Marju and Drosis and Hooleete. They're the most popular girls in school."

"The best behaved too, I bet," I said.

Grudnick gave me a funny look. She'd given me a lot of those since I first moved in with her and Em. "Why would you think that?" she asked.

"Because we were always told how perfect Zyglotian kids were," I replied.

Grudnick laughed. "We were always told the same about Earth kids," she said.

Grown-ups. They're the same on any planet.

Anyway, I felt better once I knew I wasn't going to be surrounded by hundreds of perfect little Zyglotians. Three arms I might master. Being on my best behavior for a solid school year was a **guaranteed** impossibility.

"What makes them so popular then?" I asked.

"It's their looks," Grudnick said. "They're the prettiest girls in school, and they know it."

I looked at them more carefully, which was kind of hard, because they (and everyone else at school) were staring at me. "I think you're prettier," I said to Grudnick. I did too.

"Oh no," Grudnick said. "They're real beauties. Look at their eyes."

Which was pretty funny, because for the week I'd been on Zyglot, the one thing I'd been trying hard not to look at was eyes. It had been pretty easy avoiding the eyes, since I'd been spending most of my time looking down at my third arm, willing it to behave itself. But the other thing is, there's only so much different you can accept at any one time, and Zyglotian eyes were past my threshold level.

But I figured if they were going to stare at me, I might as well stare back. Grudnick was right about their eyes. Three girls, nine eyes amongst them, each eye a **distinctive** color.

"They're very pretty," I said, although I didn't mean a word of it. I've got two eyes, myself, both

ASK YOURSELF

- How is Zyglot different from Earth?

Think about the kind of place Zyglot is and compare it to Earth.

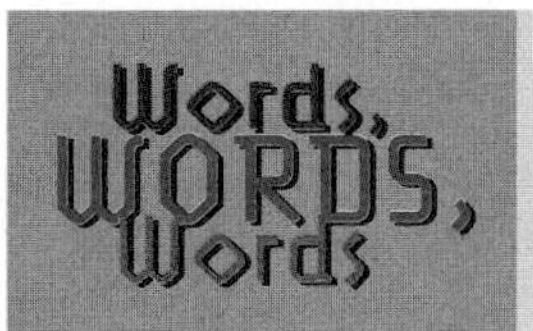

consisted: made up of
equivalent: equal in value
guaranteed: certain that something will happen
distinctive: clearly different

"Everyone laughed except for this one boy. . . . He smiled at me."

blue, and I have to admit that's how I like it. Of course I used to feel that way about two arms too.

Marju whispered something to Drosis and Hooleete, and they all giggled. I couldn't be sure, but I had the feeling they were laughing at me.

I know they were when I bumped into my first door of the day. Everyone laughed then, except for this one boy.

"Let me help you," he said.

I could tell by Zyglotian standards this guy was a looker. He would have done okay for himself on Earth for that matter. Three big eyes, red, yellow, and green. They sparkled like traffic lights as he smiled at me.

"Thank you," I mumbled.

"I like your accent," he said.

"I like yours too," I said, which was pretty dumb, because he didn't have one. I mean, he sounded just like all the other Zyglotians. But it's hard to flirt when you keep noticing you have fifteen fingers, and you can't quite tell which eye you're supposed to make eye contact with.

He just laughed and walked off. Marju, I noticed, scurried after him. I found Grudnick again, and she led me to my first class, which was Zyglotian History. A subject I happened to be extremely up on, since they'd been shoveling it down my throat since I'd been named an exchange student.

I knew a lot of answers to the questions, and I figured this was a good time to show off, since I only had to raise one arm to get called on. Besides, I figured they'd be pleased I'd learned all that stuff. And I could see the teacher was getting a kick out of me, the Earth kid, knowing the dates and places of important events on Zyglot.

ASK YOURSELF

- How do you think the Zyglotian girls feel when the cute guy smiles at the Earth girl?

Read on and pay attention to what Marju does.

I guess it annoyed the other students though, because after the teacher had called on me three or four times, I could hear some murmurings. The teacher could hear them too.

"You Zyglotians should be ashamed of yourselves," he said. "This Earth girl knows all about your history. And she's a perfect example of Earth youth. Polite, respectful, and attentive. You should all try to be more like her."

I wanted to say I wasn't at all the way he was describing me, that Earth kids were always being told how perfect the Zyglotian kids were, but it was my first day, and I didn't think it was such a good idea to annoy the teacher. After a while, I was sure he and everybody else on Zyglot would lose their **illusions** about me.

Besides, it was a kick and a half to be held up to the class like I was some kind of perfect Earth kid. I guess you'd have to have sat through that awful assembly about perfect Zyglotian youths to know how it felt.

The rest of my morning classes I didn't show off though. I'd tried to learn about Zyglotian literature, but there was no way I could hold my own there. And math on any planet is not my best subject. But I did okay, and just as long as the doors were open, I didn't make a total fool of myself.

Not until gym at least. But that was a nightmare.

Back home I'm a pretty fair athlete. My **specialty** is track events, and I've run some pretty respectable times. But even with two arms and two eyes, my hand-eye **coordination** isn't the best. It's no big deal. I stick to sports where I don't have to throw or catch things, and I do fine.

Only that day in gym, they were playing Boodlach. Boodlach, in case you missed it during the last Intergallactic Olympics, is the team sport of Zyglot. It's exclusively a middle-arm game. You get **penalized** if your right or left arm touches the ball. And you lose style points if the ball goes below your forehead, which is where both of my blue eyes happen to be located.

I was the last one picked for the team. Not that I could blame them, but it was an awful feeling as girl after girl was selected and I stood there feeling, well, feeling like the only two-eyed two-armed kid in the school.

Eventually they ran out of other kids, and somebody selected me. I knew they were all hoping nobody would hit the ball anywhere near me.

Of course the other team's entire strategy was to aim the ball my way. Which they did, over and over again.

I tried. I mean, I really tried. I tried holding my right arm with my left one, behind my back, so I wouldn't be tempted to take a swing at it. But it seemed like every time I tried hitting the ball my middle arm was too weak and too late, and the ball kept landing on my nose.

The final score was 128 to 7. That means my nose got bopped 128 out of 135 times.

Lunch followed gym. I took one look at the typical Zyglot school lunch and bolted to the girls' room. They can tell you a hundred times that what you're used to isn't necessarily better, but when you've just made a total fool of yourself and your nose hurts and your chest is black and blue, the last thing you want to deal with is a plate of still-wriggling worms, no matter how good the sauce is.

Luckily for me, and all the other Earth women who find themselves on Zyglot, we go to the bathroom the same way. I found myself an empty stall, and sat down for what I anticipated would be a good twenty-minute cry.

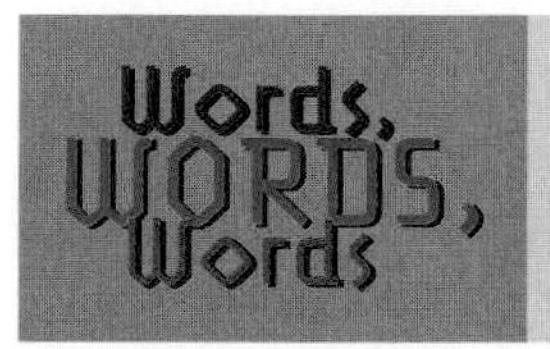

illusions: things that appear to exist but really do not
specialty: something you are good at doing
coordination: ability to combine two or more things successfully
penalized: punished for something done wrong

But before I had a chance to let myself go, I heard three girls enter.

"Don't worry, Marju," one of them said. "Tradbeam will never look at her twice."

"Hooleete's right," another girl said. "The way she showed off in history class? He hates that kind of stuff."

"And she was awful in gym," Hooleete said. "I loved how you kept hitting the ball right at her."

"I'm surprised she still has a nose left," Drosis said.

"But the way he looked at her," Marju said.

"It's only because she's new here," Hooleete said. "Tradbeam always flirts with new girls."

"Besides, think about her eyes," Drosis said. "Just two and they're both the same color."

"That's true," Marju said. "She does have the ugliest eyes I've ever seen."

The girls kept on talking, and I kept on hiding. Eventually they left, and when they did, I let the tears stream out of both my baby blues.

I guess I stayed in the girls' room long enough for Grudnick to worry, because after a while she showed up calling for me.

I let myself out of the stall (after bumping into its door).

"You've been crying," she said. She reached out to comfort me with her middle arm.

"I don't fit in," I said. "And I never will. My arms. My eyes." It was all I could do to keep from blubbering again.

"You'll get better with your arm," Grudnick said. "We'll work on it every night. And as far as your eyes go, why don't we just give you a third one."

ASK YOURSELF

- How would this story be different if it were taking place on Earth?

Think about what is happening to the Earth girl.

"What?" I said. I could just imagine what Mom would say when she got the bill for a surgically **implanted** third eye.

"We'll put it on with makeup," Grudnick said. She took out some eyebrow pencil and outlined a perfect third eye for me. It was about as useful as my third arm, but I didn't care.

"What color do you want it?" she asked.

"Blue," I said, because I hadn't gotten out of the Earth mindset about eyes matching. "No, pink. Do you have pink?"

"Of course I have pink," Grudnick said. She painted the center of the eye a bright pink. It just about matched my red nose.

"Now you look like a Zyglotian," Grudnick said.

I stared at myself in the mirror. I did too. It was a shame two of my eyes were the same color, but except for that and the fact I wasn't bald, I looked just like all the other girls.

"If you want, we can shave your hair off when we get home today," Grudnick said. "Then you'll really fit in."

It's funny. Grudnick couldn't have been nicer. And she was saying just what I'd been wishing for a moment earlier. So I guess it wasn't the arms or the eyes. I guess it was the hair.

But whatever it was, I knew right then that no matter what Grudnick did, I wasn't going to fit right in. Not if I **pretended** to be a Zyglotian for the entire school year.

"No," I said. "I'm from Earth and everyone might as well know it."

"Your hair means a lot to you, doesn't it," Grudnick said.

Of course it did. I'd brought a year's worth of shampoo with me. But that wasn't what decided me.

It was the thought of all us Earth kids being taught Zyglot kids were perfect. And all the Zyglot kids being taught the same thing about us.

I was on Zyglot to show kids what Earth kids were really like. It was possible one day one of the kids I was in school with would hold major **political** office on Zyglot, or be involved in intergallactic trade with Earth. And they had to know what Earth people, real Earth people were like. Two eyes and all.

"It's a lovely eye," I said, tearing off some toilet paper and wiping it away gently. "Thank you, Grudnick, but it just isn't me. I'll keep the extra arm, though. It seems to be the only way to open doors around here."

"I'm from Earth and everyone might as well know it."

Grudnick looked hard at me. Then she swung her arms up and removed contact lenses from two of her eyes.

"Your eyes!" I said. "They match. They're all orange."

Grudnick nodded. "I've been wearing lenses for years now," she said, "because I've been so ashamed."

"I think your eyes are beautiful," I said. "Of course, I only have two of them to see you with."

Grudnick laughed. "I guess we won't win the Miss Zyglot beauty **pageant**," she said.

"Frankly, I'm not going to bother entering," I said. And then I found myself humming the song "My Way."

"What's that?" Grudnick asked.

"It's my great-great-great-grandfather's favorite song," I told her. "He sings it all the time. His grandmother once knew someone who dated Frank Sinatra."

"Who's he?" Grudnick asked.

"He's a singer," I said. "They used to call him Old Blue Eyes. He only had two of them too."

"I guess that makes you Young Blue Eyes," Grudnick said.

"I guess so," I said. I rubbed my back against hers, which is how they hug on Zyglot. "You're the best, Grudnick. Or should I call you Young Orange Eyes?"

And we left the girls' room, laughing out loud, the two of us proud and strong, walking hand in hand together. ●

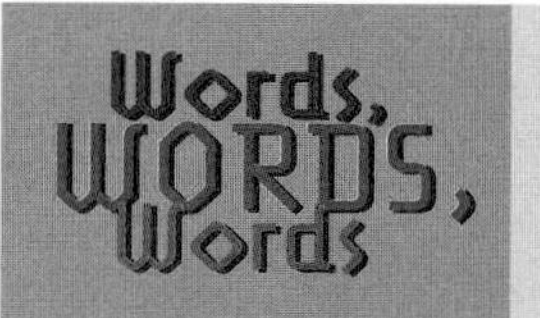

implanted: put something in or on your body by surgery
pretended: made believe
political: having to do with the government
pageant: a public show

Hi-Tech Eyes

by Miguel Vilar

One day you may be able to get money from your bank in a blink of an eye. What's this amazing technology all about?

Time: 7:30 P.M.
Place: ATM Machine

It's Saturday night and your older sister has invited you to a movie. She's low on cash. So she makes a quick stop at a cash machine. She stands in front of it and just stares. She doesn't have a bank card, or a PIN (personal identification number) to punch in. Who cares? The ATM instantly spits out $40. What gives? Is the cash machine on the blink?

No, *she* blinked. And with the press of a button, the ATM scanned her "eyeprint." A special camera inside the ATM took a picture of your sister's *iris*—or colored ring around her pupil. It then matched it to a picture of her iris it had stored in the bank's computer. Since no two irises are alike, no one else but your sister could have gotten that money from her account.

Welcome to the world of hi-tech IDs. Scientists are working very hard so that your iris, fingerprints, and even your voice will work as your ID card in the future. The use of certain parts of the human body to identify a person is called *biometrics.*

A FOOLPROOF IDEA

This kind of identity system is not new. Two thousand years ago, the Chinese used fingerprints to seal important letters and documents. Since no two fingerprints are alike, they knew it was a foolproof way to check a person's identity.

"Your irises are different from those of everyone else on Earth. In fact, your left iris is distinct from your right!"

Today computers have become very advanced. People have also become more concerned about security. As a result, biometrics has taken off. With scanners and color printers, anyone can create a fake ID that could pass for the real thing. But when you use your iris as an ID, even your identical twin couldn't pass for you.

Each iris is totally unique. Because of the way the muscle around an eye's pupil works, each iris has a different pattern. Your irises are different from those of everyone else on Earth. In fact, your left iris is distinct from your right!

HOW DOES IT WORK?

Suppose your school wanted to use iris IDs to make sure only students enter the building. Here's how it might work: First, a photographer uses a computerized camera to take a close-up picture of your left or right eye. The picture captures the pattern of your iris, which is then fed into a computer. The computer stores the picture, scans it, then turns it into a special code. It's called the "IrisCode." The code is stored in the computer's memory as a bar code (see photo).

Next time you walk into school you will have to face a camera. It will photograph and scan your iris. Then, it will search its memory for your IrisCode, and let you in or not. This all takes less than two seconds. In more than 2 billion tests on millions of eyes, the iris ID system has never mistakenly identified anyone. Not once.

Experts predict that within several years iris scanners may replace credit cards. Imagine paying for clothes with a quick look at a camera. You'd better shop with your eyes closed! ●

Each person's IrisCode and bar code (below) are unique. A computer has never mistakenly identified anyone in tests on millions of eyes.

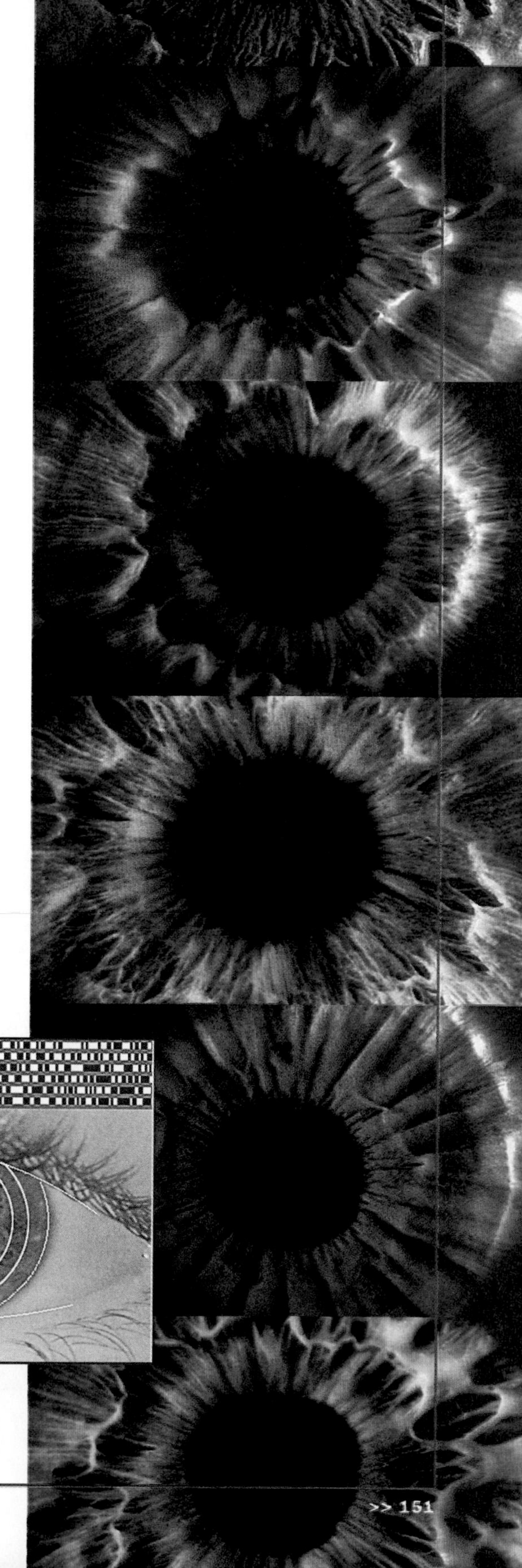

Talk About It

Now that you've read "Young Blue Eyes" and "Hi-Tech Eyes," what do you have to say about these questions?

- What do some people in your school do to try to fit in?
- In addition to replacing bank cards, how else might eyeprints be used in the future?

Comprehension Check

Write your answers to the questions below. Use information from the story and the article to support your answers.

1. Name two ways that schools in Zyglot and Earth are alike.
2. Why do you think that Marju keeps hitting the ball right at the main character during gym class?
3. How did Grudnick prove to be a good friend?
4. What advantage does an eyeprint have over an old-fashioned ID?
5. How are Zyglotian irises different from irises on Earth?

Vocabulary Check

Complete each sentence starter below. Before you answer, think about the meaning of the vocabulary word in bold.

1. I was glad that the item was **guaranteed** because . . .
2. My most **distinctive** quality is . . .
3. In some sports you can be **penalized** for . . .
4. The secret sauce **consisted** of . . .
5. An example of two **equivalent** things are . . .

Write About It

Choose one of the writing prompts below.

- Write a letter from the main character to her family back home on Earth. In this letter explain what the main character has learned and how she feels.
- Would you like to be an exchange student? Write an essay explaining where you'd like to go and why.
- Write an ad for the first bank to use eyeprints instead of bank cards. In the ad, explain how this will be a great new service for bank customers.

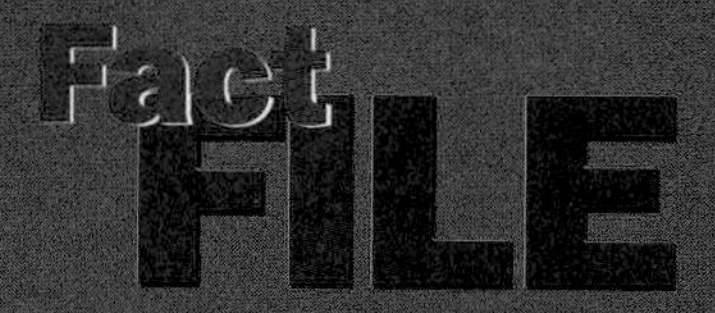

If you like "Young Blue Eyes," you might enjoy watching these science fiction classics on video.

E.T.: The Extra-Terrestrial

Directed by Steven Spielberg and written by Melissa Mathison

In 1982, *E.T.* became an instant success. It tells the story of a lonely young boy, Elliott, who finds a creature from another planet. With E.T., Elliott discovers adventures beyond his wildest imagination.

The Star Wars Saga

Created by George Lucas

It all began with *Star Wars*. In this classic, Luke Skywalker uses the Force to battle Darth Vader and his Evil Empire. The fight continues over the next two episodes, *The Empire Strikes Back* and *Return of the Jedi*. *The Phantom Menace* takes you back in time to when Luke's father, Anakin Skywalker, was only a boy. Two more episodes follow. They show how Anakin Skywalker becomes Darth Vader.

Information searching

Searching the Web

You're really interested in learning about the Detroit Tigers baseball team. You decide to search the Web. You type the word *tiger* into a search engine, and you get a list of 18,000 Web sites! How do you know which ones to visit?

Check out this home page. Find out how to make the Web work for you.

Search Engine Home Page

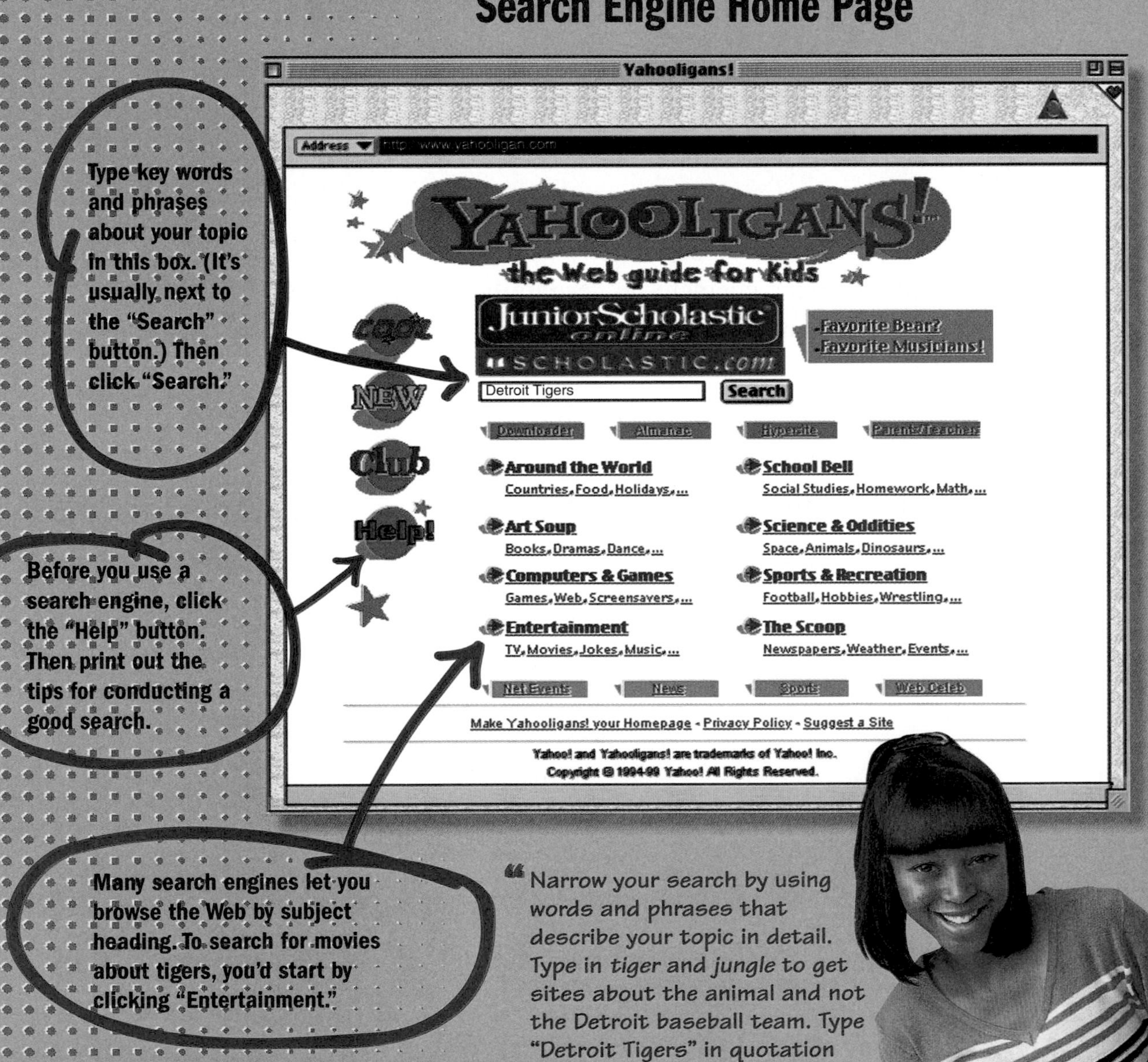

Type key words and phrases about your topic in this box. (It's usually next to the "Search" button.) Then click "Search."

Before you use a search engine, click the "Help" button. Then print out the tips for conducting a good search.

Many search engines let you browse the Web by subject heading. To search for movies about tigers, you'd start by clicking "Entertainment."

"Narrow your search by using words and phrases that describe your topic in detail. Type in *tiger* and *jungle* to get sites about the animal and not the Detroit baseball team. Type "Detroit Tigers" in quotation marks to get only sites that include that phrase."

Surf's Up!

Ready to go surfing for information? Review the home page and the tips on the left. Then use them to answer the questions below. Write your answers on your own paper.

1. You want to know what to feed your lizard. You decide to narrow your search by adding one word to the key word **lizard.** Which one of the following words would help you the most?
   a. green **c.** desert
   b. diet **d.** shedding

2. You want to know where lizards live in the wild, so you check under one of the categories on the home page. Which one do you choose?

3. You want to order some food for your lizard over the Web. Which search entry would help you find a way to do that?
   a. lizard and chameleon
   b. shopping and pet supplies
   c. lizard and dog food

4. You did one search and got information on all these topics: hammerheads, the movie *Jaws*, a San José hockey team, and deep-sea fishing. What word did you enter?
   a. hockey **c.** sharks
   b. movies **d.** sports

5. You want to narrow the search from #4. What word or phrase could you use if you wanted only sites about the hockey team?

Find It Fast

Here are a few things you might want to find on the Web. List the words and phrases you would use to search for each one.

- a Web site that sells CDs
- career home-run leaders in major-league baseball
- a group devoted to fighting drug abuse in schools
- help with your math homework
- places to go skateboarding in San Francisco

Test It Out

Go to the computer and complete one of the searches that you planned above. How did you do?

"Find a site you like? Most browsers have a 'bookmark' feature that lets you mark sites so you can go back to them easily."

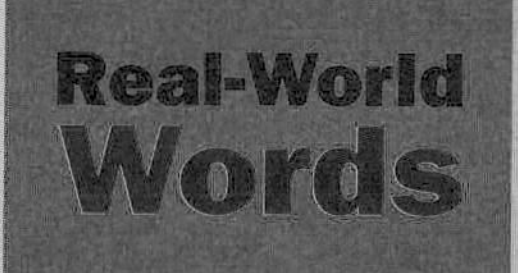

browser: software that lets you move around the Web
home page: the main menu page of a browser or Web site

nonfiction article

Teenagers are special targets of stores and advertisers. Learn their tricks and you'll save a bundle.

You're going out with your friends this weekend. You want to buy some new jeans so you'll look good. So you cruise the aisles of your favorite clothing store. Before long, you're leaving the cash register feeling strangely . . . uh . . . empty. Sure, you bought some jeans you like. You also bought a jacket, a cool sweater (50 percent off!), and a belt. But there's a problem. What's empty is your wallet. You don't have enough money left to do anything or go anywhere. You'll be stuck at home while everyone else is at the movies.

Welcome to the world of retail. What's retail? It's a multibillion-dollar business designed to get you to spend money. Every store—the entire mall—is part of it. "There is a whole science to selling," says Lynn Kahle, a marketing professor at the University of Oregon. "Especially when it comes to selling to kids and teens."

Teenagers are special targets of marketers, the experts hired by stores and advertisers to help sell a product. Why? Teenagers are big spenders. They shell out $141 billion a year, mostly on clothes, computers, food, and music.

The amount teens spend will only keep growing. One reason is sheer numbers. Right now there are 31 million teens. By 2010, says the U.S. Census Bureau, there will be about 35 million.

Where does all the money come from? Older teens may have part-time work. Younger ones have odd jobs. Others get big allowances.

In some cases, teens are being given money by their parents so they can help out with shopping and buying the family groceries. That's because working parents often don't have the time to shop themselves.

More and more, marketers are thinking of YOU when they think up ideas to get consumers to spend money. They're thinking of you when they make a special CD display. You're the reason they put that gum and candy by the cash register.

But no one can force you to empty your wallet. If you know the tricks that marketers use, you can stop wasting money on things you don't need. You can get the best deal on the things you really want to buy. Maybe, you can even have some money left over. Here's how.

1. Don't let the way that a store looks influence you.

When are you most likely to spend money? Marketers know you'll spend more when you're comfortable. So stores use their environment to influence how you shop. It's more than making a store look good. For example, the colors of the walls and rugs affect people's moods. "If you want customers to relax, use blue," says Ayn Crowley, an associate marketing professor at Iowa's Drake University. Blue encourages customers to spend time in a store. That gives salespeople more time to make a pitch which could get a customer to spend more.

WHERE TEENS GET THEIR MONEY

Parents: 53%

Gifts: 47%

Odd jobs: 46%

Part-time jobs: 38%

Full-time jobs: 6%

Their own business: 2%

0 10 20 30 40 50

Percentages do not add up to 100 because teens may list more than one source of income.
Source: Teenage Research Unlimited

Other stores make money by serving people quickly. That's why many fast-food chains decorate in red or yellow. Research has shown that these colors get customers all worked up. Their hearts actually beat faster. That encourages diners to eat and run—opening up a seat for the next customer.

Tip #1: ***Make a shopping list before you leave home. If you stick to your list, you'll be more likely to buy only what you really need to.***

2. Pay attention to your most important sense—common sense.

Marketers don't stop with how the store looks. They appeal to your other senses—smell, hearing, and sight—as well. Many stores play low-key music. That's because the music relaxes shoppers. Profits went up 38 percent in grocery stores when slow music was played, says Ronald Milliman, a marketing professor at Western Kentucky University. Shoppers relaxed. They spent more time looking at products. And they bought more.

Some stores focus on soft lighting to make their products

ASK yourself

- What might cause you to spend more than you planned?

Think about how stores try to affect your senses.

look better. Other stores even use smell to sell you. Their **scent** machines release lavender, ginger, orange, or mint fragrance. A 1996 study showed how the smells made a difference. When they were present, customers thought that the store's products were of higher quality. They also thought the products were more up-to-date.

Tip #2: ***When your senses are stimulated, you are less likely to make good buying decisions. If you feel you are losing your focus, leave the store. Go some place quieter and less distracting. Then think about what you really want to buy.***

3. Don't let sales signs fool you into paying more.

What about sale signs? There's a science behind them as well. Experts have studied how signs affect shoppers. Recently, one marketing expert did a study. He put up signs for two products. One read "25 percent off." The other said "Buy 3, get 1 free." When you did the math, the price for both products was actually the same. But the study found that suggesting a product was free caused shoppers to buy more. Shoppers may have needed only one pizza. But they bought three—and spent more than they probably needed to—to get the free one.

Don't let price signs fool you either. What may appear cheaper at first glance could actually be more expensive. In grocery stores, you'll find unit prices listed below items on the shelves. Unit prices let you compare the cost of two or more products. Let's say you're looking at chocolate chip cookies. Brand X is $1.95 for 15 ounces. Brand Y is $2.50 for 25 ounces. The unit price will show you the price per ounce. In this case, Brand X costs 13 cents per ounce and Brand Y costs 10 cents per ounce. The lowest unit price is the best deal.

Tip #3: ***Be a careful shopper. Study sale signs and use unit prices to make sure you're really getting a good deal.***

4. Avoid being tempted and stay on target.

Another trick of the trade is placement. What's placement? It's where stores actually put the merchandise. Marketing experts know things about you that you'd never guess. For example, you—and 85 percent of other shoppers—usually turn right when you enter a space. So stores put tempting high-priced items to the right of the door. Most shoppers also are more likely to buy something that is at eye-level. Since products move fastest in that spot, that's

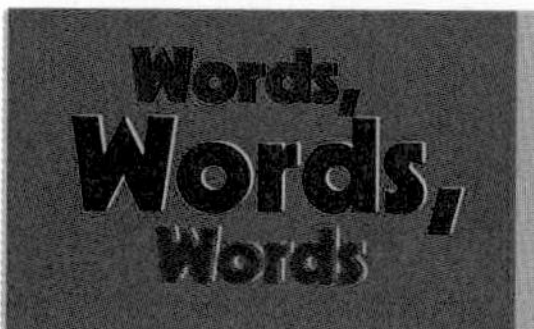

influence: have an effect upon; affect; change
scent: a pleasant smell
tempted: to want something or want to do something; attracted

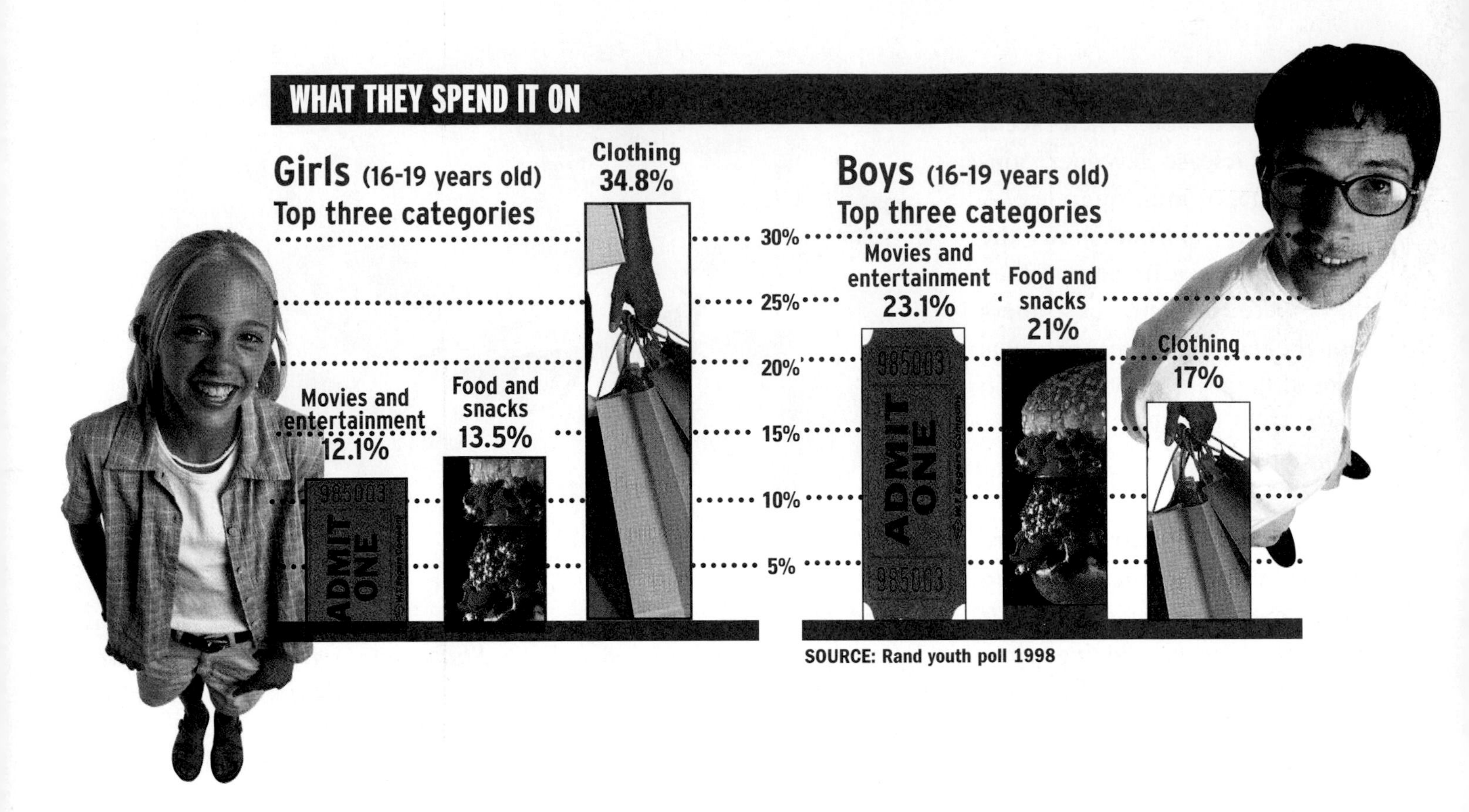

where stores tend to place their most expensive items.

Another example? Grocery stores often put the most important products—say, the milk—at the very back. That way, customers have to walk past other goodies to get to it. The more shoppers walk around, the more unplanned items they're likely to buy. Stores also **display** products that can be used together—say, corn flakes and raisins or a skirt and top—side-by-side. That way they lure shoppers into buying both.

What else do marketers know? They have found that people are more likely to buy things at the end of an aisle than in the middle. Also, people are more likely to buy things while they wait on line.

One trick is to put small "**impulse** buys" near the cash registers. For example, brightly colored key rings may tempt you at the counter of a hardware store. Magazines, candy, and gum clutter checkout aisles in grocery stores. Retailers hope that you will scoop up these small items as you wait for service. But the cost on counter items is often high. You may not be getting a very good deal.

Tip #4: ***Figure out how much you want to spend. When you go to the store, bring only enough money to buy what's on your list. That way, you won't be tempted to buy an unplanned item.***

Follow these tips next time you shop. That way you won't be fooled and spend more than you can afford! ●

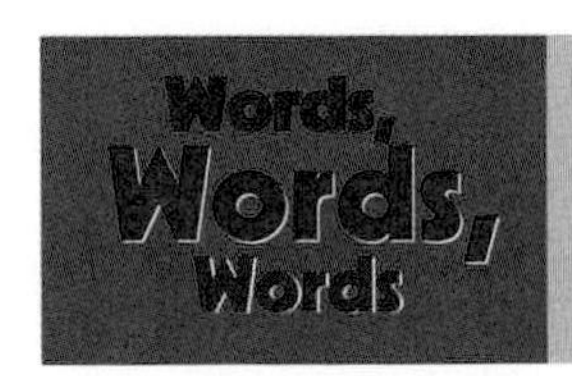

display: show
impulse: a sudden desire to do something

Is It Fair to Ban Kids From the Mall?

The Mall of America in Minnesota is the largest mall in the country. Of course, lots of teenagers like to hang out there. But on weekend evenings, this mall and other malls around the country have a rule: Kids under 16 are banned unless accompanied by an adult. Mall officials say these rules are needed because packs of kids cause trouble at the mall. But many teens—and some adults—say these rules are unfair.

What do you think? Read this debate and decide.

Malls are private property. The people who own them have the right to ban kids if they choose. Packs of kids hanging around in malls really do cause problems. They get loud and rowdy and their behavior annoys and upsets older shoppers. Plus, some kids shoplift from stores, or simply break things through careless behavior. Banning unaccompanied kids from the mall is the best way to keep kids under control and protect store owners and their customers.

If you said yes:

- If malls are off-limits, where else can kids hang out safely with their friends and have fun?

Banning kids from the mall violates their rights. Malls may be privately owned, but they are still public places. They should be open to anyone who wants to visit them. In many towns, kids have nowhere else to hang out but the mall. Besides, the majority of teen mall-goers behave perfectly well. When mall officials catch kids misbehaving, they should ask those individuals to leave. It's not fair to punish everyone for the problems caused by just a few troublemakers.

If you said no:

- How can you stop unaccompanied kids from causing trouble at the mall?

What's your point of view?

Talk About It

Now that you've read "Don't Be Fooled" and "Is It Fair to Ban Kids From the Mall?" what do you have to say about these questions?

- ▶ Should stores be forced to be more honest in the way they market to teens? Why or why not?
- ▶ Do teenagers create a problem at malls in your community? Explain your answer.

Comprehension Check

Write your answers to the questions below. Use information from the reading to support your answers.

1. What are two things stores do to encourage shoppers to spend more money?
2. According to information in the graph, "What They Spend It On," which types of stores might be more likely to target girls than boys?
3. What might happen if teens became smarter shoppers?
4. Why do some people want to ban kids from the mall?
5. Does it make sense for stores to want to ban some of their best customers? Explain your opinion.

Vocabulary Check

Answer each question below with a complete sentence. Before you answer, think about the meaning of the vocabulary word in bold.

1. What is your favorite **scent**?
2. Who or what has had the greatest **influence** on your life? Why?
3. When was the last time you were **tempted** to buy something?
4. What's the last thing you bought on **impulse**?
5. What's one way to **display** a prized collection?

Write About It

Choose one of the writing prompts below.

- Write a list of the last ten items you purchased. Then describe why you bought each one.
- Write a letter to a store complaining about a defective product you recently purchased.
- Create a "Smart Shopping" guide for other kids. Be sure to include bulleted tips and add at least one of your own.

Take ACTION

Have you ever wanted to complain about a store or find out more about shopping scams? Here are some places that can help you.

Better Business Bureaus are great places to file complaints or find out about scams. Look in the phone book for your local BBB. Or get more information from:

- Council of Better Business Bureaus, Inc.
  4200 Wilson Blvd., Suite 800
  Arlington, VA 22203-1838
  www.bbb.org
- The Consumer Information Center
  Pueblo, CO 81009
  www.pueblo.gsa.gov
- The Federal Trade Commission
  CRC-240
  Washington, DC 20580
  www.ftc.gov/ftc/consumer.htm

Reading a Bar Graph

You're a clerk at a career center. Your boss wants you to gather information about salaries of different jobs.

The bar graph below will help you. It shows the average salaries of nine different jobs. Look it over and answer the questions on the next page.

The vertical line shows how much money each job pays per year.

The taller the bar, the bigger the salary. The shorter the bar, the smaller the salary.

Annual Salaries of Selected Jobs

AVERAGE SALARIES PER YEAR

$225,000
$200,000
$175,000
$150,000
$125,000
$100,000
$75,000
$50,000
$25,000
$0

Barber | Fast-Food Manager | Flight Attendant | Lawyer | Local TV News Anchor | Movie/TV Actor | Private Detective | Surgeon | U.S. President

JOBS

Source: *America's Fastest Growing Jobs*, 4th Edition by Michael J. Farr (JIST Works, Inc. 1997); *Occupational Outlook Handbook, 1996-97 Edition* (U.S. Depatment of Labor, 1996).

The horizontal line gives the name of each job included on the graph.

"How much does a surgeon make? Go to the top of the bar above "surgeon." Then go straight across the graph, all the way to the left. A surgeon's salary is about $225,000 per year."

You Do the Math

A bar graph is a quick way to see how different sums compare to each other. Review the graph and the tips. Then use them to answer the questions below. Write your answers on your own paper.

1. On average, how much does a lawyer earn each year?
   a. about $15,000
   b. about $100,000
   c. about $115,000
   d. about $225,000

2. Bob manages a fast-food restaurant. How many years will he have to work to earn as much as a surgeon earns in one year?
   a. 3 years
   b. 5 years
   c. 7 years
   d. 9 years

3. List all the jobs on the graph in order, from the highest-paying job to the lowest. Number them from 1 to 9. Which jobs are numbers 1, 5, and 9?
   a. movie/TV actor, local TV news anchor, surgeon
   b. surgeon, private detective, movie/TV actor
   c. lawyer, U.S. president, barber
   d. lawyer, local TV news anchor, flight attendant

4. **Write about it.** Should a surgeon make more than the president? Why or why not?

Imagine That!

Suppose each bar on the graph stands for one person. Tell what each of these people's salaries would be if

- the surgeon's salary drops by $50,000.
- the barber has a new hit salon and his salary triples.
- the detective gets a $20,000 bonus.

Graph-o-Matic

Using your list from "Imagine That!," make a new bar graph.

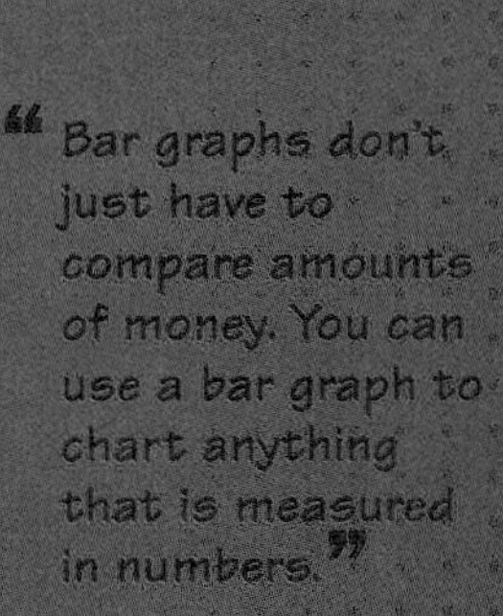

"Bar graphs don't just have to compare amounts of money. You can use a bar graph to chart anything that is measured in numbers."

Real-World Words

annual: per year; every year
horizontal: parallel to the ground
vertical: running up and down; upright

profile

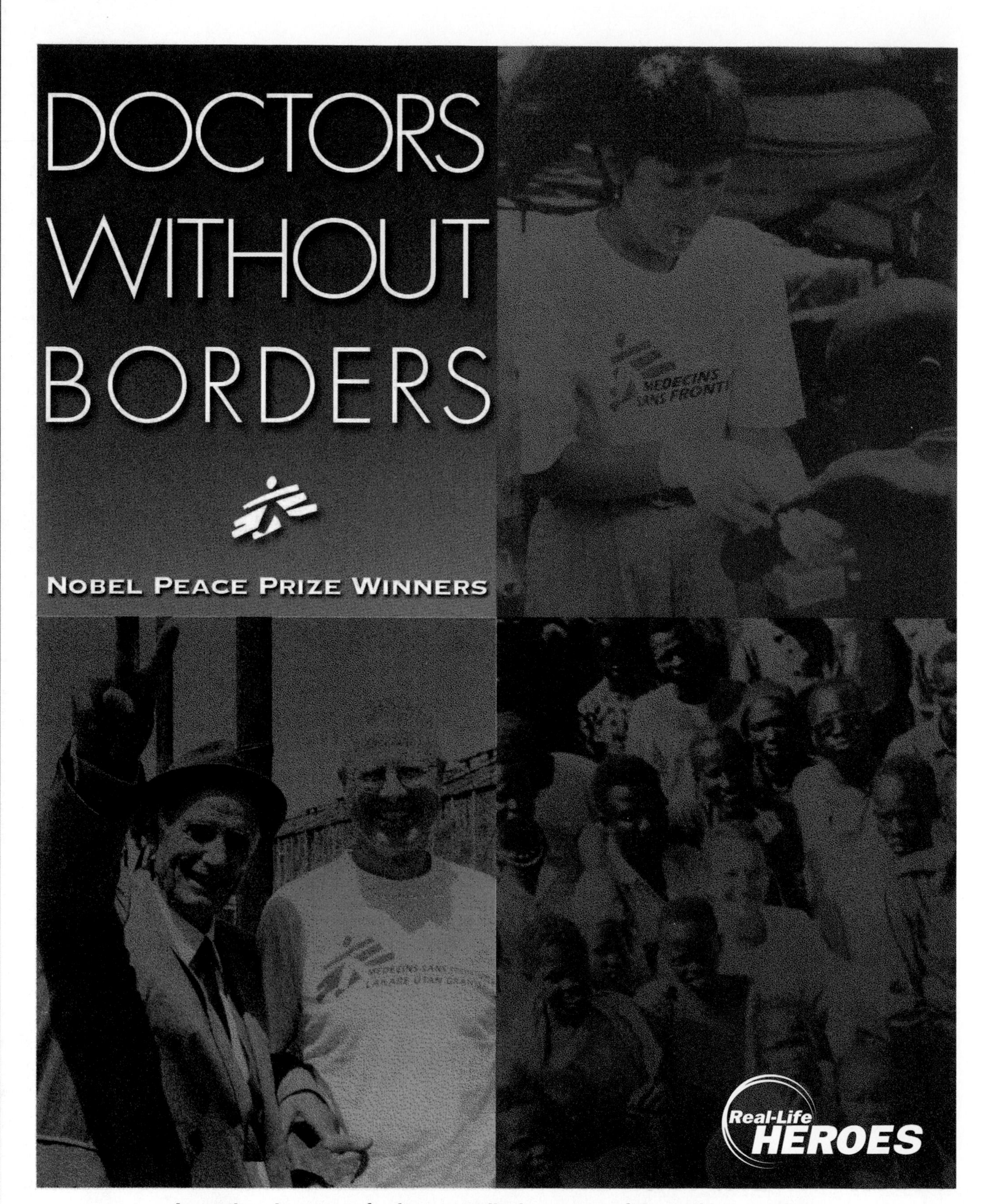

An earthquake, war, or famine can strike in any part of the world at any time.
Doctors Without Borders is there to help.

MSF VOLUNTEERS ARE A SPECIAL BREED. THEY'LL WORK BACKBREAKING HOURS TO GET WATER, MEDICINE, AND FOOD TO PEOPLE WHO MIGHT DIE WITHOUT IT.

Christine Nadori is not your average nurse. She's a volunteer for Doctors Without Borders. At any time, Christine is ready to travel to any part of the world that needs her help.

In 1998, Doctors Without Borders sent Christine to Sudan, a country in East Africa. She especially remembers helping a girl there in an orange dress.

The girl stumbled into the feeding center Christine was running. She may have been nine, possibly ten. She carried her baby brother with her. Her dress hung limp on her starving body. The area the girl lived in was being strangled by famine and war. This little girl had gotten the worst of it. She was so thin that she could barely walk.

The girl dug into the food Doctors Without Borders offered her. She had a huge will to survive. Every day, she made sure she and her brother got their ration of milk and cornmeal porridge.

Christine left the center for five days while the girl was still struggling. When she came back she couldn't believe her eyes. "There she was with her brother, and the dress was starting to burst," recalls Christine, 32. "I thought, this can't be her. She was suddenly a woman, and she was beautiful."

Ready to Help

The history of Doctors Without Borders is full of stories like this. A group of French doctors started the organization in 1971. It was called Médecins Sans Frontières or MSF, which means "doctors without borders" in French. MSF's goal was to offer medical help to people in crisis as quickly as possible without regard to race, religion, or politics.

For thirty years, MSF has been sending volunteers like Christine to the most desperate corners of the earth. They are mostly doctors and nurses. They stay in a place from a couple of weeks to a year. They provide health care to people suffering from a war, a natural disaster, famine, or poverty.

Sometimes MSF is invited into a country to help. Other times, it's not. MSF rarely takes no for an answer if people are suffering. In Afghanistan, volunteers were determined to help victims of a civil war. So, they dressed up like local residents. They slipped into the Middle Eastern country secretly with medicines and supplies. They risked their lives to provide medical care to the war's victims. In 1999, MSF's dedication brought them the highest honor the world has to offer: the Nobel Peace Prize.

A Special Breed

MSF won such a special prize because MSF volunteers are a special breed of people. They're willing to leave jobs, homes, family, and friends behind at a moment's notice. They pack their bags and take off for a country they've never seen before. They land in deserts or cities burned out by war, where no one speaks their language. And there they stay, often in difficult or dangerous conditions. They'll work backbreaking hours to get water, medicine, and food to people who might die without it.

How hard is the work? Ask William Conk. He works most of the year as a housing manager at the University of New Hampshire. He's not a doctor, but his engineering skills are desperately needed at Doctors Without Borders. In the summer of 1999, William spent his vacation working 14-hour days in Albania, a country in Eastern Europe.

Every day William visited old factories and warehouses that

An MSF volunteer on her way to help.

were overflowing with refugees. The refugees had fled from neighboring Kosovo because of a war going on there. As many as 500 people might be packed into a single room with no working toilets. William's job was to get clean water, good toilets, and working showers to the refugees. He slaved nonstop for six weeks. He only got two days off and spent most of them planning how to fix a drainage problem or a water leak.

"I guess the biggest feeling I had is of being **overwhelmed**," William wrote back to his family. "I have watched as refugees get off buses, looking at their new 'home,' which is a warehouse with 200 people already living there. I find this situation so unreal and so sad that I am anxious about letting it all sink in at once."

ASK YOURSELF

- What does Doctors Without Borders do to help people who are suffering?

As you read, think about the problems they are able to solve.

Toughing It Out

Volunteers generally have little more comfort than the people they're helping. In Sudan, Christine and 22 other workers lived in tents. They often went hungry with the Sudanese children.

In 1999, Stefano Sereno fought a meningitis outbreak in the desert of northern Sudan. Meningitis is a rare and often fatal disease. When Stefano, a 27-year-old Mexican doctor, arrived to help with the outbreak, there was no electricity. There was also very little water, and no shelter.

When he returned home three months later to Guadalajara, Mexico, nothing seemed the same. "At home, you wake up and turn on the water and you have it," he says. "You open the fridge and there is food. As a volunteer often there is no running water, there is no fridge. You drink hot water in hot weather. You learn to give value to things that we have and take for granted every day."

Doctors in Danger

In many places, life as an MSF volunteer is more than just uncomfortable. It's also very dangerous. Stefano spent seven months in Chechnya in 1997, just after its brutal war for independence with Russia. Even though fighting had stopped, tensions were still simmering. A couple of people working for other **relief** organizations were kidnapped and killed. MSF warned Stefano and other volunteers to stay inside after dark.

"At times like that you can think, why am I here?" says Stefano. "But in those moments you must also think, I am doing the right thing. It's like saying, who is going to be more stubborn? Who's going to win? Those who want to destroy or those who want to help?"

It's that **determination** and spirit that has kept Doctors Without Borders going for thirty years. Christine says that everyone comes home from a **mission** a little frustrated. They always wish they could have done more. "That's the strength of it," she says, "to never be **indifferent** in the face of something that you could have an impact on."

The Power of Caring

For Christine, the small miracles keep her volunteering for MSF. In Sudan, it was two orphans who kept everyone smiling even though they'd lost their entire family. In Kenya, another African country, it was a survey that brought kids into the feeding center to be weighed. Everyone was just standing around laughing, she says. For a minute the children were having a great time. They laughed, even though half their family had died since the last time the survey was done.

"The trap is to think you can save the world," says Stefano. "You can't change the world. But you can help one person in a single place. If you travel thousands of miles just to go and put a bandage on someone, this is already very important."

All over the world, there are people who know that what Stefano says is very true. Just ask one little Sudanese girl. Thanks to Doctors Without Borders, she lived to outgrow an orange dress. ●

Doctors Without Borders RESUMÉ

NAME Doctors Without Borders or Médecins Sans Frontières (MSF)

FOUNDED 1971

GOALS
- to help all victims of war or disaster without regard to race, religion, or politics
- to speak out against human rights abuses

WORK HISTORY
- sends nearly 3,000 volunteers out each year
- maintains missions in 80 countries
- spends about $250 million a year helping victims

MAJOR ACHIEVEMENTS
- helped thousands of Vietnamese and Cambodian refugees in Thailand in 1976
- sent 550 doctors to Afghanistan in 1979 during civil war despite Afghani government opposition
- aided thousands of Somali refugees during 1991 civil war
- launched biggest cholera program to date in Rwanda, 1994
- vaccinated 4.5 million Nigerians against meningitis in 1996
- arrived to aid Turkish earthquake victims within two days of quake in 1999
- won Nobel Peace Prize in 1999

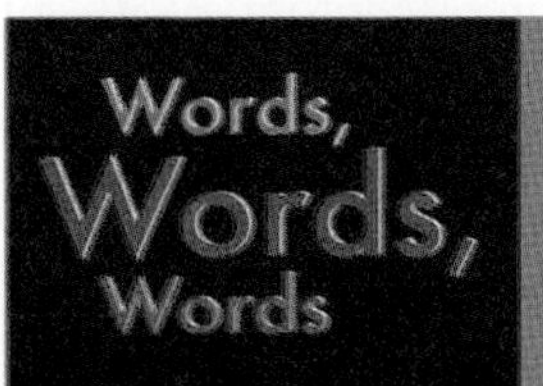

overwhelmed: having too many problems and worries to deal with
relief: a bringing of comfort or a reduction of pain
determination: a strong passion to complete a task despite its difficulty
mission: a special job or task
indifferent: not caring or concerned about something

No Time to Waste

Every minute counts when you're trying to save people's lives. Here's how Doctors Without Borders gets to a world crisis fast.

On Tuesday, August 17, 1999, a massive earthquake rumbled through Turkey. Thousands of people were trapped under shattered buildings. Before dawn the next day, four volunteers from Doctors Without Borders had rushed to the scene. By Thursday, the first of many cargo planes had arrived, packed with supplies. Four teams of doctors were hard at work tending to the victims—just 48 hours after the earthquake struck.

How does Doctors Without Borders get to a crisis so fast?

The answer is simple: hard work and careful organization. The group has dozens of volunteers who are willing to fly anywhere in the world on a moment's notice. When a disaster happens, a team is picked out and at the scene within 24 hours. Often, it's two doctors and an engineer. Right away, they start checking out the damage and sending reports back to a main office in Paris, France.

By this time, a crisis team has been set up. Each person in the crisis team is in charge of something different. One figures out how many volunteers to send. Others determine food needs, medical needs, housing needs, sanitation needs, and so on.

Within two days, word goes out to volunteers around the world about the mission they'll be working on. A separate message goes to two large warehouses in Belgium and France. The warehouses stock a huge amount of supplies in ready-to-go kits. There are hundreds of kits and each one serves a different need. One provides shelter for 100 families. Another has medical supplies that will treat 10,000 people for three months. Yet another will treat 625 patients for the disease cholera.

The crisis team decides which kits are needed and how many. Usually within 48 hours of the disaster, the first cargo plane leaves ready to help out with tons of supplies and a team of doctors. And that is only the beginning. Supplies and volunteers keep flowing until Doctors Without Borders decides it has done its job.

Study the maps on the next page. They'll help introduce you to several places around the world where Doctors Without Borders has worked fast to provide much-needed help.

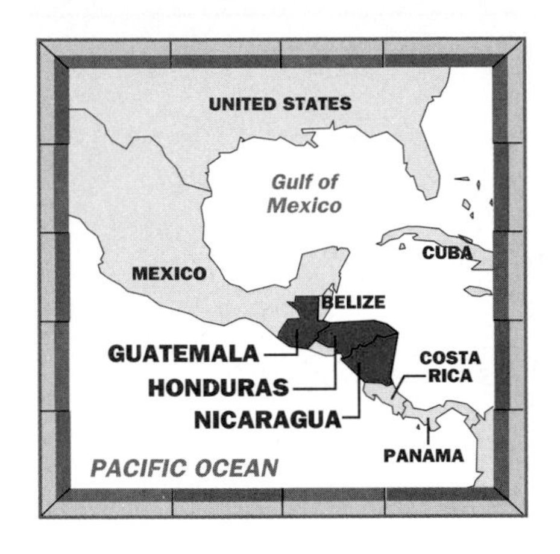

Countries: Honduras, Guatemala, and Nicaragua
Continent: North America
Population: 21.5 million

• The Crisis:

During the last weekend in October 1998, the worst hurricane in memory hit Honduras, Nicaragua, and Guatemala. Thousands were left homeless and disease began to spread quickly. Within a few days, more than 10,000 people were reported dead, and 10,000 were missing.

• How Doctors Helped:

Before the hurricane had fully disappeared, Doctors Without Borders was rushing medical supplies and water to the area. For months after, volunteers helped treat victims for cholera, diarrhea, and other diseases. In the end, 100 tons of drugs and medical supplies were sent in.

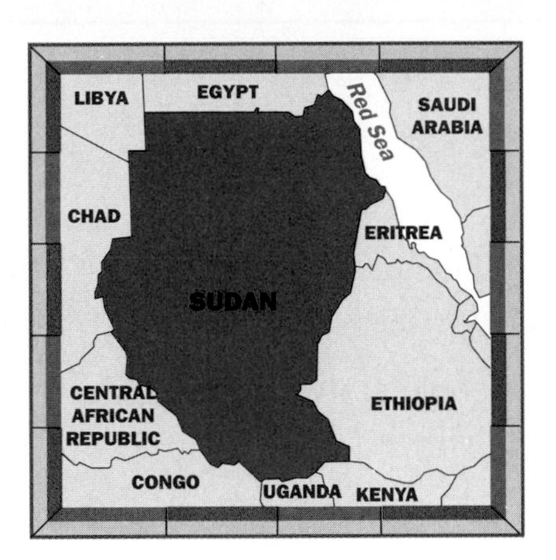

Country: Sudan
Continent: Africa
Population: 28.1 million

• The Crisis:

In 1998, a massive famine struck southern Sudan. It was caused by a 15-year civil war and a severe drought. During the worst of the famine, 1.2 million people were near death from hunger. More than half of the children in some villages didn't have enough to eat.

• How Doctors Helped:

Doctors Without Borders sent over 130 volunteers. Nurses set up feeding centers to give emergency food to the hungriest children. Doctors treated thousands for disease. Many stayed on and trained local health care workers around the country.

Province: Kosovo
Country: Republic of Serbia, Federation of Yugoslavia
Continent: Europe
Population: 1.9 million

• The Crisis:

In 1998, Kosovo was a province of Serbia. But 90 percent of its people were ethnic Albanians. They wanted independence from Serbia. In 1998, Serbian troops began attacking Albanians in Kosovo. The following year, refugees started pouring out of Kosovo into neighboring countries.

• How Doctors Helped:

MSF rushed volunteers to the area. By the summer they had 112 workers helping at refugee camps. Cargo planes flew in emergency supplies. Engineers built water supply systems. Doctors vaccinated people and distributed food. ●

Talk About It

Now that you've read "Doctors Without Borders" and "No Time to Waste," what do you have to say about these questions?

- ▶ Why do you think people are willing to risk their lives to help others? Would you? Why or why not?
- ▶ Why do you think some governments do not want the help of Doctors Without Borders?

Comprehension Check

Write your answers to the questions below. Use information from the profile and the article to support your answers.

1. How do the volunteers feel at the end of a mission?
2. What do you think might have happened to the girl in the orange dress if Doctors Without Borders wasn't there to help?
3. What kinds of sacrifices are the volunteers willing to make when they leave home at a moment's notice?
4. How did volunteers respond to the famine in Sudan?
5. Why is it important to act quickly during a crisis?

Vocabulary Check

Complete each sentence starter below. Before you answer, think about the meaning of the vocabulary word in bold.

1. When I have a cold, I get **relief** from . . .
2. Sometimes, I'm **overwhelmed** by . . .
3. You need **determination** to . . .
4. It's hard to be **indifferent** about a test because . . .
5. My idea of a dangerous **mission** is . . .

Write About It

Choose one of the writing prompts below.

- Write a thank-you letter to Christine Nadori from the girl in the orange dress. Explain how her help made a difference.
- Imagine that you are an MSF volunteer. Write a journal entry describing your experience during one crisis.
- Write an ad to persuade people to become MSF volunteers. Use details from the reading to explain why volunteers are needed. Then explain what people might get out of the experience.

Take ACTION

Doctors Without Borders is not the only group that takes fast action during a world crisis. Here's a list of others:

The International Committee of the Red Cross

This organization, founded in 1863, provides assistance to victims everywhere. Write to them in Switzerland at:

International Committee of the Red Cross
Promotion and Private Fundraising Sector
19 Avenue de la Paix
CH 1202 Genève
Switzerland
www.icrc.org

Oxfam International

This is a group of organizations that all send aid to places in crisis. Contact them in the United States at:

Oxfam America
26 West Street
Boston MA 02111
(617) 728-2594
www.oxfaminternational.org

Using an Airline Schedule

You live in Denver, Colorado. You and your family are going to your grandparents' house in Washington, D.C., for the holidays. You'll be there from December 23 through December 30. Which airline will you fly?

Look over the airline schedules below. Then get ready to fly the friendly skies.

Airline Schedules

A nonstop, or direct, flight is one that doesn't make any stops along the way.

Swifty Travel

You'll love our prices—and our free cookies!

Option #1 National Air $374 (nonstop)

Date	Leave	Arrive
12/23	**Leave:** Denver, CO 10:30 A.M.	**Arrive:** Washington, D.C. 3:34 P.M.
12/30	**Leave:** Washington, D.C. 8:45 A.M.	**Arrive:** Denver, CO 10:27 A.M.

Discount for 7-day advance purchase: $30 off each ticket

Option #2 Unified Airplanes $414

Date	Leave	Arrive
12/23	**Leave:** Denver, CO 6:15 A.M.	**Arrive:** St. Louis, MO 7:15 A.M.
12/23	**Leave:** St. Louis, MO 8:25 A.M.	**Arrive:** Washington, D.C. 1:33 P.M.
12/30	**Leave:** Washington, D.C. 8:15 A.M.	**Arrive:** St. Louis, MO 10:49 A.M.
12/30	**Leave:** St. Louis, MO 11:29 A.M.	**Arrive:** Denver, CO 12:30 P.M.

Discount for 14-day advance purchase: $75 off each ticket

Option #3 Trans-State Airlines $392

Date	Leave	Arrive
12/23	**Leave:** Denver, CO 10:27 A.M.	**Arrive:** Chicago, IL 1:40 P.M.
12/23	**Leave:** Chicago, IL 3:00 P.M.	**Arrive:** Washington, D.C. 5:55 P.M.
12/30	**Leave:** Washington, D.C. 6:30 A.M.	**Arrive:** Chicago, IL 7:24 A.M.
12/30	**Leave:** Chicago, IL 8:30 A.M.	**Arrive:** Denver, CO 9:54 A.M.

Many airlines offer discounts on advance-purchase tickets.

On some flights, you have to change planes on your way to your destination. The wait between planes is called a layover.

"Before you leave for the airport, call the airline to confirm your flight. Departure or arrival times can suddenly change."

Now Boarding

You don't want to miss your flight or pay big bucks for a ticket bought at the last minute. Air travel takes planning. Review the airline schedule. Then use it to answer these questions. Write your answers on your own paper.

1. Which airline has a direct flight from Denver, Colorado, to Washington, D.C.?
   a. National Air
   b. Unified Airplanes
   c. Trans-State Airlines

2. Which airline should you fly if you want to arrive in Washington, D.C., as early in the day as possible?

3. Which is the cheapest airline to fly if you can't buy your tickets in advance?
   a. National Air
   b. Unified Airplanes
   c. Trans-State Airlines

4. How much will it cost you and three family members to fly round-trip between Denver and Washington, D.C., on Unified Airplanes? (You'll buy the tickets 14 days in advance.)
   a. $300
   b. $1,356
   c. $1,656

5. Your grandparents in Washington, D.C., want to pick you up from the airport around 4:00 P.M. On which airline would you make a reservation?

Check It Out

You're a travel agent. You need to buy tickets for a basketball team traveling from Denver to Washington, D.C. The two forwards like to sleep late and don't want to change planes. The two guards like to travel early in the morning, and the center wants to buy souvenirs at the St. Louis airport. Using the schedule to the left, pick flights for all the players.

Look It Up

Plan your dream vacation. Decide your destination and dates of travel. Then use the Web tip below to find out how much your flights would cost.

"Almost all airlines have their own Web sites. Search for airlines' names on an Internet search engine."

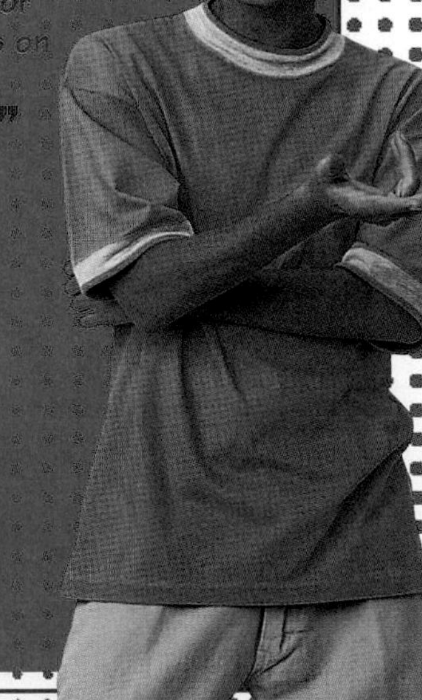

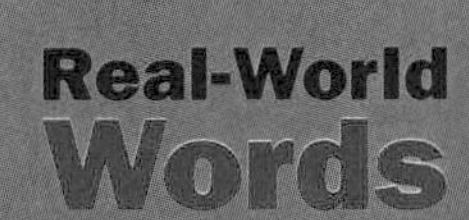

confirm: to make sure that something is going to happen
destination: place you are traveling to
reservation: something that is held for your use

novel

MEET THE WEIRD WATSONS

How cool is too cool? Kenny Watson's older brother finds out the hard way.

by Christopher Paul Curtis

Many people in Flint, Michigan, find the Watson family a little strange. In this excerpt from The Watsons Go to Birmingham–1963, *you'll find out why. The year is 1963. It's winter and freezing cold, even inside the house. To get warm, the Watsons decide to visit mean old Aunt Cydney. Mr. Watson sends Kenny, and his older brother Byron, out to scrape the ice off the windshield of their car nicknamed the Brown Bomber.*

Ever laugh out loud? You may by the end of this story!

Dad went out to try and get the Brown Bomber started. That was what we called our car. It was a 1948 Plymouth that was dull brown and real big. Uncle Bud gave it to Dad when it was thirteen years old and we'd had it for two years. Me and Dad took real good care of it but some of the time it didn't like to start up in the winter.

After five minutes Dad came back in huffing and puffing and slapping his arms across his chest.

"I should have known that the only reason Buphead and By would want to play with me was to do something mean."

"Well, it was touch and go for a while, but the Great Brown One pulled through again!" Everyone cheered, but me and Byron quit cheering and started frowning right away. By the way Dad smiled at us we knew what was coming next. Dad pulled two ice scrapers out of his pocket and said, "O.K., boys, let's get out there and knock those windows out."

We moaned and groaned and put some more coats on and went outside to scrape the car's windows. I could tell by the way he was pouting that Byron was going to try and get out of doing his share of the work.

"I'm not going to do your part, Byron, you'd better do it and I'm not playing either."

"Shut up, punk."

I went over to the Brown Bomber's passenger side and started hacking away at the scab of ice that was all over the windows. I finished Momma's window and took a break. Scraping ice off of windows when it's that cold can kill you!

I didn't hear any sound coming from the other side of the car so I yelled out, "I'm serious, Byron, I'm not doing that side too, and I'm only going to do half the windshield, I don't care what you do to me." The windshield on the Bomber wasn't like the new 1963 cars, it had a big bar running down the middle of it, dividing it in half.

"Shut your mouth, I got something more important to do right now."

I peeked around the back of the car to see what By was up to. The only thing he'd scraped off was the outside mirror and he was bending down to look at himself in it. He saw me and said, "You know what, square? I must be adopted, there just ain't no way two folks as ugly as your momma and daddy coulda give birth to someone as sharp as me!"

He was running his hands over his head like he was brushing his hair.

I said, "Forget you," and went back over to the other side of the car to finish the back window. I had half of the ice off when I had to stop again and catch my breath. I heard Byron mumble my name.

I said, "You think I'm stupid? It's not going to work this time." He mumbled my name again. It sounded like his mouth was full of something. I knew this was a trick, I knew this was going to be How to Survive a **Blizzard,** Part Two.

How to Survive a Blizzard, Part One had been last night when I was outside playing in the snow and Byron and his running buddy, Buphead, came walking by. Buphead has **officially** been a juvenile delinquent even longer than Byron.

"Say, kid," By had said, "you wanna learn somethin' that might save your stupid life one day?"

I should have known better, but I was bored and I think maybe the cold weather was making my brain slow, so I said, "What's that?"

"We gonna teach you how to survive a blizzard."

"How?"

Byron put his hands in front of his face and said, "This is the most important thing to remember, O.K.?"

"Why?"

"Well, first we gotta show you what it feels like to be trapped in a blizzard. You ready?" He whispered something to Buphead and they both laughed.

"I'm ready."

I should have known that the only reason Buphead and By would want to play with me was to do something mean.

"O.K.," By said, "first thing you gotta worry about is high winds."

Byron and Buphead each grabbed one of my arms and one of my legs and swung me between them going, "*Wooo*, blizzard warnings! Blizzard warnings! *Wooo!* Take cover!"

Buphead counted to three and on the third swing they let me go in the air. I landed headfirst in a snowbank.

But that was O.K. because I had on three coats, two sweaters, a T-shirt, three pairs of pants and four socks along with a scarf, a hat and a hood. These guys couldn't have hurt me if they'd thrown me off the Empire State Building!

After I climbed out of the snowbank they started laughing and so did I.

"Cool, Baby Bruh," By said, "you passed that part of the test with a B-plus, what you think, Buphead?"

Buphead said, "Yeah, I'd give the little punk a A."

They whispered some more and started laughing again.

"O.K.," By said, "second thing you gotta learn is how to keep your balance in a high wind. You gotta be good at this so you don't get blowed into no polar bear dens."

They put me in between them and started making me spin round and round, it seemed like they spun me for about half an hour. When slob started flying out of my mouth they let me stop and I wobbled around for a while before they pushed me back in the same snowbank.

When everything stopped going in circles I got up and we all laughed again.

They whispered some more and then By said, "What you think, Buphead? He kept his balance a good long time, I'm gonna give him a A-minus."

"I ain't as hard a grader as you, I'ma give the little punk a double A-minus."

"O.K., Kenny, now the last part of Surviving a Blizzard, you ready?"

"Yup!"

"You passed the wind test and did real good on the balance test but now we gotta see if you ready to graduate. You remember what we told you was the most important part about survivin'?"

"Yup!"

"O.K., here we go. Buphead, tell him 'bout the final exam."

Buphead turned me around to look at him, putting my back to Byron. "O.K., square," he started, "I wanna make sure you ready for this one, you done so good so far I wanna make sure you don't blow it at graduation time. You think you ready?"

I nodded, getting ready to be thrown in the snowbank real hard this time. I made up my mind I wasn't going to cry or anything, I made up my mind that no matter how hard they threw me in that snow I was going to get up laughing.

"O.K.," Buphead said, "everything's cool, you 'member what your brother said about puttin' your hands up?"

"Like this?" I covered my face with my gloves.

"Yeah, that's it!" Buphead looked over my shoulder at Byron and then said, "*Wooo!* High

ASK YOURSELF

- Why is Kenny afraid of Byron? Consider how Byron treats Kenny.

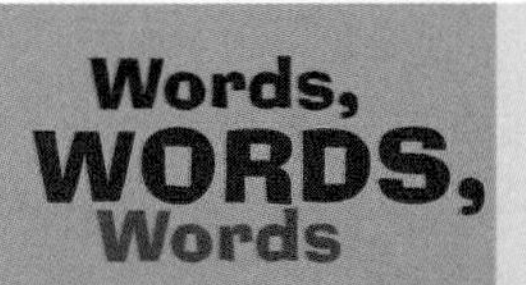

officially: in a formal way that is approved by authority
blizzard: a heavy snowstorm

winds, blowing snow! *Wooo!* Look out! Blizzard a-comin'! Death around the corner! Look out!"

Byron mumbled my name and I turned around to see why his voice sounded so funny. As soon as I looked at him Byron blasted me in the face with a mouthful of snow.

Man! It was hard to believe how much stuff By could put in his mouth! Him and Buphead just about died laughing as I stood there with snow and spit and ice dripping off of my face.

Byron caught his breath and said, "Aww, man, you flunked! You done so good, then you go and flunk the Blowin' Snow section of How to Survive a Blizzard, you forgot to put your hands up! What you say, Buphead, F?"

"Yeah, double F-minus!"

It was a good thing my face was numb from the cold already or I might have froze to death. I was too embarrassed about getting tricked to tell on them so I went in the house and watched TV.

So as me and By scraped the ice off the Brown Bomber I wasn't going to get fooled again. I kept on chopping ice off the back window and ignored By's mumbling voice.

The next time I took a little rest Byron was still calling my name but sounding like he had something in his mouth. He was saying, "Keh-ee! Keh-ee! Hel'. . . hel' . . . !" When he started banging on the door of the car I went to take a peek at what was going on.

By was leaned over the outside mirror, looking at something in it real close. Big puffs of steam were coming out of the side of the mirror.

I picked up a big, hard chunk of ice to get ready for Byron's trick.

"Keh-ee! Keh-ee! Hel' me! Hel' me! Go geh Mom-ma! Go geh Mom-ma! Huwwy uh!"

"I'm not playing, Byron! I'm not that stupid! You'd better start doing your side of the car or I'll tear you up with this iceball."

He banged his hand against the car harder and started stomping his feet. "Oh, please, Keh-ee! Hel' me, go geh Mom-ma!"

I raised the ice chunk over my head. "I'm not playing, By, you better get busy or I'm telling Dad."

I moved closer and when I got right next to him I could see boogers running out of his nose and tears running down his cheeks. These weren't tears from the cold either, these were big juicy crybaby tears! I dropped my ice chunk.

"By! What's wrong?"

"I moved closer. I couldn't believe my eyes! Byron's mouth was frozen on the mirror! He was as stuck as a fly on flypaper!"

"Hel' me! Keh-ee! Go geh hel'!"

I moved closer. I couldn't believe my eyes! Byron's mouth was frozen on the mirror! He was as stuck as a fly on flypaper!

I could have done a lot of stuff to him. If it had been me with my lips stuck on something like this he'd have **tortured** me for a couple of days before he got help. Not me, though, I nearly broke my neck trying to get into the house to rescue Byron.

As soon as I ran through the front door Momma, Dad and Joey all yelled, "Close that door!"

"Momma, quick! It's By! He's froze up outside!"

No one seemed too **impressed.**

I screamed, "Really! He's froze to the car! Help! He's crying!"

That shook them up. You could cut Byron's head off and he probably wouldn't cry.

"Kenneth Bernard Watson, what on earth are you talking about?"

"Momma, please hurry up!"

Momma, Dad and Joey threw on some extra coats and followed me to the Brown Bomber.

The fly was still stuck and buzzing. "Oh, Momma! Hel' me! Geh me offa 'ere!"

"Oh my Lord!" Momma screamed, and I thought she was going to do one of those movie-style faints, she even put her hand over her forehead and staggered back a little bit.

Joey, of course, started crying right along with Byron.

Dad was doing his best not to explode laughing. Big puffs of smoke were coming out of his nose and mouth as he tried to squeeze his laughs down. Finally he put his head on his arms and leaned against the car's hood and howled.

ASK YOURSELF

- Which piece of news causes the family to help Byron?

Think about how Byron usually acts and how he's acting now.

"Byron," Momma said, gently wiping tears off his cheeks with the end of her scarf, "it's O.K., sweetheart, how'd this happen?" She sounded like she was going to be crying in a minute herself.

Dad raised his head and said, "Why are you asking how it happened? Can't you tell, Wilona? This little knucklehead was kissing his reflection in the mirror and got his lips stuck!" Dad took a real deep breath. "Is your tongue stuck too?"

"No! Quit teasin', Da-ee! Hel'! Hel'!"

"Well, at least the boy hadn't gotten too **passionate** with himself!" Dad thought that was **hilarious** and put his head back on his arms.

Momma didn't see anything funny. "Daniel Watson! What are we gonna do? What do y'all do when this happens up he-uh?" Momma started talking Southern-style when she got worried. Instead of saying "here" she said "he-uh" and instead of saying "you all" she said "y'all."

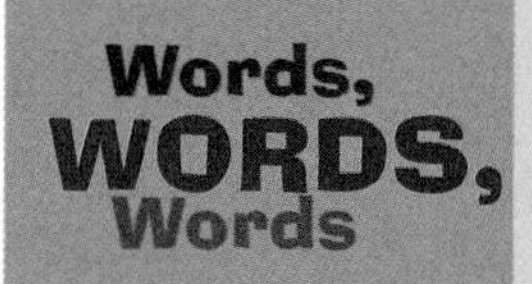

tortured: caused extreme pain and suffering
impressed: affected strongly, influenced
passionate: having or showing very strong feelings
hilarious: very funny

Dad stopped laughing long enough to say, "Wilona, I've lived in Flint all my life, thirty-five years, and I swear this is the first time I've ever seen anyone with their lips frozen to a mirror. Honey, I don't know what to do, wait till he thaws out?"

"Pull him off, Dad," I suggested. Byron went nuts! He started banging his hands on the Brown Bomber's doors again and mumbling, "No! No! Mom-ma, doe leh him!"

Joey blubbered out, "This is just like that horrible story Kenny read me about that guy Nar-sissy who stared at himself so long he forgot to eat and starved to death. Mommy, please save him!" She went over and hugged her arms around stupid Byron's waist.

Momma asked Dad, "What about hot water? Couldn't we pour enough hot water on the mirror so it would warm up and he could get off?" She kept wiping tears off By's cheeks and said, "Don't you worry, Baby, we gonna get you off of this." But her voice was so shaky and Southern that I wondered if we'd be driving around in the summer with a skeleton **dangling** from the outside mirror by its lips.

Dad said, "I don't know, pouring water on him might be the worst thing to do, but it might be our only chance. Why don't you go get some hot tap water and I'll stay to wipe his cheeks."

Joey told By, "Don't worry, we'll come right back." She stood on her tiptoes and gave By a kiss, then she and Momma ran inside. Dad cracked up all over again.

"Well, I guess this means no one can call you Hot Lips, can they?" He tugged on Byron's ear a little, pulling his face back.

By went nuts again. "Doe do dat! Mom-ma! Mom-ma, hel'! Keh-ee, go geh Mom-ma! Huwwy!"

ASK YOURSELF

- Why is Byron afraid when Dad tugs on his ear and pulls his face back?

Think about what might happen to Byron's lips.

"Hmm, I guess that's not going to work, is it?"

Every time he wiped away the tears and the little mustache of boogers on Byron's lip Dad couldn't help laughing, until a little river of tears was coming out of his eyes too.

Dad tried to straighten his face out when Momma and Joey came running back with a steaming glass of hot water, but the tears were still running down his cheeks.

Momma tried to pour water on the mirror but her hands were shaking so much, she was splashing it all over the place. Dad tried too, but he couldn't look at Byron without laughing and shaking.

That meant I had to do it.

I knew that if my lips were frozen on something and everybody was shaking too much to pour water on them except for Byron he'd do some real cruel stuff to me. He probably would have **"accidentally"** splashed my eyes until they were frozen open or put water in my ears until I couldn't hear anything, but not me. I gently poured a little stream of water over the mirror.

Dad was right! This was the worst thing we could do! The water made a cracking sound and froze solid as soon as it touched the mirror and By's lips!

Maybe By's mouth was frozen but his hands sure weren't and he popped me right in the forehead. Hard! I hate to say it but I started crying too.

It's no wonder the neighbors called us the Weird Watsons behind our backs. There we were, all five of us standing around a car with the **temperature** about a million degrees below zero and each and every one of us crying!

"'top! 'top!" By yelled.

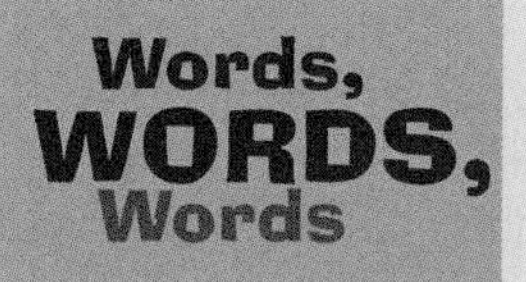

dangling: swinging or hanging down loosely
accidentally: unexpectedly
temperature: the degree of heat or cold in weather

"Daniel Watson, what're we gonna do?" Momma went nuts. "You gotta get this boy to the hospital! My baby is gonna die!"

Dad tried to look serious real quick.

"Wilona, how far do you think I'd get driving down the street with this little clown attached to the mirror? What am I supposed to do, have him run beside the car all the way down to the emergency room?"

Momma looked real close at By's mouth, closed her eyes for a second like she was praying and finally said, "Daniel, you get in there and call the hospital and see what they say we should do. Joey and Kenny, go with your daddy."

Dad and Joey went crying into the house. I stayed by the Brown Bomber. I figured Momma was clearing everybody out for something. Byron did too and looked at Momma in a real nervous way.

Momma put her scarf around Byron's face and said, "Sweetheart, you know we gotta do something. I'ma try to warm your face up a little. Just relax."

"O.K., Mom-ma."

"You know I love you and wouldn't do anything to hurt you, right?" If Momma was trying to make Byron relax she wasn't doing a real good job at it. All this talk about love and not getting hurt was making him real nervous.

"Wah are you gonna do? Huh? Doe hur' me! Keh-ee, hel'!"

Momma moved the scarf away and put one hand on Byron's chin and the other one on his forehead.

"No! Hel'! Hel' me, Keh-ee!"

Momma gave Byron's head a good hard snatch and my eyes automatically shut and my hands automatically flew up to cover my ears and my mouth automatically flew open and screamed out, "Yeeeowwww!"

I didn't see it, but I bet Byron's lips stretched a mile before they finally let go of that mirror. I bet his lips looked like a giant rubber band before they snapped away from that glass!

I didn't hear it, but I bet Byron's lips made a sound like a giant piece of paper being ripped in half!

When I opened my eyes Byron was running to the house with his hands over his mouth and Momma following right behind him. I ran over to the mirror to see how much of Byron's mouth was still stuck there.

The dirty dogs let Byron get away with not doing his share of the windows and I had to do the whole car myself. When we were finally going to Aunt Cydney's house I decided to pay Byron back for punching me in the forehead and getting out of doing his part of the window scraping. Joey was sitting between us so I felt kind of safe. I said to her, loud, "Joetta, guess what. I'm thinking about writing my own comic book."

"What about?"

"Well, it's going to be about this real mean criminal who has a terrible accident that turns him into a superhero."

Joey knew I was going to **tease** Byron so she sat there looking like I should be careful what I said. Finally I asked her, "Do you want to know what I'm going to call this new superhero?"

"What?"

"I'm going to call him the Lipless **Wonder.** All he does is beat up superheroes smaller than him and the only thing he's afraid of is a cold mirror!"

All the Weird Watsons except Byron cracked up. Momma's hand even covered her mouth. I was the only one who saw Byron try to whisper without **smearing** all the goop Momma had put on his lips, "You wait, I'm gonna get you." Then he made his eyes go crossed, which was his favorite way of teasing me, but I didn't care, I knew who had won this time! ●

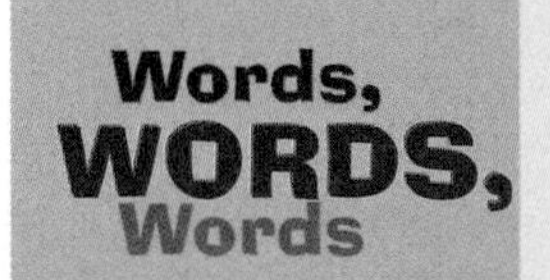

tease: to say mean and hurtful things to someone
wonder: someone who is talented at something
smearing: rubbing something around an area

CHRISTOPHER PAUL CURTIS

It's no joke! Christopher Paul Curtis can turn a family problem into something to laugh at.

Christopher Paul Curtis grew up in Flint, Michigan, just like Kenny Watson. His family was not known as the Weird Curtises, though. In fact, Curtis says that very few parts of *The Watsons Go to Birmingham–1963* were *exactly* like things that happened to him. But he did come from a close-knit family, and he did know some wacky people.

After high school, Curtis took a job in a car factory. He used the money to pay for college. There, he won a writing award for an early draft of *The Watsons Go to Birmingham.* In this interview, Curtis answers students' questions about his popular book.

Does this book have anything to do with your life?

I think all books have some relationship to the author's life. One fun thing about writing is that you can take events that happen to you, change them a little bit, and make them part of your story. For instance, Byron and his pal, Buphead, act a lot like the bullies who went to my grade school.

Why were the Watsons called the Weird Watsons?

Something crazy was always happening at the Watsons' house—like Byron getting his lips stuck on the car. The Watsons' neighbors thought they were different—in other words, weird. So that's why I used the name "Weird Watsons."

Kenny calls Byron the "Lipless Wonder." It's a mean but funny nickname. How did you think of it?

Byron's nickname came to me the way a lot of things do. I let my imagination run wild and I came up with "Lipless Wonder." It struck me as the kind of thing that a kid might really make up.

Did you know a family like the Watsons growing up?

I didn't know any one family that was *just* like them. But there are pieces of my own family and my friends' families in the Watsons. Plus, there are kids everywhere who have mean older brothers and bratty little sisters. Lots of families have a kid like Byron. And Dad and Momma Watson are like a lot of parents. They love their kids a lot, but they get really fed up with them sometimes. ●

Other Books by Christopher Paul Curtis

The Watsons Go to Birmingham—1963
Read the rest of the Watsons' story. The Watson family travels to Alabama to leave Byron with his strict grandmother. There, the family witnesses a terrible event in American history.

Bud, Not Buddy
Bud Caldwell is an orphan on the run from a mean foster family in 1930s Michigan. Will he ever find Herman Calloway—a musician who just might be his father?

TALK ABOUT IT

Now that you've read "Meet the Weird Watsons" and the author profile, what do you have to say about these questions?

- Do you think the Watsons are weird? Why or why not?
- If you had an older brother like Byron, what would you do?

COMPREHENSION CHECK

Write your answers to the questions below. Use information from the story and the profile to support your answers.

1. How did Byron get his lips stuck to the mirror?
2. How did Mom and Dad Watson react to Byron's problem?
3. If you were in Kenny's place, how would you react to Byron's problem? Explain.
4. Where does Christopher Paul Curtis get some of his ideas?
5. How does Chistopher Paul Curtis's life compare to Kenny Watson's?

VOCABULARY CHECK

Answer each question below with a complete sentence. Think about the meaning of the vocabulary word in bold, and use that word in your sentence.

1. What is the most **hilarious** movie you've ever seen? Why?
2. What would you say if you **accidentally** dialed a friend's number?
3. How might you **officially** enter a contest?
4. When was the last time you were really **impressed**?
5. How would you explain a kite **dangling** from a tree?

WRITE ABOUT IT

Choose one of the writing prompts below.

- Kenny invents a superhero called "The Lipless Wonder" to tease Byron. Make up a short story that features that character in a silly adventure.
- What is one of your family's favorite funny stories? Write about it in one or two paragraphs.
- Author Christopher Paul Curtis gets ideas from real life. Do you know someone who would make a great character in a story? Write a description of this person. Include details to show why this person is so funny, interesting, etc.

Fact FILE

In "Meet the Weird Watsons," Joey says, "This is just like that horrible story Kenny read me about that guy Nar-sissy who stared at himself so long he forgot to eat and starved to death." The story Joey is talking about is a Greek myth.

In Greek mythology, Narcissus is a very handsome young man who thinks he is much too good for anyone else. The gods decide to punish Narcissus. They cause him to fall in love with his own reflection. Staring into a pool of water, he pines away for love of himself. He refuses to move or even eat. Eventually he dies. In that very spot, some flowers grew. They are called narcissus, also known as daffodils.

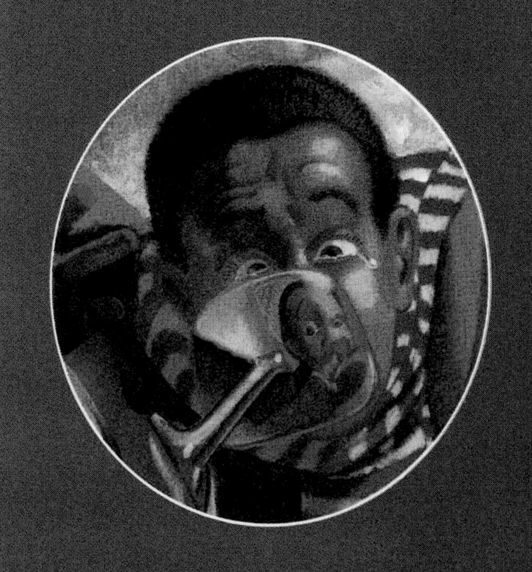

Reading Road Signs

You're too young to drive. But you're not too young to learn to read road signs. Check out the common signs below. Most of them don't have any words. That's because they're meant for all drivers, no matter what language the drivers speak. Can you figure out what these signs mean?

Common Road Signs

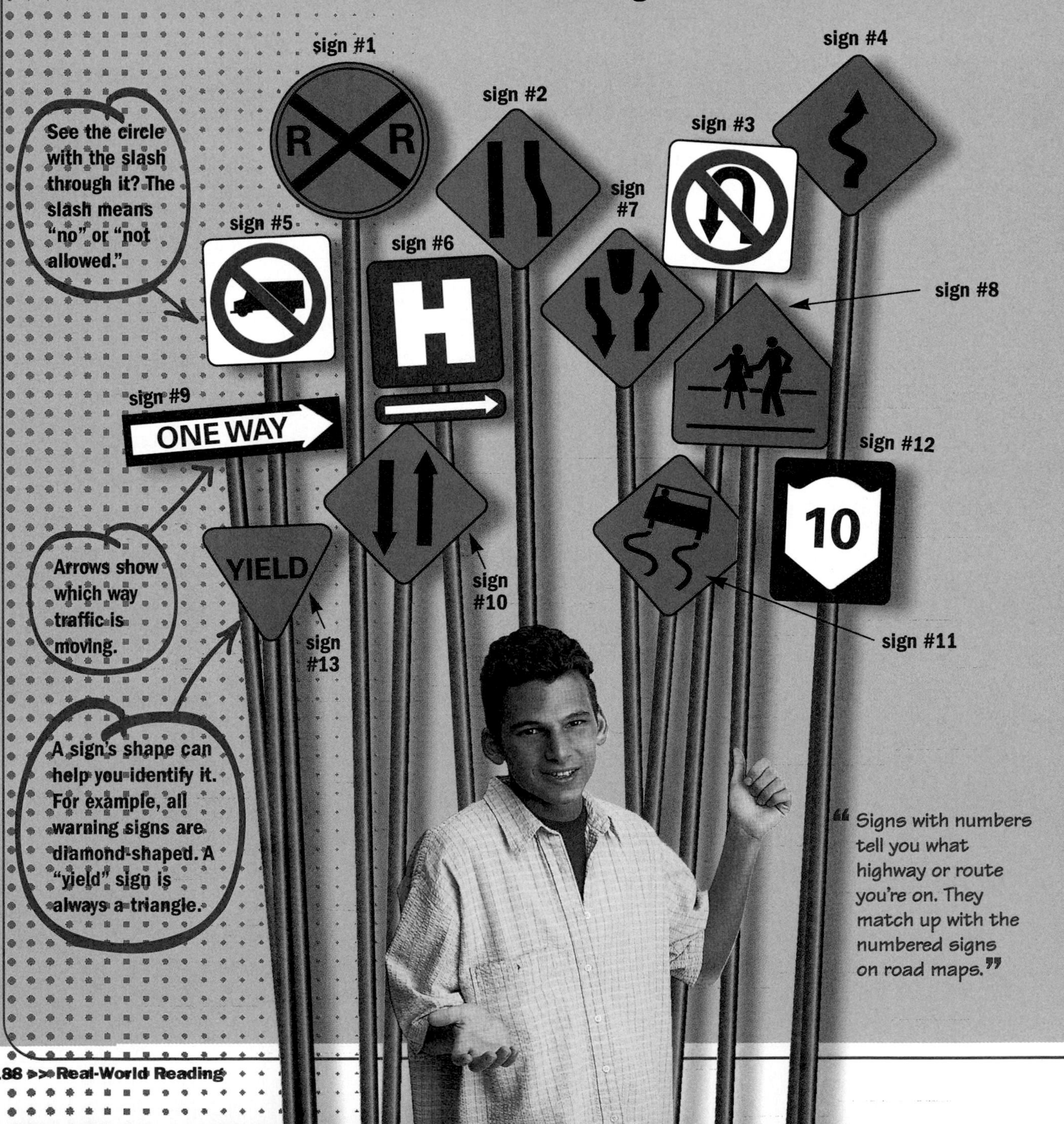

Learn Sign Language

Are you ready for your road test? Review the signs on the left and reread the tips that go with them. Then use the signs to answer each question below.

1. What do you think sign #11 means?
   a. Please leave skid marks here.
   b. Road is slippery when wet.
   c. Road is extremely hot.

2. What do you think sign #3 means?
   a. Drive in circles.
   b. No U-turns.
   c. U-turns allowed.

3. You're driving on a two-lane highway. The lanes are beside each other. Then you see sign #7. It shows that a divided highway is beginning. What does that mean?
   a. There will be a car lane and a motorcycle lane.
   b. The highway will go through a tunnel.
   c. The lanes will be separated by a divider.

4. You're driving down the road in your truck. You see sign #5. What should you do?
   a. Keep driving at the next green light.
   b. Turn off the road. No trucks are allowed.
   c. Keep going—this is a special road just for trucks.

5. Sign #8, a children crossing sign, is placed on streets where there's a school. Sign #6 points the way to a hospital. Why do you think these signs are needed?

Watch the Road

Check out your neighborhood streets. Do you see any bad driving going on? Make a list of three mistakes you've seen drivers make in your area.

Solve the Problem

Review your list of driving mistakes from "Watch the Road." Design a sign that would help solve each problem. Use what you learned about road signs in this lesson.

"Want to learn more about driving? Your state's Department of Motor Vehicles (DMV, for short) probably has a Web site."

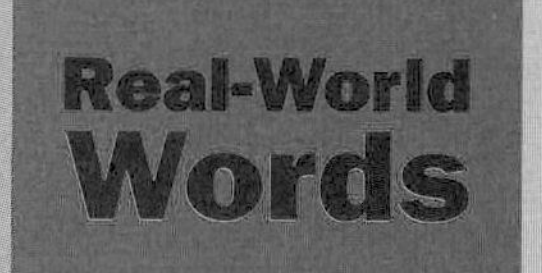

U-turn: a turn in the shape of a "U," made by a driver in order to go in the opposite direction
yield: to let a driver in another lane go in front of you

short story

The All-American Slurp

Can a *Chinese* family learn to eat American style? Can an *American* family learn to use chopsticks?

by Lensey Namioka

The first time our family was invited out to dinner in America, we disgraced ourselves while eating celery. We had emigrated to this country from China, and during our early days here we had a hard time with American table manners.

In China we never ate celery raw, or any other kind of vegetable raw. We always had to disinfect the vegetables in boiling water first. When we were presented with our first relish tray, the raw celery caught us unprepared.

We had been invited to dinner by our neighbors, the Gleasons. After arriving at the house, we shook hands with our hosts and packed ourselves into a sofa. As our family of four sat stiffly in a row, my younger brother and I stole glances at our parents for a clue as to what to do next.

Mrs. Gleason offered the relish tray to Mother. The tray looked pretty, with its tiny red radishes, curly sticks of carrots, and long, slender stalks of pale green celery. "Do try some of the celery, Mrs. Lin," she said. "It's from a local farmer, and it's sweet."

Mother picked up one of the green stalks, and Father followed suit. Then I picked up a stalk, and my brother did too. So there we sat, each with a stalk of celery in our right hand.

Mrs. Gleason kept smiling. "Would you like to try some of the dip, Mrs. Lin? It's my own recipe: sour cream and onion flakes, with a dash of Tabasco sauce."

Most Chinese don't care for dairy products, and in those days I wasn't even ready to drink fresh milk. Sour cream sounded perfectly revolting. Our family shook our heads in unison.

Mrs. Gleason went off with the relish tray to the other guests, and we carefully watched to see what they did. Everyone seemed to eat the raw vegetables quite happily.

Mother took a bite of her celery. *Crunch.* "It's not bad!" she whispered.

Father took a bite of his celery. *Crunch.* "Yes, it *is* good," he said, looking surprised.

I took a bite, and then my brother. *Crunch, crunch.* It was more than good; it was delicious. Raw celery has a slight sparkle, a zingy taste that you don't get in cooked celery. When Mrs. Gleason came around with the relish tray, we each took another stalk of celery, except my brother. He took two.

There was only one problem: long strings ran through the length of the stalk, and they got caught in my teeth. When I help my mother in the kitchen, I always pull the strings out before slicing celery.

I pulled the strings out of my stalk. *Z-z-zip, z-z-zip.* My brother followed suit. *Z-z-zip, z-z-zip, z-z-zip.* To my left, my parents were taking care of their own stalks. *Z-z-zip, z-z-zip, z-zzip.*

Suddenly I realized that there was dead silence except for our zipping. Looking up, I saw that the eyes of everyone in the room were on our family. Mr. and Mrs. Gleason, their daughter Meg, who was my friend, and their neighbors the Badels—they were all staring at us as we busily pulled the strings of our celery.

That wasn't the end of it. Mrs. Gleason announced that dinner was served and invited us to the dining table. It was lavishly covered with platters of food, but we couldn't see any chairs around the table. So we helpfully carried over some dining chairs and sat down. All the other guests just stood there.

Mrs. Gleason bent down and whispered to us, "This is a buffet dinner. You help yourselves to some food and eat it in the living room."

"I wasn't sure how Meg would feel about me after the spectacle our family made at the party."

Our family beat a retreat back to the sofa as if chased by enemy soldiers. For the rest of the evening, too **mortified** to go back to the dining table, I nursed a bit of potato salad on my plate.

Next day Meg and I got on the school bus together. I wasn't sure how Meg would feel about me after the spectacle our family made at the party. But she was just the same as usual, and the only **reference** she made to the party was, "Hope you and your folks got enough to eat last night. You certainly didn't take very much. Mom never tries to figure out how much food to prepare. She just puts everything on the table and hopes for the best."

I began to relax. The Gleasons' dinner party wasn't so different from a Chinese meal after all. My mother also puts everything on the table and hopes for the best.

Meg was the first friend I had made after we came to America. I eventually got **acquainted** with a few other kids in school, but Meg was still the only real friend I had.

My brother didn't have any problems making friends. He spent all his time with some boys who were teaching him baseball, and in no time he could speak English much faster than I could—not better, but faster.

ASK YOURSELF

- How can you tell that the Lin family wants to fit in?

Look for examples of how the Lins are acting.

I worried more about making mistakes, and I spoke carefully, making sure I could say everything right before opening my mouth. At least I had a better accent than my parents, who never really got rid of their Chinese accent, even years later. My parents had both studied English in school before coming to America, but what they had studied was mostly written English, not spoken.

Father's approach to English was a scientific one. Since Chinese verbs have no tense, he was fascinated by the way English verbs changed form according to whether they were in the present, past imperfect, perfect, pluperfect, future, or future perfect tense. He was always making diagrams of verbs and their inflections, and he looked for opportunities to show off his mastery of the pluperfect and future perfect tenses, his two favorites. "I shall have finished my project by Monday," he would say smugly.

Mother's approach was to memorize lists of polite phrases that would cover all possible social situations. She was constantly muttering things like "I'm fine, thank you. And you?" Once she accidentally stepped on someone's foot, and hurriedly blurted, "Oh, that's quite all right!" Embarrassed by her slip, she resolved to do better next time. So when someone stepped on *her* foot, she cried, "You're welcome!"

In our own different ways, we made progress in learning English. But I had another worry, and that was my appearance. My brother didn't have to worry, since Mother bought him blue jeans for school, and he dressed like all the other boys. But she insisted that girls had to wear skirts. By the time she saw that Meg and the other girls were wearing jeans, it was too late. My school clothes were bought already, and we didn't have money left to buy new outfits for me. We had too many other things to buy first, like furniture, pots, and pans.

The first time I visited Meg's house, she took me upstairs to her room, and I wound up trying on her clothes. We were pretty much the same size, since Meg was shorter and thinner than average. Maybe that's how we became friends in the first place. Wearing Meg's jeans and T-shirt, I looked at myself in the mirror. I could almost pass for an American—from the back, anyway. At least the kids in school wouldn't stop and stare at me in the hallways, which was what they did when they saw me in my white blouse and navy blue skirt that went a couple of inches below the knees.

When Meg came to my house, I invited her to try on my Chinese dresses, the ones with a high collar and slits up the sides. Meg's eyes were bright as she looked at herself in the mirror. She struck several sultry poses, and we nearly fell over laughing.

The dinner party at the Gleasons' didn't stop my growing friendship with Meg. Things were getting better for me in other ways too. Mother finally bought me some jeans at the end of the month, when Father got his paycheck. She wasn't in any hurry about buying them at first, until I worked on her. This is what I did. Since we didn't have a car in those days, I often ran down to the neighborhood store to pick up things for her. The groceries cost less at a big supermarket, but the closest one was many blocks away. One day, when she ran out of flour, I offered to borrow a bike from our neighbor's son and buy a ten-pound bag of flour at the big supermarket. I mounted the boy's bike and waved to Mother. "I'll be back in five minutes!"

Before I started pedaling, I heard her voice behind me. "You can't go out in public like that! People can see all the way up to your thighs!"

"I'm sorry," I said innocently. "I thought you were in a hurry to get the flour." For dinner we were going to have pot-stickers (fried Chinese dumplings), and we needed a lot of flour.

"Couldn't you borrow a girl's bicycle?" complained Mother. "That way your skirt won't be pushed up."

"There aren't too many of those around," I said. "Almost all the girls wear jeans while riding a bike, so they don't see any point buying a girl's bike."

We didn't eat pot-stickers that evening, and Mother was thoughtful. Next day we took the bus downtown and she bought me a pair of jeans. In the same week, my brother made the baseball team of his junior high school, Father started taking driving lessons, and Mother discovered rummage sales. We soon got all the furniture we needed, plus a dart board and a 1,000-piece jigsaw puzzle (fourteen hours later, we discovered that it was a 999-piece jigsaw puzzle). There was hope that the Lins might become a normal American family after all.

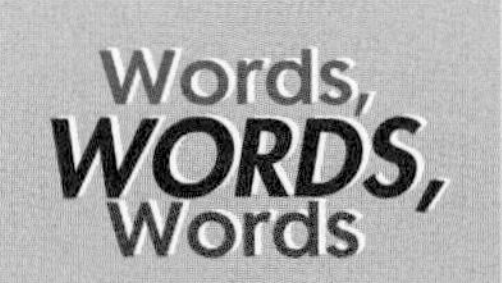

mortified: embarrassed enough to feel one's pride is hurt
reference: a mention of someone or something
acquainted: having been brought into social contact

Then came our dinner at the Lakeview restaurant.

The Lakeview was an expensive restaurant, one of those places where a headwaiter dressed in tails conducted you to your seat, and the only light came from candles and flaming desserts. In one corner of the room a lady harpist played tinkling melodies.

Father wanted to celebrate, because he had just been promoted. He worked for an electronics company, and after his English started improving, his superiors decided to **appoint** him to a position more suited to his training. The promotion not only brought a higher salary but was also a tremendous boost to his pride.

Up to then we had eaten only in Chinese restaurants. Although my brother and I were becoming fond of hamburgers, my parents didn't care much for western food, other than chow mein.

But this was a special occasion, and Father asked his coworkers to recommend a really elegant restaurant. So there we were at the Lakeview, stumbling after the headwaiter in the murky dining room.

At our table we were handed our menus, and they were so big that to read mine I almost had to stand up again. But why bother? It was mostly in French, anyway.

Father, being an engineer, was always **systematic.** He took out a pocket French dictionary. "They told me that most of the items would be in French, so I came prepared." He even had a pocket flashlight, the size of a marking pen. While Mother held the flashlight over the menu, he looked up the items that were in French.

"*Pâté en croûte,*" he muttered. "Let's see . . . *pâté* is paste . . . *croûte* is crust . . . hmm . . . a paste in crust."

The waiter stood looking patient. I squirmed and died at least fifty times.

At long last Father gave up. "Why don't we just order four complete dinners at random?" he suggested.

"Isn't that risky?" asked Mother. "The French eat some rather peculiar things, I've heard."

"A Chinese can eat anything a Frenchman can eat," Father declared.

The soup arrived in a plate. How do you get soup up from a plate? I glanced at the other diners, but the ones at the nearby tables were not on their soup course, while the more distant ones were invisible in the darkness.

Fortunately my parents had studied books on western **etiquette** before they came to America. "Tilt your plate," whispered my mother. "It's easier to spoon the soup up that way."

She was right. Tilting the plate did the trick. But the etiquette book didn't say anything about what you did after the soup reached your lips. As any respectable Chinese knows, the correct way to eat your soup is to slurp. This helps to cool the liquid and prevent you from burning your lips. It also shows your appreciation.

We showed our appreciation. *Shloop,* went my father. *Shloop,* went my mother. *Shloop, shloop,* went my brother, who was the hungriest.

The lady harpist stopped playing to take a rest. And in the silence, our family's consumption of soup suddenly seemed unnaturally loud. You know how it sounds on a rocky beach when the tide goes out and the water drains from all those little pools? They go *shloop, shloop, shloop.* That was the Lin family, eating soup.

At the next table a waiter was pouring wine. When a large *shloop* reached him, he froze. The bottle continued to pour, and red wine flooded the tabletop and into the lap of a customer. Even the customer didn't notice anything at first, being also hypnotized by the *shloop, shloop, shloop.*

It was too much. "I need to go to the toilet," I mumbled, jumping to my feet. A waiter, sensing my urgency, quickly directed me to the ladies' room.

I splashed cold water on my burning face, and as I dried myself with a paper towel, I stared into the mirror. In this perfumed ladies' room, with its pink-and-silver wallpaper and marbled sinks, I looked completely out of place. What was I doing here? What was our family doing in the Lakeview restaurant? In America?

The door to the ladies' room opened. A woman came in and glanced curiously at me. I retreated into one of the toilet cubicles and latched the door.

Time passed—maybe half an hour, maybe an hour. Then I heard the door open again, and my mother's voice. "Are you in there? You're not sick, are you?"

There was real concern in her voice. A girl can't leave her family just because they slurp their soup. Besides, the toilet cubicle had a few drawbacks as a permanent **residence.** "I'm all right," I said, undoing the latch.

Mother didn't tell me how the rest of the dinner went, and I didn't want to know. In the weeks following, I managed to push the whole thing into the back of my mind, where it jumped out at me only a few times a day. Even now, I turn hot all over when I think of the Lakeview restaurant.

But by the time we had been in this country for three months, our family was definitely making progress toward becoming Americanized. I remember my parents' first PTA meeting. Father wore a neat suit and tie, and Mother put on her first pair of high heels. She stumbled only once. They met my homeroom teacher and beamed as she told them that I would make honor roll soon at the rate I was going. Of course Chinese etiquette forced Father to say that I was a very stupid girl and Mother to protest that the teacher was showing favoritism toward me. But I could tell they were both very proud.

ASK YOURSELF

- What makes the trip to the French restaurant a total disaster?

Retell what happens in your own words.

The day came when my parents announced that they wanted to give a dinner party. We had invited Chinese friends to eat with us before, but this dinner was going to be different. In addition to a Chinese-American family, we were going to invite the Gleasons.

"Gee, I can hardly wait to have dinner at your house," Meg said to me. "I just *love* Chinese food."

That was a relief. Mother was a good cook, but I wasn't sure if people who ate sour cream would also eat chicken gizzards stewed in soy sauce.

Mother decided not to take a chance with chicken gizzards. Since we had western guests, she set the table with large dinner plates, which we never used in Chinese meals. In fact we didn't use individual plates at all, but picked up food from the platters in the middle of the table and brought it

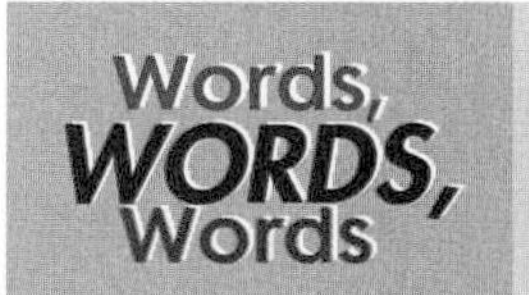

appoint: to choose someone for a job
systematic: having a method or a plan
etiquette: rules of polite behavior
residence: a place where someone lives

directly to our rice bowls. Following the practice of Chinese-American restaurants, Mother also placed large serving spoons on the platters.

The dinner started well. Mrs. Gleason exclaimed at the beautifully arranged dishes of food: the colorful candied fruit in the sweet-and-sour pork dish, the noodle-thin shreds of chicken meat stir-fried with tiny peas, and the glistening pink **prawns** in a ginger sauce.

At first I was too busy enjoying my food to notice how the guests were doing. But soon I remembered my duties. Sometimes guests were too polite to help themselves and you had to serve them with more food.

I glanced at Meg, to see if she needed more food, and my eyes nearly popped out at the sight of her plate. It was piled with food: the sweet-and-sour meat pushed right against the chicken shreds, and the chicken sauce ran into the prawns. She had been taking food from a second dish before she finished eating her helping from the first!

Horrified, I turned to look at Mrs. Gleason. She was dumping rice out of her bowl and putting it on her dinner plate. Then she ladled prawns and gravy on top of the rice and mixed everything together, the way you mix sand, gravel, and cement to make concrete.

I couldn't bear to look any longer, and I turned to Mr. Gleason. He was chasing a pea around his plate. Several times he got it to the edge, but when he tried to pick it up with his chopsticks, it rolled back toward the center of the plate again. Finally he put down his chopsticks and picked up the pea with his fingers. He really did! A grown man!

All of us, our family and the Chinese guests, stopped eating to watch the activities of the Gleasons. I wanted to giggle. Then I caught my mother's eyes on me. She frowned and shook her head slightly, and I understood the message: the Gleasons were not used to Chinese ways, and they were just **coping** the best they could. For some reason I thought of celery strings.

When the main courses were finished, Mother brought out a platter of fruit. "I hope you weren't expecting a sweet dessert," she said. "Since the Chinese don't eat dessert, I didn't think to prepare any."

"Oh, I couldn't possibly eat dessert!" cried Mrs. Gleason. "I'm simply stuffed!"

Meg had different ideas. When the table was cleared, she announced that she and I were going for a walk. "I don't know about you, but I feel like dessert," she told me, when we were outside. "Come on. I could use a big chocolate milkshake!"

Although I didn't really want anything more to eat, I insisted on paying for the milkshakes. After all, I was still **hostess.**

Meg got her large chocolate milkshake and I had a small one. Even so, she was finishing hers while I was only half done. Toward the end she pulled hard on her straws and went *shloop, shloop.*

"Do you always slurp when you eat a milkshake?" I asked, before I could stop myself.

Meg grinned. "Sure. All Americans slurp."

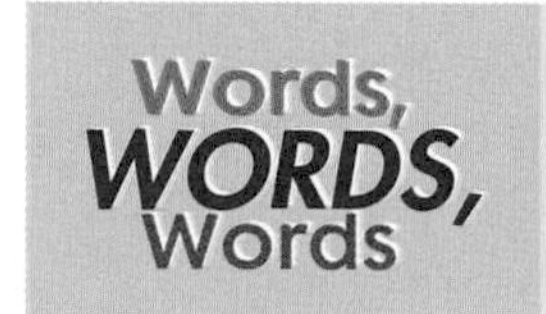

prawns: shrimp
coping: dealing with something successfully
hostess: a woman who entertains guests

Lensey Namioka

The Lin family wants to fit in. Lensey Namioka knows exactly how that feels.

Lensey Namioka knows what it's like to be an outsider. Her family moved from China to the United States when she was in grade school. In fact, "The All-American Slurp" is based on something that really happened to her. At first, Namioka hated the way her family stood out in their new country. Later, she learned to enjoy—and sometimes laugh at—their differences.

Today Namioka writes books about everything from modern Chinese immigrant kids to ancient samurai warriors. But almost all of her books share a common theme: The main characters are outsiders. Here, Namioka talks about her life and career.

Did you always want to be a writer?

Well, I wrote my first novel when I was eight. It was an action novel called *The Princess with the Bamboo Sword.* Our house was filled with stacks of Chinese paperback action novels. Their covers all had pictures of warriors—male and female. My princess was modeled after the female warriors. But *Princess* had no sequels. About 30 years went by before I thought about writing as a career. I became a college math teacher in the meantime.

What made you switch to writing?

When my daughters were little, I wanted to work at home. So I went to work translating a book about Chinese restaurants. It was fun, and it made me want to write. Next, I wrote some short newspaper stories about Asian culture.

How did you begin writing kids' fiction about Asian characters?

I used to play big April Fool's Day jokes every year, so my husband decided I was creative. He encouraged me to use my creativity on something else—like writing stories. My first novel—a mystery called *White Serpent Castle*—was meant for adults. But everybody who read it saw it as a book for young people. I think that my writing appeals to kids because in some ways I have never grown up!

Other Books by Lensey Namioka

Den of the White Fox
Two samurai roam the countryside looking for work. Instead, they wind up searching for the mysterious White Fox. Is it a human or a spirit out for revenge?

Ties That Bind, Ties That Break
A young girl hopes to break from Chinese tradition by going to school—and by escaping the crippling ritual of foot-binding. Will she get what she wants?

Talk About It

Now that you've read "The All-American Slurp" and the author profile, what do you have to say about these questions?

- What kinds of problems do you think the Gleasons might have if they moved to China?
- Why does Lensey Namioka think of herself as an "outsider"?

Comprehension Check

Write your answers to the questions below. Use information from the story and the profile to support your answers.

1. How does the main character convince her mother to buy her blue jeans?
2. Why do you think the story is called "The All-American Slurp"?
3. If you belonged to the Lin family, would you want people to ignore your mistakes or tell you about them? Why?
4. How did Lensey Namioka become a writer?
5. What do the main character and Lensey Namioka have in common?

Vocabulary Check

Answer each question below with a complete sentence. Think about the meaning of the vocabulary word in bold, and use that word in your sentence.

1. What might make you feel **mortified**?
2. What would your ideal **residence** be like?
3. How did you become **acquainted** with your best friend?
4. What makes **coping** with lots of homework easier for you?
5. What would be an example of something done in a **systematic** way?

Write About It

Choose one of the writing prompts below.

- Write a list of five to seven tips about etiquette (or manners) that might help someone from another culture fit into yours.
- Create a menu that you might serve if you wanted someone to experience your family's favorite foods. Then write a short paragraph explaining why you chose the foods you did.
- Have you ever felt like an "outsider" as Lensey Namioka said she did? Write a paragraph explaining what made you feel that way and what you did about it.

Fact FILE

Do you have good table manners? How about when it comes to using chopsticks? Read these rules of etiquette and see how much you know.

- **Don't lick your chopsticks.**
- **Don't bite your chopsticks.**
- **Never use chopsticks to point at someone.**
- **Don't stab food with the chopsticks. (Instead, hold food between two chopsticks.)**
- **Don't leave chopsticks standing up in your bowl. (Instead, place chopsticks on a holder or in front of the bowl, on the side closest to you.)**
- **When taking food from a bowl that's not your own, never use the end of the chopsticks that enters your mouth. (Instead, turn the chopsticks around and pick up the food with the opposite end.)**

Reading a Menu

You're going to a great new restaurant with a friend. But you're not sure you even know how—or what—to order at such a fancy place. What will you do?

Check out the menu below. It's got a few pointers for you. Read all about it. Then get ready to order.

Menu for the Greenhouse Café

An appetizer is a small dish served before the main course.

An entree is the main course, or dish.

Menu

Appetizers $5.25 each
Fruit Cocktail Little Neck Clams
Shrimp Cocktail Baked Stuffed Clams
Tossed Green Salad $3.50

Soup $3.75
Lentil Clam Chowder Chicken
Chicken with Asparagus

**Dinner is served with an appetizer, choice of soup or salad, potato, vegetables, dessert, beverage.*

ENTREES	*DINNER**	*A LA CARTE*
Broiled Flounder	*$19*	*$15*
Baked Brook Trout	*$20*	*$16*
Sautéed Bay Scallops	*$18*	*$14*
Lobster Tail	*$22*	*$18*
Grilled Shell Steak	*$19*	*$15*
Grilled Short Ribs of Beef	*$18*	*$14*
Bowtie Pasta with Broccoli and Garlic	*$18*	*$14*
Vegetable Pot Pie	*$19*	*$15*
Roasted Chicken with Fresh Herbs	*$19*	*$15*
Wiener Schnitzel	*$19*	*$15*

Coffee, Tea, or Milk $.90

DESSERTS $5.00
Cheesecake Apple Strudel
Chocolate Cake Melon in Season
Homemade Ice Cream Sorbet

If you order your main dish "à la carte," you'll get the main dish only. Soup, salad, and other dishes will cost extra.

"It's a good idea to check the menu before you choose a restaurant. Most restaurants post their menus in the window. Some restaurants even post their menus on the Web."

Time for Dinner

The waiter's been circling your table. It's high time to place your order. So what's it going to be? It's time to find out whether you're really ready for dinner. Answer each question below on your own paper.

1. You've been on a steady diet of peanut-butter-and-jelly sandwiches. Tonight, you're in the mood for some beef. Which entrees could you choose?

2. Your friend, on the other hand, does not eat meat at all—not even seafood. Which two of these entrees could he or she choose?
   a. bowtie pasta with broccoli and garlic
   b. sautéed bay scallops
   c. vegetable pot pie
   d. grilled short ribs of beef

3. You've decided on the shell steak. You'd also like the lentil soup and chocolate cake. Should you order each item à la carte, or should you order the shell steak dinner? Why?

4. The Wiener Schnitzel sounds interesting—but what is it, anyway? You might want to order it. Who could you ask to find out what it is?

5. Was the service good? Don't forget to tip the waiter! The standard tip is 15% of the cost of your meal. Your bill came to $40. How much should you leave for a tip? (Hint: Multiply $40 \times .15$)

Cooking Up Words

Look up five of these food terms in a dictionary and write what they mean: *bay scallops, broiled, chowder, flounder, herbs, sautéed, shell steak, short ribs, sorbet, strudel, Wiener Schnitzel.*

Open for Business

You're opening a restaurant. What dishes will you serve? Create a menu. You can use the menu on the left as a model.

"Items on a menu sometimes have unusual names. Don't be afraid to ask the waiter if you're not sure what something is."

dish: food made in a certain way, as in a *chicken dish*
course: a part of a meal served by itself
tip: money given as thanks for good service

short story collection

Sandra Cisneros: STORYTELLER

Sandra Cisneros knows the secret to great writing: You don't need a lot of words to tell an unforgettable story.

Sandra Cisneros is a writer. But she isn't just any writer. She's known the world over for the careful way she uses words. Her stories are very short. And yet, after reading each one, you feel like you know the person you're reading about. You feel like you're standing next to characters as they experience life's joys and sorrows.

The five Cisneros stories you are about to read come from her two most famous books, The House on Mango Street *and* Woman Hollering Creek. *To write them, Cisneros drew on her Mexican heritage and used memories from her experiences growing up in a Hispanic neighborhood in Chicago. But you don't have to be Hispanic to understand what they're about . . . as you'll soon find out.*

MY NAME

In English my name means hope. In Spanish it means too many letters. It means sadness, it means waiting. It is like the number nine. A muddy color. It is the Mexican records my father plays on Sunday mornings when he is shaving, songs like sobbing.

It was my great-grandmother's name and now it is mine. She was a horse woman too, born like me in the Chinese year of the horse—which is supposed to be bad luck if you're born female—but I think this is a Chinese lie because the Chinese, like the Mexicans, don't like their women strong.

My great-grandmother. I would've liked to have known her, a wild horse of a woman, so wild she wouldn't marry. Until my great-grandfather threw a sack over her head and carried her off. Just like that, as if she were a fancy chandelier. That's the way he did it.

And the story goes she never forgave him. She looked out the window her whole life, the way so many women sit their sadness on an elbow. I wonder if she made the best with what she got or was she sorry because she couldn't be all the things she wanted to be. Esperanza. I have inherited her name, but I don't want to inherit her place by the window.

At school they say my name funny as if the syllables were made out of tin and hurt the roof of your mouth. But in Spanish my name is made out of a softer something, like silver, not quite as thick as sister's name—Magdalena—which is uglier than mine. Magdalena who at least can come home and become Nenny. But I am always Esperanza.

I would like to baptize myself under a new name, a name more like the real me, the one nobody sees. Esperanza as Lisandra or Maritza or Zeze the X. Yes. Something like Zeze the X will do.

ELEVEN

What they don't understand about birthdays and what they never tell you is that when you're eleven, you're also ten, and nine, and eight, and seven, and six, and five, and four, and three, and two, and one. And when you wake up on your eleventh birthday you expect to feel eleven, but you don't. You open your eyes and everything's just like yesterday, only it's today. And you don't feel eleven at all. You feel like you're still ten. And you are—underneath the year that makes you eleven.

Because the way you grow old is kind of like an onion or like the rings inside a tree trunk or like my little wooden dolls that fit one inside the other, each year inside the next one.

Like some days you might say something stupid, and that's the part of you that's still ten. Or maybe some days you might need to sit on your mama's lap because you're scared, and that's the part of you that's five. And maybe one day when you're all grown up maybe you will need to cry like if you're three, and that's okay. That's what I tell Mama when she's sad and needs to cry. Maybe she's feeling three.

Because the way you grow old is kind of like an onion or like the rings inside a tree trunk or like my little wooden dolls that fit one inside the other, each year inside the next one. That's how being eleven years old is.

You don't feel eleven. Not right away. It takes a few days, weeks even, sometimes even months before you say Eleven when they ask you. And you don't feel smart eleven, not until you're almost twelve. That's the way it is.

Only today I wish I didn't have only eleven years **rattling** inside me like pennies in a tin Band-Aid box. Today I wish I was one hundred and two instead of eleven because if I was one hundred and two I'd have known what to say when Mrs. Price put the red sweater on my desk. I would've known how to tell her it wasn't mine instead of just sitting there with that look on my face and nothing coming out of my mouth.

"Whose is this?" Mrs. Price says, and she holds the red sweater up in the air for all the class to see. "Whose? It's been sitting in the coatroom for a month."

"Not mine," says everybody. "Not me."

"It has to belong to somebody," Mrs. Price keeps saying, but nobody can remember. It's an ugly sweater with red plastic buttons and a collar and sleeves all stretched out like you could use it for a jump rope. It's maybe a thousand years old and even if it belonged to me I wouldn't say so.

Maybe because I'm skinny, maybe because she doesn't like me, that stupid Sylvia Saldívar says, "I think it belongs to Rachel." An ugly sweater like that, all **raggedy** and old, but Mrs. Price believes her. Mrs. Price takes the sweater and puts it right on my desk, but when I open my mouth nothing comes out.

"That's not, I don't, you're not . . . Not mine," I finally say in a little voice that was maybe me when I was four.

"Of course it's yours," Mrs. Price says. "I remember you wearing it once." Because she's older and the teacher, she's right and I'm not.

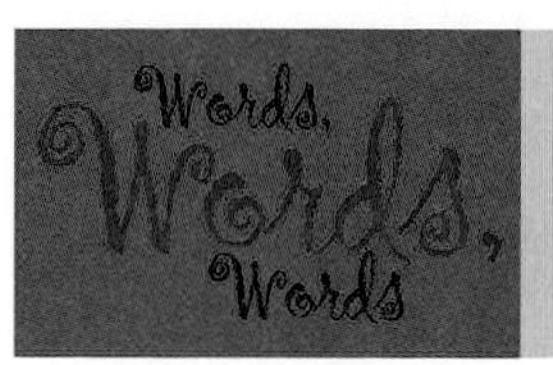

rattling: moving noisily
raggedy: torn and worn out
nonsense: silly or annoying behavior
hiccups: sounds in the throat caused by a spasm of the diaphragm

Not mine, not mine, not mine, but Mrs. Price is already turning to page thirty-two, and math problem number four. I don't know why but all of a sudden I'm feeling sick inside, like the part of me that's three wants to come out of my eyes, only I squeeze them shut tight and bite down on my teeth real hard and try to remember today I am eleven, eleven. Mama is making a cake for me for tonight, and when Papa comes home everybody will sing Happy birthday, happy birthday to you.

But when the sick feeling goes away and I open my eyes, the red sweater's still sitting there like a big red mountain. I move the red sweater to the corner of my desk with my ruler. I move my pencil and books and eraser as far from it as possible. I even move my chair a little to the right. Not mine, not mine, not mine.

In my head I'm thinking how long till lunchtime, how long till I can take the red sweater and throw it over the schoolyard fence, or leave it hanging on a parking meter, or bunch it up into a little ball and toss it in the alley. Except when math period ends Mrs. Price says loud and in front of everybody, "Now, Rachel, that's enough," because she sees I've shoved the red sweater to the tippy-tip corner of my desk and it's hanging all over the edge like a waterfall, but I don't care.

"Rachel," Mrs. Price says. She says it like she's getting mad. "You put that sweater on right now and no more **nonsense**."

"But it's not—"

"Now!" Mrs. Price says.

This is when I wish I wasn't eleven, because all the years inside of me—ten, nine, eight, seven, six, five, four, three, two, and one—are pushing at the back of my eyes when I put one arm through one sleeve of the sweater that smells like cottage cheese, and then the other arm through the other and stand there with my arms apart like if the sweater hurts me and it does, all itchy and full of germs that aren't even mine.

- Why does Rachel feel that the red sweater is an insult to her?

Think about the way the sweater looks and smells.

That's when everything I've been holding in since this morning, since when Mrs. Price put the sweater on my desk, finally lets go, and all of a sudden I'm crying in front of everybody. I wish I was invisible but I'm not. I'm eleven and it's my birthday today and I'm crying like I'm three in front of everybody. I put my head down on the desk and bury my face in my stupid clown-sweater arms. My face all hot and spit coming out of my mouth because I can't stop the little animal noises from coming out of me, until there aren't any more tears left in my eyes, and it's just my body shaking like when you have the **hiccups**, and my whole head hurts like when you drink milk too fast.

But the worst part is right before the bell rings for lunch. That stupid Phyllis Lopez, who is even dumber than Sylvia Saldívar, says she remembers the red sweater is hers! I take it off right away and give it to her, only Mrs. Price pretends like everything's okay.

Today I'm eleven. There's a cake Mama's making for tonight, and when Papa comes home from work we'll eat it. There'll be candles and presents and everybody will sing Happy birthday, happy birthday to you, Rachel, only it's too late.

I'm eleven today. I'm eleven, ten, nine, eight, seven, six, five, four, three, two, and one, but I wish I was one hundred and two. I wish I was anything but eleven, because I want today to be far away already, far away like a runaway balloon, like a tiny *o* in the sky, so tiny-tiny you have to close your eyes to see it.

OUR GOOD DAY

If you give me five dollars I will be your friend forever. That's what the little one tells me.

Five dollars is cheap since I don't have any friends except Cathy who is only my friend till Tuesday.

Five dollars, five dollars.

She is trying to get somebody to chip in so they can buy a bicycle from this kid named Tito. They already have ten dollars and all they need is five more.

Only five dollars, she says.

Don't talk to them, says Cathy. Can't you see they smell like a broom.

But I like them. Their clothes are crooked and old.

They are wearing shiny Sunday shoes without socks. It makes their bald ankles all red, but I like them. Especially the big one who laughs with all her teeth. I like her even though she lets the little one do all the talking.

Five dollars, the little one says, only five.

Cathy is tugging my arm and I know whatever I do next will make her mad forever.

Wait a minute, I say, and run inside to get the five dollars. I have three dollars saved and I take two of Nenny's. She's not home, but I'm sure she'll be glad when she finds out we own a bike. When I get back, Cathy is gone like I knew she would be, but I don't care. I have two new friends and a bike too.

My name is Lucy, the big one says. This here is Rachel my sister.

I'm her sister, says Rachel. Who are you?

And I wish my name was Cassandra or Alexis or Maritza—anything but Esperanza—but when I tell them my name they don't laugh.

We come from Texas, Lucy says and **grins**. Her was born here, but me I'm Texas.

You mean *she,* I say.

No, I'm from Texas, and doesn't get it.

This bike is three ways ours, says Rachel who is thinking ahead already. Mine today, Lucy's tomorrow and yours day after.

But everybody wants to ride it today because the bike is new, so we decide to take turns *after* tomorrow. Today it belongs to all of us.

I don't tell them about Nenny just yet. It's too complicated. Especially since Rachel almost put out Lucy's eye about who was going to get to ride it first. But finally we agree to ride it together. Why not?

Because Lucy has long legs she pedals. I sit on the back seat and Rachel is skinny enough to get up on the handlebars which makes the bike all wobbly as if the wheels are spaghetti, but after a bit you get used to it.

We ride fast and faster. Past my house, sad and red and crumbly in places, past Mr. Benny's grocery on the corner, and down the avenue which is dangerous. Laundromat, junk store, drugstore, windows and cars and more cars, and around the block back to Mango.

People on the bus wave. A very fat lady crossing the street says, You sure got quite a load there.

Rachel shouts, You got quite a load there too. She is very **sassy.**

Down, down Mango Street we go. Rachel, Lucy, me. Our new bicycle. Laughing the crooked ride back.

grins: cheerfully smiles
sassy: being rude or fresh to someone
ache: to feel pain

PAPA WHO WAKES UP TIRED IN THE DARK

Your *abuelito* is dead, Papa says early one morning in my room. *Está muerto,* and then as if he just heard the news himself, crumples like a coat and cries, my brave Papa cries. I have never seen my Papa cry and don't know what to do.

I know he will have to go away, that he will take a plane to Mexico, all the uncles and aunts will be there, and they will have a black-and-white photo taken in front of the tomb with flowers shaped like spears in a white vase because this is how they send the dead away in that country.

Because I am the oldest, my father has told me first, and now it is my turn to tell the others. I will have to explain why we can't play. I will have to tell them to be quiet today.

My Papa, his thick hands and thick shoes, who wakes up tired in the dark, who combs his hair with water, drinks his coffee, and is gone before we wake, today is sitting on my bed.

And I think if my own Papa died what would I do. I hold my Papa in my arms. I hold and hold and hold him.

MANGO SAYS GOODBYE SOMETIMES

I like to tell stories. I tell them inside my head. I tell them after the mailman says, Here's your mail. Here's your mail, he said.

I make a story for my life, for each step my brown shoe takes. I say, "And so she trudged up the wooden stairs, her sad brown shoes taking her to the house she never liked."

I like to tell stories. I am going to tell you a story about a girl who didn't want to belong.

We didn't always live on Mango Street. Before that we lived on Loomis on the third floor, and before that we lived on Keeler. Before Keeler it was Paulina, but what I remember most is Mango Street, sad red house, the house I belong but do not belong to.

I put it down on paper and then the ghost does not **ache** so much. I write it down and Mango says goodbye sometimes. She does not hold me with both arms. She sets me free.

One day I will pack my bags of books and paper. One day I will say goodbye to Mango. I am too strong for her to keep me here forever. One day I will go away.

Friends and neighbors will say, What happened to that Esperanza? Where did she go with all those books and paper? Why did she march so far away?

They will not know I have gone away to come back. For the ones I left behind. For the ones who cannot out. ●

ASK yourself

- Why does Esperanza tell stories?

Think of how writing makes her feel and how the last story ends.

Talk About It

Now that you've read "Sandra Cisneros: Storyteller," what do you have to say about these questions?

- ▶ How important is a person's name?
- ▶ What would you have done if someone had insisted that a raggedy piece of clothing was yours?

Comprehension Check

Write your answers to the questions below. Use information from the reading to support your answers.

1. Why does Esperanza dislike her name?
2. Why does Rachel want her birthday to be "far away already, far away like a runaway balloon?"
3. How does Esperanza feel about her father? How can you tell?
4. Which character from these stories do you like better, Esperanza or Rachel? Why?
5. From what you've read about each character, do you think Esperanza and Rachel might become good friends? Explain.

Vocabulary Check

Complete each sentence with the correct vocabulary word.

rattling raggedy nonsense ache grins

1. These days _______ clothes are very popular at my school.
2. The hard workout at practice yesterday made my muscles _______.
3. We could hear the windows _______ during the storm.
4. My little sister always _______ when I hug her.
5. I have a pet parrot who talks, and everything he says is _______.

Write About It

Choose one of the writing prompts below.

- Write a letter from Rachel to Mrs. Price about the sweater. In this letter, explain how the sweater made Rachel feel.
- Use Esperanza's description of the neighborhood on Mango Street as a model to write a description of a place you know well.
- Write a new ending to the story that tells what happens when Esperanza's sister learns of their new bike.

About the AUTHOR

Sandra Cisneros was raised mainly in a Hispanic neighborhood in Chicago. Her father was Mexican and her mother was Mexican-American. She says that her six brothers all paired off when she was growing up, leaving her to spend a lot of time alone.

She spent some of that time reading. One of her favorite books was Virginia Lee Burton's *The Little House.* The book captured her dream "of a house where one family lived and grew old and didn't move away."

Comparing Prices

When you go grocery shopping you want to get the best deal you can. Sometimes that's not so easy. How do you know which brand or size of a product is the cheapest?

You need to know the unit price. That's how much something costs per unit of measure. Look at the label and chart below. Do you see how they work?

Unit Prices

Sometimes supermarkets figure out unit prices for you. Look for a label like this under each item.

BRAND: MUCHO MACHO
FOOD: SALSA
TOTAL WEIGHT: 8 OZ.
UNIT PRICE: $ .38 PER OUNCE

This is how much this salsa costs per ounce. Compare this price to the unit prices of other salsas.

Item	Size	Price	Unit Price
· Clean It Up Napkins	75 napkins	$1.50	$ .02
· Tidy Napkins	100 napkins	$1.00	$ .01
· Wipe 'n' Go Napkins	150 napkins	$4.50	$ .03
· Señor Spicy's Salsa	5 ounces	$2.30	$ .46
· Mucho Macho Salsa	8 ounces	$3.04	$ .38
· Hot and Chile Salsa	14 ounces	$3.64	$ .26
· Tasty Cola	1 liter	$.99	$ .99
· Fizzy Cola	2 liters	$1.89	$ .95
· Zippy Cola	3 liters	$2.80	$ .93

"Figuring out unit prices isn't hard. Just take the total price of an item and divide by the quantity. So for Mucho Macho Salsa, divide $3.04 by 8 ounces. Your answer: $.38 per ounce."

The unit price is often lower when you buy a product in a large size. But don't buy something you'll never finish.

Good Deal!

Do you know how to find the good deals? Remember, you can't compare the price of a 5-ounce jar with the price of an 14-ounce jar. You need to know the unit price. Reread the label, chart, and tips. Then use them to answer the questions below. Write your answers on your own paper.

1. What is the unit price of Clean It Up Napkins?
   a. $.03 per napkin
   b. $.26 per napkin
   c. $.02 per napkin

2. What is the cheapest napkin you can buy? How much money will you save per napkin over the most expensive brand you can buy?

3. Suppose you want to get the best deal on cola. Which one should you buy? How much will it cost per liter?

4. Which salsa is the best deal?
   a. Hot and Chile
   b. Mucho Macho
   c. Señor Spicy's

5. Suppose your supermarket also has the large economy size of Mucho Macho Salsa. It weighs two pounds and costs $6.40. What would its unit price be? (Remember, there are 16 ounces in a pound.)

Total It Up

It's time to throw a party. You'll use 50 napkins, 14 ounces of salsa, and 3 liters of cola. You want to spend as little as possible. Which brands should you buy? How much money will you spend?

Smart Shopping

It's important to save money. But what else should you think about when you're buying food? Write a list.

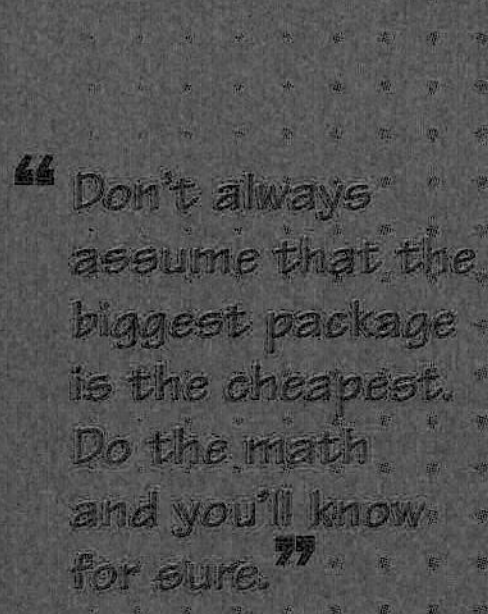

"Don't always assume that the biggest package is the cheapest. Do the math and you'll know for sure."

Real-World Words

liter: a unit of measurement; about 1.1 quarts
unit of measure: ounces, pounds, liters, etc. Sometimes individual items, such as one napkin, can be a unit of measure.

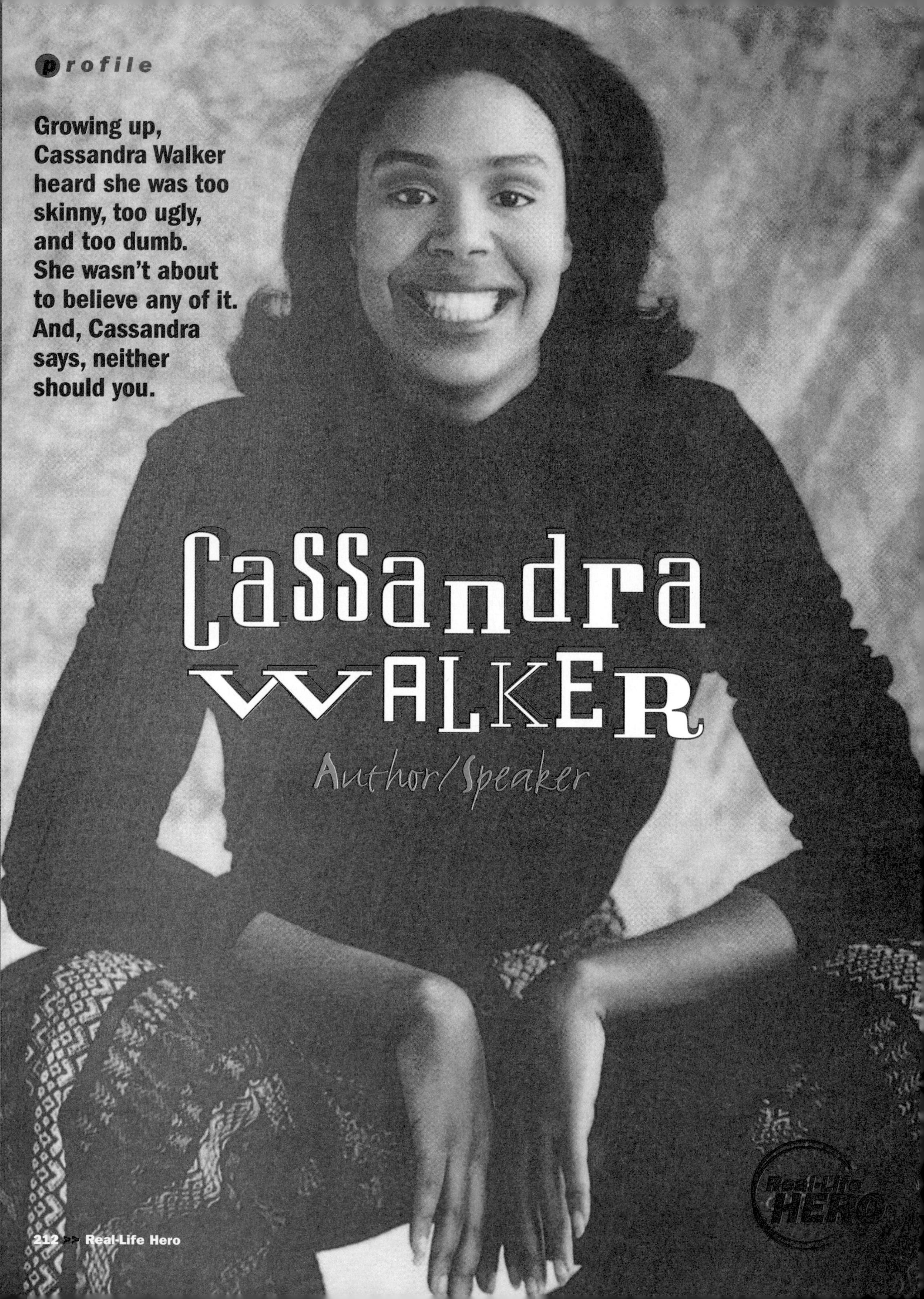

profile

Growing up, Cassandra Walker heard she was too skinny, too ugly, and too dumb. She wasn't about to believe any of it. And, Cassandra says, neither should you.

Cassandra Walker

Author/Speaker

Real-Life HERO

"You were born to be a winner and to succeed, and that is what you can do."

Grade school was not kind to Cassandra Walker. She can still remember the insults. "Big Lips," the boys called her. Then there was her weight: "You're so skinny you can only fit one stripe on your pajamas." Or, worst of all: "You're so skinny I don't know how you can hold up those lips."

High school wasn't a whole lot easier. Cassandra wanted to go to college, but she bombed on the entrance exams. She wanted to be a writer. Instead, she got straight C's in senior English. In 1984, she went into college, embarrassed to be in a special program for people who don't quite meet the requirements.

It seemed the message Cassandra had been hearing all her life was that she was too skinny, too ugly, and too dumb. She decided to ignore it.

Ten years later Cassandra had started her own TV show, written her first book, and appeared on "Oprah." She's now a successful author, public speaker, and mother of three. With endless energy, she's helped thousands of young people have faith in themselves. Especially when things aren't going their way.

"You know," she says, "I try to tell people that for every bad thing that happens, something good can come of it. You just have to believe in yourself. Life has its ups and downs and you just have to keep going."

A Voice of Hope

Cassandra devotes her life to getting that message out. She's written two award-winning books for kids that retell all the ups and downs of her childhood. She also speaks in classrooms, churches, and conferences around the country to share her lessons on living.

"I have people come up to me in tears, saying you changed my life," she says. "Kids are really hurting. They feel bad about themselves. They don't know who to talk to."

In Cassandra, they find someone they can relate to. She was never perfect and freely admits it. But she learned from every setback. She set goals for herself and refused to believe she couldn't reach them.

Cassandra's grade school days helped teach her one of life's most important lessons: Protect your self-esteem. When all the teasing about her "big" lips got to her, Cassandra started biting her bottom lip to hold it in. Her mother noticed one day and told her, "You know, in the African-American culture, full lips are normal."

Cassandra's mother suggested she look in the encyclopedia and find animals that are long and thin like herself. Cassandra picked out graceful gazelles and majestic giraffes. She started to think of her lips as "full" instead of "big." And pretty soon, the teasing just rolled off her back.

"You were created to be unique, and unique is what you are," writes Cassandra. "You were born to be a winner and to succeed, and that is what you can do."

Learning From Life

Cassandra says this is not a lesson you simply learn once, before riding it straight to the top. You have to keep teaching yourself all the way through life. Cassandra's writing career is a case in point.

Cassandra knew she wanted to be a writer when she was nine or ten. While the boys were

When Cassandra shares the story of her life with others, there's one thing for sure: She practices what she preaches.

smirking about her lips and her weight, she would come home from school and hole up in her room with her journal. "I wrote everything down," she says. "My mother would have to come looking for me to say why don't you go out and play."

Around that time, Cassandra got inspired by *Blubber*, a novel by Judy Blume about a girl who gets teased for being overweight. Knowing what it's like to be teased, Cassandra could relate to the main character. But she **identified** even more with the writer. So at ten years old, Cassandra decided she too could be a best-selling author. She wrote a story using her favorite crayon. She stuck it in an envelope and pulled a publisher's address from one of her books. Then she sent off her **masterpiece.**

A couple of months later, her story reappeared in the mail. With it was a letter suggesting she try a typewriter next time.

In 12th grade, Cassandra suffered a much more discouraging rejection. She had made it into honors English and knew she wanted to be an author someday. But every paper she wrote came back with a C on it. The teacher wrote "too creative," or "too wordy" on her papers. Eventually, the teacher told Cassandra she might as well give up trying to be a writer.

Cassandra was crushed. How stupid of her to think she could be a writer when she was barely passing senior English. Then one day she picked up one of the "A" papers in class. It read like an encyclopedia, dull enough to put someone to sleep. She realized suddenly that the teacher's opinion was just one of many. And she decided to keep writing the way she wanted. "I didn't give up," she says, "even when someone in **authority** told me I should."

Sticking With It

That attitude carried Cassandra through college and into her first job: newspaper reporter for the Chicago Heights *Star.* Then she moved to television and started as a receptionist. In two years she was writing and hosting her own kids' show. Despite her C's in English, she was making it as a writer.

ASK YOURSELF

- Whose opinion means the most to Cassandra?

Consider her reaction to the "A" paper that she read.

Then, in 1992, a piece of news crossed Cassandra's desk that changed her life. Alex Haley, who turned the story of his family's African-American heritage into the ground-breaking book, *Roots*, had died. Cassandra had interviewed him once and he'd encouraged her to write. *Roots*, he said, had been rejected 40 times before becoming a huge bestseller.

"It jolted me and I felt like there was a reason I had met him," says Cassandra. After all, if one of the best-selling writers of all time

Words, Words, Words

identified: considered as the same
masterpiece: a person's finest piece of work or achievement
authority: a high position of power

had to fight through so much rejection, maybe there was hope for her. So she started writing her first book; a book of help and hope.

Getting the Message Out

This time she used a computer instead of a crayon. Still, for a year she got nothing but rejections. When she finally received an invitation to meet with a publisher, they went on and on about all the ways she could change the manuscript to make it better. Cassandra thought to herself, okay, maybe they'll like it better next time. But at the end of the conversation, the editor asked if Cassandra was ready to talk about her book contract. "I couldn't believe it," says Cassandra. "I said, 'Oh . . . you mean you want it?' "

In 1994, Cassandra's first book, *Becoming Myself*, was published. The book was full of stories of Cassandra's struggles and helpful advice.

Within months, the letters started pouring in. One girl wrote to thank Cassandra for restoring her self-esteem. She suffered from a condition that had paralyzed part of her face. To avoid the giggles and glares of her classmates, she never went to school functions and rarely hung out with friends. *Becoming Myself* gave her the confidence to ignore the teasing. Not only did she start going out, she launched a support group at school for kids with physical disabilities.

Another 19-year-old girl thanked Cassandra for giving her the strength to believe she could rebuild her life even though she was a teen mother.

Letters like these make it all worthwhile for Cassandra. Since then, she's published another book and is working on a third.

"Put your best foot forward and respect people," Cassandra says. "You get back what you put out. If you put out anger and rudeness, that's what you're going to get back. You'll be complaining all your life and you won't reach your potential."

When Cassandra shares the story of her life with others, there's one thing for sure: She practices what she preaches. ●

Cassandra Walker RESUMÉ

Name: Cassandra Walker

Born: 1966

Goals:
- to build hope and self-esteem in young people
- to help kids learn to respect each other and never give up

Work History:
- **1988–89:** Reporter for the Chicago Heights *Star*
- **1989–90:** Public relations director for Harvey, Illinois
- **1992–94:** Writer and star of "Youth Corner" TV show
- **1994–present:** Author, columnist, public speaker

Education:
- bachelors in mass communication, Western Illinois University

Major Achievements:
- published two books that helped thousands of kids
- spoken to 50–100,000 kids around the country
- winner of the 1997 Athena Award; Book as Mentor: Teen

Life's Lessons

by Cassandra Walker

Cassandra Walker has inspired thousands of young people with her stories about growing up. Here are a couple for you to read from her two books, *Becoming Myself* and *Stories of My Life.* Who knows? They may inspire you, too.

Teasing Isn't Funny

By the time I reached eighth grade, I'd heard every joke about being tall and skinny. I was called such names as "Too Tall Bones," "Olive Oyl," "Jolly Green Giant," etc. You get the picture. I just couldn't take it anymore. So, I felt relieved when another tall and skinny girl arrived at our school. She was a new seventh grader named Charlotte.

Charlotte was a quiet girl, with big eyes and long black hair. She walked down the halls with her books held close to her body. I'm sure she felt intimidated by the older kids, especially those who teased and mocked her as she walked by. Some of the eighth graders made what they referred to as "Charlotte jokes." They tried to come up with the funniest thing to say about how Charlotte walked or looked, or any other cruel remark. I wish I could say that I didn't laugh at these jokes, but I did. Although I didn't think the jokes were funny, I laughed just so those kids wouldn't tease me.

We noticed that Charlotte often didn't show up for school. And when we'd go outside for gym, Charlotte would watch us from a classroom window. For some reason, she didn't ever come outdoors during gym, and this just gave everyone another thing to tease her about.

One day, when we were outside, I hurt myself and had to go to the nurse's office. The nurse immediately gave me ice. (She always gave students ice. Whether you had cramps, a bump on your head, or internal bleeding, she first gave you ice.) I sat down with my ice pack, and, out of the corner of my eye, noticed that Charlotte was sitting near me. She smiled.

I looked around to make sure that no other kids could tease me for talking to Charlotte, and, seeing that the coast was clear, I smiled back. I decided to ask her how she was doing. She said she was fine and asked me if I had enjoyed gym class. I said I had, and then I found the courage to ask her why she never came outside during gym. What she said really had an effect on me and the way I treated people from that point on.

"I can't go outside because I can't do all of the physical activities required in gym," said Charlotte. "I have a bad heart, and I have to take medicine to keep it working. I've had to be in the hospital and doctors' offices all my life. That's why I miss so much school. But I don't fall behind in my school work because I study while I'm in the hospital or at home.

Growing up, Cassandra learned from her many different friends and experiences. Here, she visits with some fellow eighth graders.

"It's hard for me to make friends because I'm absent from school so much," Charlotte added. "Kids tease me but that's because they don't understand me. I'm really a very nice person."

I found out in a short amount of time that Charlotte and I had a lot in common: We were both tall and got teased, we both had big feet, and we both were given ice whenever we went to see the nurse.

I realized that Charlotte was nice and had a good sense of humor. After a few more minutes of talking, Charlotte had to go back to class. But before she left, she said: "On Friday, I'll be going to the hospital for open-heart surgery. I'm glad that I'll have this operation, even though it's kind of scary. After the operation, I'll be different. No more doctors all the time, no more needles, and no more pain. I'll be a new person. Will you pray for me and tell the other kids to, also? It would make me feel good. I'll see you when I get back."

When I returned to class, I told my friends what had happened. Some of them were kind and said they would remember Charlotte in their prayers. But some of them weren't so kind and started telling new Charlotte jokes about how she had an "old lady heart."

On Friday, when Charlotte was going in for her operation, the principal told everyone to make get-well cards for Charlotte during homeroom. He said that on Monday he would give us the hospital name and the address so we could mail the cards. When Monday arrived, I could hardly wait to get the address so I could send the special card to my new friend. The principal's voice came over the loudspeaker, giving us an update on Charlotte.

Charlotte had been right when she said that after the operation there would be no more doctors, needles, or pain. We found out at that moment that Charlotte had died on the operating table. She was only eleven years old when she died. The classroom was quiet. We were all asked to walk to the gym, where we would have a mock funeral for Charlotte. Everyone was upset, and some kids were crying. I cried, too.

For weeks afterward, I'd find myself looking back at the classroom window during gym, as if Charlotte might be there watching us. I just couldn't believe she was gone.

*

I learned in a very hard way that other people's feelings count. I was so concerned about what others might think of me that I had completely ignored Charlotte's feelings and laughed at the jokes. If you see someone being made fun of, I hope you'll have more courage than I did and that you'll stick up for the person getting teased. Or, at the very least, don't join in the teasing or laughter. I regret that I never really got to know a wonderful person who probably could have taught me a lot about life.

Don't Give Up

In high school, I took an honors English class, and I was very excited. I had always liked English, and now I would have the opportunity to do college level work and read advanced novels. I would also get the chance to write creatively. I dreamed of being an author someday, and this would be good practice.

Our first assignment was a book report. I read the book and wrote what I thought was a great report. When the teacher started handing back the papers, I noticed quite a few A's and B's and I could hardly wait to get mine. Then she handed me my paper. A C-minus. WHAT?!

The teacher then told me that she was being generous.

On paper after paper, I couldn't get better than a C. The teacher told me I was being "too creative," so I toned it down. Still a C. Then she said I was being "too wordy," so I cut back. Still a C. After a while I stopped trying and I just turned in any old thing. Still a C.

I had told the teacher that I wanted to be an author. Finally she told me that I should consider another occupation, because I really didn't have what it takes to be a writer and especially not an author. I was crushed.

I almost gave up until I read one of my classmates' book reports. It was boring and dull. It told exactly what happened in the book, with no interpretation or personal reaction. And this was an A paper.

Suddenly it all made sense. The teacher didn't like my reports because I included opinions and suggestions. I tried to make my reports **humorous** as well as informative. She didn't want to read anything but the facts. It was her personal opinion that was giving me C's. The teacher had a style of writing, and mine was not following it.

I decided then that I was going to keep writing like I had been, and one day someone would **appreciate** it. I got a C for my final grade, but because it was an honors course it was counted as a B. I knew that the teacher meant me no harm. She just didn't like my writing style. For some reason, she thought her style was the only acceptable one.

I did continue to write. I wrote my way into a reporter's job at a local newspaper. Then I wrote my way into my own chil-

Words, Words, Words

regret: to be sad or sorry about something
humorous: funny
appreciate: enjoy or value something

dren's TV segment on a major television station. I didn't give up, even when someone in authority told me I should.

I have a friend who didn't give up either. Her name is Linda J. Adkins. She went to junior high and high school with me. Here is her story:

Per-se-ver-ance. Such a long word for a young person. "What does it mean?" I asked my father during one of our many "it's-time-to-talk" conversations. He replied, "It means a sense of determination and endurance in the pursuit of a desired goal."

At the time, that wasn't exactly what I was thinking about. I was in high school, where I was a cheerleader, gymnast, student council member, and regular socialite. Why worry about anything besides having fun? Yet I knew there would be life after high school. I was a junior, and it was time to make decisions about my future.

I wanted to become a doctor. This goal seemed sort of comical, coming from someone with mediocre grades. I remember approaching my counselor with the idea. I could see the dismay in his eyes as he searched for a way to tell me that I probably should consider other alternatives.

"How about attending the vocational school?" he suggested. "There's a nursing assistance course. Maybe that is what you should consider." Although I was upset that he was not taking my aspirations seriously, I knew I still wanted to become a doctor.

I attended vocational school, and I learned a lot about the medical profession. I reassured myself that I wanted to be a health professional—not a nurses' assistant, lab technician, or therapist, but a doctor. I was positive I could do it. I guess this was perseverance.

I remember a day in high school history class when I almost became discouraged. The teacher informed us that only honor students are expected to become the doctors and lawyers of the future. I knew in my heart that the goals I had set for myself were attainable.

To make a long story short, this is how it goes: After vocational school, I went to college with doubts from everyone including former teachers, counselors, and peers. Even my new college pre-med counselor tried to dissuade me from my career choice. He explained that pre-med was a difficult program and my prior course work was not indicative of a strong science background. I listened politely, yet I was determined to persevere.

It took a tremendous amount of hard work. I sure wished I had paid more attention to class work in junior high and high school instead of focusing on trying to be popular. I had a lot of catching up to do.

I never gave up, and after four years of college and a Bachelor of Science in biology I was accepted into all the post-graduate schools I applied to. I cried a lot, I often became discouraged, and I didn't graduate at the top of my class, but I did fulfill my dream. I persevered. . . . Just call me Doctor.

Talk About It

Now that you've read "Cassandra Walker" and "Life's Lessons," what do you have to say about these questions?

- Why do you think kids often tease those who look or act different?
- Do you think most people would be discouraged by failure and rejection? Explain.

Comprehension Check

Write your answers to the questions below. Use information from the profile and the essays to support your answers.

1. How did Alex Haley inspire Cassandra to follow her dream of writing a book?
2. How would you describe Cassandra's character?
3. Why do you think people are encouraged by Cassandra's story?
4. Why did the kids tease Charlotte?
5. What part of Cassandra's story was most interesting to you? Why?

Vocabulary Check

Answer each question below with a complete sentence. Before you answer, think about the meaning of the vocabulary word in bold.

1. What is something you might **regret**?
2. What do you think people **appreciate** most about you?
3. When was the last time you **identified** with someone?
4. Who has a position of **authority** in your school?
5. What is the most **humorous** thing that has happened to you lately?

Write About It

Choose one of the writing prompts below.

- Imagine you are one of the kids at school who had teased Charlotte. Write a letter to Charlotte and explain how you feel about that now that you know she is seriously ill.
- Write a short report about a book you have recently read. Try to make it funny and include personal reactions.
- Write about a true story from your life or someone else's that you think will inspire or teach others. Use Cassandra's stories as a model for your writing.

More to READ

Are you interested in inspirational books like those by Cassandra Walker? If so, check out these titles.

Real Kids, Real Adventures

by Deborah Morris

This book contains three true-life stories that are as incredible as they are inspiring. In "A Sudden Shark Attack," a young girl on a family vacation finds herself battling a hungry shark. In "A Ski Slope Rescue!" a high schooler risks his own life to save a young girl. In "A Thirty-Five Foot Fall," a nine-year-old saves her father after an accident. It's true: Heroes come in all sizes.

Louis Braille: The Boy Who Invented Books for the Blind

by Margaret Davidson

Blinded in an accident at the age of three, Louis Braille depended on his fantastic memory to do well in school. In those days, you couldn't read what you couldn't see. Or so everyone thought. But not Louis. Working for years, he developed a simple alphabet of raised dots for blind people to read with their fingers. And he was only 15!

job skills

Using Help-Wanted Ads

You need a job. How can you find out what's available? A good way to start is by checking the help-wanted ads. You'll find them in the classified-ads section of your newspaper.

Check out the help-wanted ads below. Are you ready to get to work?

Help-Wanted Ads

Want ads are grouped in categories, according to type of business. For example, a job in a store would be listed under "retail."

RETAIL

CASHIER

Part-time help needed. To $500/wk. Grab 'n' Save Supermarket. Several shifts avail., incl. M-F 4-8, S&S 8-4. Send resumé to Grab 'n' Save, 14 Main St.

CHILDCARE

MOTHER'S HELPER

needed for 2-yr.-old 5 mornings/wk. Also laundry, cleaning. Own transportation. No exp. nec., but refs. required. Please call 555-8921.

Here are some common abbreviations in want ads: wk.=week; hrs.=hours; exp.=experience; nec.=necessary; refs.=references; flex.=flexible.

RESTAURANT

BUS PERSON/DISHWASHER NEEDED

Must be avail. nights. $8/hr. Some exp. preferred. Apply in person at NIGHTHAWK DINER, corner of Maple and Vine.

Check ads in more than one category. For example, the job of dishwasher could be found under "food service" or "restaurant."

ODD JOBS

YARD WORKER

20 hrs./wk. Flex. hrs.
$7/hr.
Mow, rake, garden, other odd jobs.
No exp. nec. Call 555-3423 after 6 P.M.

FOOD SERVICE

HAPPY BURGER

Many positions open. Full and part-time. $7-12/hr., depending on exp. Apply in person.

"The salary, hours, and required experience may be listed in the ad, or you may need to ask for this information."

Start Your Job Hunt

When you first look at want ads, you might think they're written in code. Luckily, the code is not hard to crack. Reread the want ads and tips. Then use them to answer these questions. Write your answers on your own paper.

1. Which shift is not available at Grab 'n' Save?
a. Saturday, from 8 A.M. to 4 P.M.
b. Saturday, from 4 P.M. to 8 P.M.
c. Tuesday, from 4 P.M. to 8 P.M.
d. Friday, from 4 P.M. to 8 P.M.

2. You need a job that allows you to work after school and on weekends. Which of the jobs should you **not** apply for?
a. cashier
b. yard worker
c. mother's helper
d. bus person/dishwasher

3. You get an interview at Happy Burger. Which question are they likely to ask to determine your salary?
a. How much money do you need?
b. Have you worked at a fast-food restaurant before?
c. Do you like burgers?
d. Do you have experience as a receptionist?

4. Which of the following would you need to get the mother's helper job? (Choose three.)
a. gardening experience
b. child-care experience
c. transportation
d. adults who will recommend you

Real-World Words

position: a job
required: necessary; something that you must have
salary: the amount that an employee is paid

Be a Career Counselor

Use the ads to help you choose the job that suits each of these three people. **Karen** wants to work outdoors. **Ray** wants to learn to cook. **Jason** loves kids.

Help Wanted

You run a hot dog stand. You need to hire workers. Create the want ad that you would place in the paper. Use the ads to the left as models for your ad.

"Your newspaper is not the only place to find want ads. You can also find job listings on the Web."

MY NATIVE TONGUE

During World War II, a small group of Navajo risked their lives on a secret mission that helped America win the war. Their weapon was words. Here's their true story.

by Kathy Sorensen

When Japan bombed Pearl Harbor on December 7, 1941, the United States entered World War II. The U.S. Marine Corps wanted to create a secret code. They wanted to communicate with their troops in a code that the Japanese wouldn't be able to crack.

They turned to the Navajo for help. Navajo language is so complex that it is almost impossible for outsiders to learn.

Despite a bitter history with the U.S. military, young Navajos worked side by side on the battlefield with U.S. soldiers. They braved bombs and dodged bullets to use their special skills and saved many American lives. This play is inspired by the little-known true story of the Navajo "code talkers."

CHARACTERS

Joe, a 15-year-old Navajo boy *

Narrator 1 | Joe, retelling
Narrator 2 | his story*

Paul, a 15-year-old Navajo boy *

Father, Joe's father

Mother, Joe's mother

BIA Agent, from the Bureau of Indian Affairs

Sergeant Grayhorse, a Navajo

Drill Sergeant

Medicine Man

Navajo Marine 1

Navajo Marine 2

Officer *

Soldier

*** Starred parts are major roles.**

SCENE ONE

Narrator 1: I live on the Navajo Reservation in Arizona. It is a beautiful land of deserts, canyons, and rock formations.

When I was young, my family taught me to live in the Navajo way. I learned to follow the traditions of my **ancestors.** I lived in **harmony** with nature and spent my days herding sheep.

Narrator 2: One day when I was ten years old, an agent from the Bureau of Indian Affairs came to our hogan to speak to my mother. The BIA agent had brought along a Navajo boy to interpret. The agent could not speak Navajo, and my family could not speak English. I could not hear what was said. But my mother was upset and angry. Later I overheard my parents talking about it.

Father: Our son must go away to an English-speaking school? Why?

Mother: The agent says that all Navajos must learn English. They must follow the ways of the white people.

Father: But he doesn't need to know their ways. We live off the land, off our sheep. I don't want outsiders teaching my son.

Mother: We have no choice. The government will take our sheep if he doesn't go to Navajo boarding school. We can't live without our sheep.

Narrator 1: My mother was right. The sheep were our **livelihood.** We used their wool for clothes and blankets. We used their meat for food. Finally, I couldn't listen anymore. I burst into the room.

Joe: I'm not going away to school! I want to stay here and help our family. You need me!

Narrator 2: My mother's eyes filled with tears. But she remained firm.

Mother: You must go to school. You must do it *for* your family.

ASK YOURSELF

- How does Joe feel about going away to school?

Read on and see how the change in setting affects him.

SCENE TWO

Narrator 1: I left my family for the first time and went to the boarding school. It was only 12 miles from home. But it felt like a different world. All the kids were Navajo, but I didn't realize it at first. They all wore jeans and spoke English!

Narrator 2: Back then, I'd never talked to white people, eaten their food, or worn their clothes. I was terrified. Finally, I got up the nerve to speak to another student.

Joe *(in Navajo)*: Hey, you! Are you Navajo?

Paul *(whispering)*: My name's Paul. And we're all Navajo, stupid. Just don't let them catch you *speaking* Navajo. You can get beaten for it. So can I.

Joe *(whispering back)*: What happened to everybody's hair? Why is it so short?

Paul: The teachers cut it off—like they will yours. Now, shut up! I'm not kidding about speaking Navajo.

Joe: But I don't know English.

Paul: Then don't say anything. When the teachers talk to you, just nod. You'll learn it eventually.

Narrator 1: A moment later, a white teacher took me by the arm. He led me to a small room where another man cut off my long hair. Then they made me change into uncomfortable new clothes. When it was over, they brought out a mirror. When I looked at myself, I couldn't believe what I saw.

Native American schoolchildren in 1900

Narrator 2: I wanted to run away. But I knew I had to stay—for my family. Later, I found my way to the dining room. The strange food didn't taste good to me. I looked around and saw Paul eating at the same table.

Joe *(in Navajo)*: Look what they did to me.

Narrator 1: A teacher yelled something from across the room. Paul looked down. The teacher stomped over to us, still yelling. She wanted me to answer her. But I did not know what she was saying.

Narrator 2: I guessed she was mad because we were speaking Navajo. She dragged Paul and me out of the room. We did not get supper that night. Later, I began to recognize some of the words she had used. They were words like "savage," "brute," and "animal."

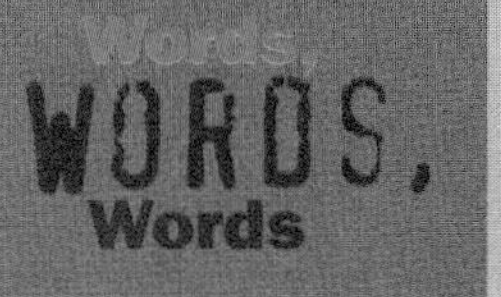

ancestors: members of your family who lived a long time ago
harmony: agreement
livelihood: the way you make money to support yourself

"NO MATTER WHAT, OUR HOMELAND IS AT STAKE! THIS IS OUR CHANCE TO PROTECT OUR PEOPLE *AND* PROVE OURSELVES TO THE WHITE MAN. . . . COME ON. LET'S JOIN UP."

SCENE THREE

Narrator 1: I was lonely for my old Navajo life. I missed my relatives. I missed being outside all day. I missed running in the sunshine. I couldn't understand why the teachers wanted us to forget the Navajo teachings. At least Paul shared my feelings. He became my closest friend. When I questioned the teachers, he would speak up too. We'd both get punished. But at least I wasn't alone.

Narrator 2: Five years passed like this. I learned to speak English. I even got used to my short hair. By the time I was 15, life at school seemed almost normal. Still, I longed to leave those four walls forever. Then one day, a BIA agent came into our classroom. With him was a Navajo man in military uniform.

BIA Agent: Class, meet Sergeant Grayhorse of the United States Marine Corps.

Narrator 1: Paul and I were **startled.** We had never seen a Navajo in uniform before. The teacher and the BIA agent treated him with great respect—even though he was a Navajo. He had come with a very special mission.

Grayhorse: As you know, the United States is fighting a war against Japan. Now our country needs the aid of its first true Americans, the Navajos. We must help protect the land of our ancestors. I am asking you to enlist in the Marines. If you are at least 17 years old, come see me at the BIA recruiting center.

Narrator 2: I was interested. If nothing else, joining the Marines would get us out of our awful school. It looked like our only chance. So I talked privately with Paul.

Joe: Let's get out of here. Let's enlist. Come with me!

Narrator 1: Paul was not so easy to convince.

Paul: No way! Why should we get involved in the white man's war? Look what they've done to us!

Joe: No matter what, our homeland is at stake! This is our chance to protect our people *and* prove ourselves to the white man. Besides, we'll be able to make a living. What can we do on the reservation after we leave school? Come on. Let's join up.

ASK YOURSELF

- Why does Joe want to join the Marines?

Retell Joe's reasons in your own words.

SCENE FOUR

Narrator 2: I finally convinced Paul to come with me. The next day, we went down to the recruiting station. We were only 15. But we lied and told them we were 17. When we walked out the door, we were Marines! I went home to say goodbye to my family. My mother was not very happy.

Mother *(in Navajo)*: Son, our people have always been great warriors. But this is not our war. Why must you fight it?

Joe: Mother, the Navajo world is shrinking. The white world keeps growing. We must be part of it in order to survive. Fighting will

The Navajo code was one of the only military codes never broken by the enemy.

make the white world take us seriously. It will help all of our people.

Mother: But it's all so dangerous, so far away. . . .

Joe: The Navajo Tribal Council voted last year to defend the U.S. against **invasion.** After all, our reservation is part of this country. If this country is destroyed, our reservation will be too. I'm just doing my part. I want to protect you and my father and everyone else.

Mother: This is a bad idea. If I could keep you from going, I would. But, if you must go, we will have a Blessing Way for you before you leave.

Narrator 1: A Blessing Way is one of the ceremonies that make up the Navajo religion. It's meant to bring a person good luck and protection. A medicine man ran my Blessing Way at a big family gathering. As my relatives gathered around, the medicine man made a sand painting on the ground. Then he sang an ancient **chant.**

Medicine Man *(singing in Navajo)*: *I have come upon it. I have come upon a blessing. My people, my relatives, I have come upon a blessing. . . .*

Narrator 2: When it was all over, I felt ready to join the white people's war.

SCENE FIVE

Narrator 1: Paul and I took a bus to boot camp. Our platoon was all Navajo. Everyone else in the camp was white. They treated us pretty fairly. We ran into just a few problems.

Drill Sergeant *(to Joe)*: Give me three laps around the track, chief!

Joe *(whispering)*: What's he calling me?

Drill Sergeant *(to Paul)*: Hey, chief, you too! Get a move on!

Paul: I guess we're all "chief" to him. Too bad he doesn't know that Navajos don't have chiefs.

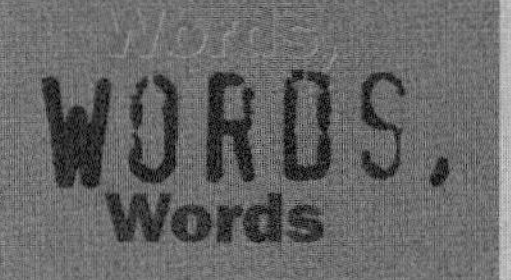

startled: surprised
invasion: taking over a country by armed force
chant: a phrase said or sung over and over again

Joe *(sarcastically)*: You tell him. I'm sure he'd be fascinated. Besides, if that's the worst thing they do to us here, we're OK.

Narrator 2: The drill sergeant was hard on us. But he was hard on everyone. We had to be in great shape if we were going to survive the war.

Drill Sergeant: Listen up, you sorry excuses for Marines! That was the worst performance I've ever seen on the obstacle course! We're going to keep doing it until I see some improvement!

Narrator 1: His drills turned us into top-notch Marines. We learned to respect him. And he learned to respect us.

Drill Sergeant: Congratulations, chiefs, you've survived boot camp. Now you're off to Marine training school. You'll get a special assignment there. Good luck.

ASK YOURSELF

- How do Joe and Paul feel about Marine boot camp?

Think about how they were treated at the boarding school.

SCENE SIX

Narrator 2: At training school, we saw Sergeant Grayhorse again.

Grayhorse: Men, you've been chosen for a secret mission. It could save thousands of American lives. And no one but you can do it. You will be code talkers. You'll **transmit** messages between soldiers on the front lines and their commanding officers, between battleships at sea and bombers in the air. You'll use the Navajo language to transmit this secret code.

Narrator 1: It was incredible! For years I'd been punished for speaking my language. Now my country wanted me to use it as a weapon in the war!

Grayhorse: As you know, Navajo is one of the most complex languages on earth. But you won't simply be speaking Navajo. We're going to scramble the Navajo language into code. Only the people in this room will be able to understand it!

Joe: I was filled with pride. Each day in class we learned the code. It combined everyday Navajo speech with 400 code words that we helped to create. While 3,600 Navajo soldiers fought in the war, only 420 of us were code talkers.

SCENE SEVEN

Narrator 2: After we learned the code, we were shipped to the Pacific. On the way, an officer gave us our instructions.

Officer: Men, our objective is to take an island called Iwo Jima. We will land on the beach. Then we'll fight our way to the mountain, the island's highest point. We expect heavy **resistance** from the enemy. If we don't capture the mountain, we'll lose the battle. Thousands of our men will die.

Narrator 1: The morning of the battle, Paul and I rose at dawn

This man, William Dean Wilson, was one of the real code talkers. Before the war, he was a sheepherder.

and prayed in the Navajo way. We faced east and touched a bit of **sacred** corn pollen to our tongues. Then we sprinkled it into the wind.

Joe and Paul *(in Navajo)*: *All is beautiful before me. All is beautiful behind me. All is beautiful above me. All is beautiful around me.*

Today I will live well. . . .

SCENE EIGHT

Narrator 2: The night before the battle, we "chiefs" were scared. One reason is that we had heard a rumor about a Navajo soldier named Joe Kieyoomia. The Japanese had captured him.

Navajo Marine 1: Kieyoomia's not a code talker. He doesn't even know the code. But the Japanese don't know that. They'll probably torture him to try to get it out of him.

Paul: That's awful! But what if one of us got captured? If one of us broke under torture, it would destroy the whole code-talking mission.

Navajo Marine 2: I'll bet if one of us got injured, the Marines would just shoot us. They couldn't risk leaving us behind for the medics. The Japanese might capture us in the meantime and get the code. The code is more important than we are.

Joe *(worried)*: Don't be ridiculous. No one would shoot us. We're Marines too. We're all serving the same country.

Narrator 1: I spoke forcefully. But I don't remember getting any sleep that night. What if the others were right?

SCENE NINE

Narrator 2: The day of the Marine invasion came. As we

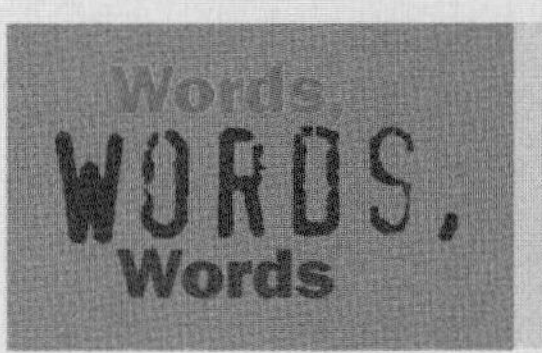

transmit: to send
resistance: fighting back
sacred: deserving great respect

"I PUT ON THE RADIO HEADSET. PAUL AND I IMMEDIATELY SENT THE MESSAGE. BOMBS WERE EXPLODING ALL AROUND US. . . . WITHIN MINUTES, THE BATTLESHIPS BEGAN HEAVING SHELLS AT THE JAPANESE WHO HAD US TRAPPED."

neared Iwo Jima, Paul and I heard gunfire and bomb explosions. Like thousands of other Marines around us, we stepped from our small boat into waist deep water. I held my radio over my head to keep it dry.

Officer: OK, men! Hit the beaches!

Narrator 1: Paul and I tried to run through the water. All around us, mortar shells were exploding. Bullets whizzed through the air. To the left and right of me, soldiers were being hit. They would collapse, dying. The water was red with blood. I had never been so frightened in my life!

Joe: Run for the sea wall!

Narrator 2: We ran for the beach with the other Marines. Then we dove for cover, plunging headfirst into the sand behind the sea wall. Bullets kept flying around us. An officer stuck his head out to call for help.

Officer: I need a code talker! Did any of the chiefs make it?

Joe: Yes, sir! We're here. Over here!

Narrator 1: With bullets whizzing past us, Paul and I crawled through the sand to the officer.

Officer: We'll be slaughtered if we stay here much longer. Send this message to the battleships. "Pinned down on Green Beach. Request immediate artillery support."

Joe: Yes, sir.

Narrator 2: I put on the radio headset. Paul and I immediately sent the message. Bombs were still exploding all around us.

Joe: . . . *shil-loh be-al-do-cid-da-hi* . . .

Narrator 1: It didn't take long for us to do what we had to do.

Paul: Sir! We've sent the message. The ships have acknowledged it. Support is on the way!

Narrator 2: Within minutes, the battleships began heaving shells at the Japanese who had us trapped. Soon, the enemy positions were destroyed.

Officer: All right, men! Move out!

ASK YOURSELF

- How did the code talkers help save the Marines?

Explain in your own words what Joe and Paul did.

SCENE TEN

Narrator 1: We left the beach and began crawling up the mountain. It was slow, dangerous going. Bullets were raining down on us the whole time. We had almost reached the top. But then the enemy blasted us with an amazing show of firepower. Suddenly, I felt a searing pain in my leg. I fell **writhing** to the ground.

Joe *(screaming in pain)*: I'm hit! I'm hit!

Narrator 2: Blood poured from my leg. Paul crawled over to me.

Paul *(to an officer)*: He's hurt! I have to take Joe back to the medical unit!

Officer: No! You can't! We can't win this mountain without your code! Send a message for him to be picked up.

Paul: Yes, sir! *(on the radio headset) Jo-kayed-goh A-zay . . . !*

Narrator 1: I pulled Paul over to me and spoke to him in Navajo. I was thinking about the conversation we'd had the night before.

Joe: Please. Don't let them shoot me! Whatever happens, don't let them shoot me.

Paul *(concerned)*: You don't have to worry, buddy. I'm here all the way. I'll fight them if I have to.

Narrator 2: We watched nervously as the officer looked around for another Marine.

Officer: Soldier!

Soldier: Yes, sir!

Narrator 1: We didn't know what he would ask the soldier to do. We waited.

Officer: Soldier, stay with this chief until the medical unit arrives. Protect him with your life. He knows the secret code. He's very valuable. We can't risk letting the Japanese capture him.

Soldier: Yes, sir. I won't let anything happen to him.

Narrator 2: I looked over at Joe. We both knew now that the Marine Corps would stand by me.

Paul: I wish I could stay with you, Joe.

Joe: Go. They need the code to save our brothers' lives. The island is lost without it.

Narrator 1: Paul reached into his pocket.

Paul: Here, take this for protection.

Narrator 2: He gave me his bag of sacred corn pollen. I smiled.

Paul: This will be the first time we've been separated since you arrived at school.

Joe: I know.

Narrator 1: Paul scrambled away, following the others. After a long time, I looked up and saw them raising the American flag on the mountaintop. All the troops cheered.

SCENE ELEVEN

Narrator 2: After the war, Paul stayed in the Marines. He became an officer. I recovered from my wounds and went back to the reservation. When I returned, a medicine man performed a traditional Enemy Way Ceremony. It helped rid me of the ghosts of war. The songs in the ceremony were ancient. But they seemed to be made just for me.

Medicine Man *(singing in Navajo)*:

> *In the center of the **turquoise** home a nice one gave its sound, so it did*
>
> *In the journey of the Warrior Boy a nice one gave its sound, so it did*
>
> *The nice child of long life and happiness just gave its sound, so it is.*

Narrator 1: Before we were discharged from the Marines, we all took an **oath** not to tell anyone—not even our wives and children—what we had done in the war. The Marine Corps wanted to be able to use the code again. They feared that soon we would have to fight the Soviet Union. But luckily that war never happened. In 1969, twenty-four years later, we Navajo code talkers finally began to get some credit for our part in the war. ●

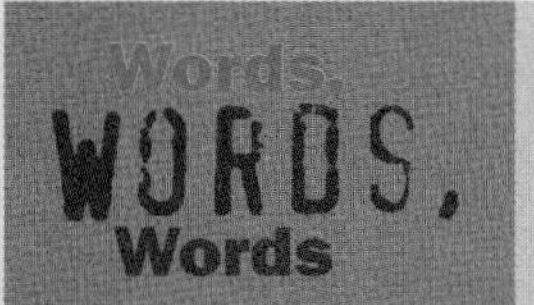

writhing: twisting and turning in pain
turquoise: a blue-green color
oath: a serious promise

The Navajo

from the *Scholastic Encyclopedia of the North American Indian*

- **Location:** Parts of Arizona, New Mexico & Utah
- **Population:** 200,000
- **Way of Life:** Hunting & Farming
- **Their Own Name:** Dineh

Besides rugs and baskets, the Navajo also make wonderful turquoise and silver jewelry. Men do the silverwork. This silversmith displays some of his work, including the silver belt he is holding in his hands.

The Navajo tribe is the largest in the western United States. Most Navajo live on America's largest reservation, a 28,000-square-mile spread located within Arizona, New Mexico, and Utah.

The Navajo's origins are different from those of their neighbors in the Southwest. That's because they migrated southward from the Subarctic about 900 years ago. The name Navajo comes from the Pueblo language and means "newcomers." The Navajo call themselves Dineh, or People. More than 100,000 people speak the Navajo dialect as their first language. About 25,000 of them speak little or no English.

ADAHOONIŁIGII

THE NAVAHO LANGUAGE MONTHLY

VOL. 2 NO. 3 WINDOW ROCK, ARIZONA JANUARY 1, 1947

'AHKEAH HONEESNÁ 'ÁKO BÉÉSH BĄĄH DAH NAAZ NILÍGÍÍ YÁ DAH NÁNÍDAAHÍ SILĮĮ'!!

Nílch'its'ósí ńdízidęę bighi' Naabeehó binant'a'í béésh bąąh dah naaznilígíí yá dah nánídaahii dooleeł biniighé Sam 'Ahkeah dóó Chéé Dodge diné naaltsoos bá 'adayiiznil. Sam 'Ahkeah naaltsoos dįįdi miil dóó ba'aan naakidi neeznádiin bá 'aníídee'. Chee Dodge t'éiyá naaltsoos naakidi miil dóó ba'aan naakidi neeznádiin bá 'aníídee'.

Sam Ahkeah k'ad naanishtsoh haa deet'ą, 'éí hoł bééhózin. Sam Ahkeah t'éiyá Naat'áanii Néézdęę' naaghá dóó k'ad 'ashdladiin binááhai lá jiní. Fort Lewis Colorado hoolghéedi 'ííłta' dóó Naat'áanii Néezgi dó' 'ííłta' jiní. 'Ólta' yits'ániyáá dóó Colorado bighi' 'akał bistłee'ii ła' yá naalnishgo tseebíí náá-hai jiní. 'Áádóó Gad Deelzha hoolghée-di (Meso Verde) ninááná lnishgo tseebíí-ts'áadah nínáánááhai jiní. Bilagáana

TSASK'EH BA HOOGHAN DIILTŁA

Hayíílką́ągo Atlanta Georgia hoolghéedi tsásk'eh bá hooghan ńt'ęę' diiltła lá jiní. 'Éí Bilagáana t'ááłáhádi neeznádiin dóó ba'aan dįįts'áadah yilt'éego nabistseed dóó neeznádiin yilt'éego t'éiyá t'óó tídadiilyaa lá jiní. T'áá

This monthly newsletter is used for teaching reading skills in the Navajo language. The Navajo language was first written down in the 1930s. That's when officials from the Smithsonian Institution created an alphabet for it. The newsletter was first published shortly after that, in 1943. Its name, *Adahooniligii,* means "Current Events."

Ceremonies and Government

Traditional Navajo spirituality is devoted to ceremonies of life and health. Each Navajo healer specializes in one kind of ceremony—the Blessing Way, for example. It is performed for good luck, and for two days the healer makes sand paintings and sings special chants.

Sand paintings are an important part of Navajo ceremonies to cure a sick person, cast out evil, or unite a person with nature. They are made by arranging pollen and colored sand on the ground to illustrate legends and spirits. After a ceremony, the sand paintings are destroyed.

Navajo government has changed a lot in the past 100 years. Traditionally, Navajo were governed by clan leaders called *naat'aanii*, or "ones who make speeches." In this informal system, leaders were chosen by clan members and served two to four years. They usually tried to persuade people to listen to them, rather than ordering them to obey.

As the Navajo nation grew, their government became more formal. In recent years there has been an elected council and president. This change is especially important to the Navajo when negotiating with outside businesses and governments.

Environment and Resources

Navajo land contains many resources, including coal, uranium, and oil. The Navajo government has earned millions of dollars by leasing land to corporations.

Because settlers did not want the Navajo's desert lands, the tribe kept most of its territory. The Navajo have raised sheep there ever since the Spanish brought sheep to the region in the 1600s. Unfortunately, sheep-raising has created problems for the environment today. When sheep graze, they usually eat plants down to the very soil. That causes the soil to wash away when heavy desert thundershowers pour down.

The Navajo hold many festivals, powwows, and ceremonies. Often, the public is invited. ●

TALK ABOUT IT

Now that you've read *My Native Tongue* and "The Navajo," what do you have to say about these questions?

- ▶ How would you feel if you were forced to adopt the ways of another culture? Explain.
- ▶ How important is it for anyone living in the U.S. to learn to speak English? Why do you think so?

COMPREHENSION CHECK

Write your answers to the questions below. Use information from the play and the encyclopedia entry to support your answers.

1. Why did the Marines want to use the Navajo language for their code?
2. Why did the code talkers fear that the Marines might shoot them if they got injured?
3. If Joe and the other Navajo students were going to school today, how do you think they would be treated?
4. What name do the Navajo use for themselves?
5. Which details about Navajo life found in "The Navajo" are also included in *My Native Tongue?* Give two.

VOCABULARY CHECK

Complete each sentence starter below. Before you answer, think about the meaning of the vocabulary word in bold.

1. I was **startled** when I heard about . . .
2. The soldiers took an **oath** to . . .
3. The first sign of the **invasion** was . . .
4. At home games the fans would **chant** . . .
5. The quarterback was **writhing** because . . .

WRITE ABOUT IT

Choose one of the writing prompts below.

- Create your own code with a partner and then exchange messages in this code. Don't forget to create a code key.
- Write a letter home from one of the Marines at Iwo Jima. In the letter, talk about the experience.
- When the code talkers were finally recognized for their brave effort, how do you think this made Joe and Paul feel? Write a letter from Joe to Paul about this.

Fact FILE

Cracking the Code

The code talkers needed to know more than just how to speak the Navajo language. When a Navajo code talker received a message, he first had to translate each Navajo word into English. Then he used only the first letter of the English word. For example, the Navajo word *wol-la-chee* (meaning "ant") stood for the letter "a." The Navajo words *be-la-sana* ("apple") and *tse-nill* ("axe") also stood for the letter "a." Having several Navajo words to represent each letter in English made the code even harder to break.

Here's an example of how the code works. One way to say the word "navy" in Navajo code would be: "tsah/wol-la-chee/ah-keh-di-glini/tsah-ah-dzoh" (translation: needle/ant/victor/yucca).

If you want to check out the Navajo Code Talkers' Dictionary, you can find it at this Web site: *www.history.navy.mil/faqs/faq 61-4.htm.*

Ordering From a Catalog

How can you go shopping without leaving home? That's easy, you can just order from catalogs!

Sometimes catalogs come in handy. But are they always the best way to shop? Take a look at the catalog page below and decide for yourself.

Couch-Potato Catalog

To keep their own records straight, mail-order companies give everything in their catalogs "item numbers."

Translation, in case you weren't sure: S = small; M = medium; L = large; XL = extra-large.

Hooded Sweatshirt
In canary, goldenrod, cornsilk, or banana. Adult sizes S, M, L, XL
#4261537 $20

Rollneck Sweater
In natural, ivory, sand, or snow.
Adult sizes S, M, L, XL
#4171352 $15
Child sizes S, M, L
#4171353 $10

Baseball Cap
One size fits all.
#5261743 $10

Pullover Jacket
In olive, hunter, or moss.
Adult sizes S, M, L, XL
#7312568 $30

Backpack
In garnet, scarlet, or just plain red.
#3468271 $18

Item Number	Page No.	Size	Color	Price	How Many	Total Price

POSTAGE & HANDLING	
Price of Order	**Charge**
Up to $75	$5
$75.01 to $125	$6
$125.01 to $175	$7
Over $175	$9

Total Price of Order	
Postage & Handling	
Grand Total	

Catalogs charge you for packing up your order and mailing it off. If you return your order, you may have to pay for that postage, too.

Mail vs. Mall

There's a huge stack of catalogs in your mailbox. Who needs the mall? Review the catalog page on the left and reread the tips that go with it. Then use them to answer each question below. Write your answers on your own paper.

1. You place an order. Your total is $60. How much will you pay in postage and handling?

2. Suppose you need a backpack, two hooded sweatshirts, and one baseball cap. How much will it cost to buy these items from the Couch-Potato Catalog? (Hint: Don't forget the postage and handling charge.)

3. You want to buy the pullover jacket. Which of these colors could you select?
   a. moss, olive, and hunter
   b. goldenrod, canary, and cornsilk
   c. ivory, snow, and sand

4. Which of the questions below are important to find out about before you order from a catalog? (Pick two.)
   a. How long do you have to return merchandise?
   b. Where was the catalog manufactured?
   c. How much must you pay for shipping and handling?

The Soft Sell

Most catalogs describe their products in a way that will make you want to buy. You know: "Soft and cozy for sitting around the fire on a snowy night." Write your own description of one product in the Couch-Potato Catalog.

Go Shopping

Copy the order form. Then fill it out with this list: 1 olive jacket, medium; 3 baseball caps; 2 canary sweatshirts, large; 3 just plain red backpacks; 1 ivory rollneck sweater, child's medium.

"Before you order, check out the return policy in the catalog. Most catalogs include a toll-free customer service number. Call it if you have questions about a product or an order."

Real-World Words

handling: preparing an item for shipping
merchandise: products that are bought and sold
postage: a fee paid for mailing a package or letter

WILMA UNLIMITED

How Wilma Rudolph Became the World's Fastest Woman

BY
KATHLEEN KRULL

ILLUSTRATED BY
DAVID DIAZ

No one expected such a tiny girl to have a first birthday. In Clarksville, Tennessee, in 1940, life for a baby who weighed just over four pounds at birth was sure to be limited.

But most babies didn't have nineteen older brothers and sisters to watch over them. Most babies didn't have a mother who knew home remedies and a father who worked several jobs.

Most babies weren't Wilma Rudolph.

Wilma did celebrate her first birthday, and everyone noticed that as soon as this girl could walk, she ran or jumped instead.

She worried people, though—she was always so small and sickly. If a brother or sister had a cold, she got double pneumonia. If one of them had measles, Wilma got measles, too, plus mumps and chicken pox.

Her mother always nursed her at home. Doctors were a luxury for the Rudolph family, and anyway, only one doctor in Clarksville would treat black people.

ASK YOURSELF

- What was Wilma's early childhood like?

Think about one statement that is true for all the facts you've read so far.

Just before Wilma turned five, she got sicker than ever. Her sisters and brothers heaped all the family's blankets on her, trying to keep her warm.

During that sickness, Wilma's left leg twisted inward, and she couldn't move it back. Not even Wilma's mother knew what was wrong.

The doctor came to see her then. Besides scarlet fever, he said, Wilma had also been stricken with polio. In those days, most children who got polio either died or were permanently crippled. There was no cure.

The news spread around Clarksville: Wilma, that lively girl, would never walk again.

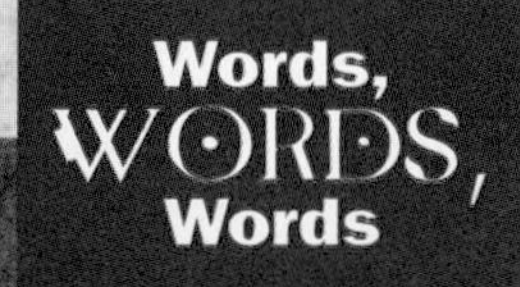

stricken: affected suddenly by an illness
permanently: forever
lively: active and full of life

But Wilma kept moving any way she could. By hopping on one foot, she could get herself around the house, to the outhouse in the backyard, and even, on Sundays, to church.

Wilma's mother urged her on. Mrs. Rudolph had plenty to do—cooking, cleaning, sewing patterned flour sacks into clothes for her children, now 22 in all. Yet twice every week, she and Wilma took the bus to the nearest hospital that would treat black patients, some fifty miles away in Nashville. They rode together in the back, the only place blacks were allowed to sit.

ASK YOURSELF

- What do you think Wilma will do?

Make your best prediction based on what you've read so far.

Doctors and nurses at the hospital helped Wilma do exercises to make her paralyzed leg stronger. At home, Wilma practiced them constantly, even when it hurt.

To Wilma, what hurt most was that the local school wouldn't let her attend because she couldn't walk. Tearful and lonely, she watched her brothers and sisters run off to school each day, leaving her behind. Finally, tired of crying all the time, she decided she had to fight back—somehow.

Words, WORDS, Words

paralyzed: helpless or unable to function
constantly: all the time
attend: go to

Wilma worked so hard at her exercises that the doctors decided she was ready for a heavy steel brace. With the brace supporting her leg, she didn't have to hop anymore. School was possible at last.

But it wasn't the happy place she had imagined. Her classmates made fun of her brace. During playground games she could only sit on the sidelines, twitchy with impatience. She studied the other kids for hours—memorizing moves, watching the ball zoom through the rim of the bushel basket they used as a hoop.

Wilma fought the sadness by doing more leg exercises. Her family always cheered her on, and Wilma did everything she could to keep them from worrying about her. At times her leg really did seem to be getting stronger. Other times it just hurt.

One Sunday, on her way to church, Wilma felt especially good. She and her family had always found strength in their faith, and church was Wilma's favorite place in the world. Everyone she knew would be there—talking and laughing, praying and singing. It would be just the place to try the bravest thing she had ever done.

She hung back while people filled the old building. Standing alone, the sound of hymns coloring the air, she unbuckled her heavy brace and set it by the church's front door. Taking a deep breath, she moved one foot in front of the other, her knees trembling violently. She took her mind off her knees by concentrating on taking another breath, and then another.

Whispers rippled throughout the gathering: Wilma Rudolph was *walking*. Row by row, heads turned toward her as she walked alone down the aisle. Her large family, all her family's friends, everyone from school—

each person stared wide-eyed. The singing never stopped; it seemed to burst right through the walls and into the trees. Finally, Wilma reached a seat in the front and began singing too, her smile triumphant.

Wilma practiced walking as often as she could after that, and when she was twelve years old, she was able to take off the brace for good. She and her mother realized she could get along without it, so one memorable day, they wrapped the hated brace in a box and mailed it back to the hospital.

As soon as Wilma sent that box away, she knew her life was beginning all over again.

After years of sitting on the sidelines, Wilma couldn't wait to throw herself into basketball, the game she had most liked to watch. She was skinny but no longer tiny. Her long, long legs would propel her across the court and through the air, and she knew all the rules and all the moves.

In high school, she led her basketball team to one victory after another. Eventually, she took the team all the way to the Tennessee state championships. There, to everyone's astonishment, her team lost.

Wilma had become accustomed to winning. Now she slumped on the bench, all the liveliness knocked out of her.

But at the game that day was a college coach. He admired Wilma's basketball playing but was especially impressed by the way she ran. He wanted her for his track-and-field team.

With his help, Wilma won a full athletic scholarship to Tennessee State University. She was the first member of her family to go to college.

Eight years after she mailed her brace away, Wilma's long legs and years of hard work carried her thousands of miles from Clarksville, Tennessee. The summer of 1960 she arrived in Rome, Italy, to represent the United States at the Olympic Games—as a runner.

Just participating in the Olympics was a deeply personal victory for Wilma, but her chances of winning a race were limited. Simply walking in Rome's shimmering heat was a chore, and athletes from other countries had run faster races than Wilma ever had. Women weren't thought to run very well, anyway; track-and-field was considered a sport for men. And the pressure from the public was intense—for the first time ever, the Olympics would be shown on television, and all the athletes knew that more than one hundred million people would be watching. Worst of all, Wilma had twisted her ankle just after she arrived in Rome. It was still swollen and painful on the day of her first race.

ASK YOURSELF

- What can you say about the way Wilma faces hardship? Consider what you've already read about her.

Yet once it was her turn to compete, Wilma forgot her ankle and everything else. She lunged forward, not thinking about her fear, her pain, or the sweat flying off her face. She ran better than she ever had before. And she ran better than anyone else.

Grabbing the attention of the whole world, Wilma Rudolph of the United States won the 100-meter dash. No one else even came close. An Olympic gold medal was hers to take home.

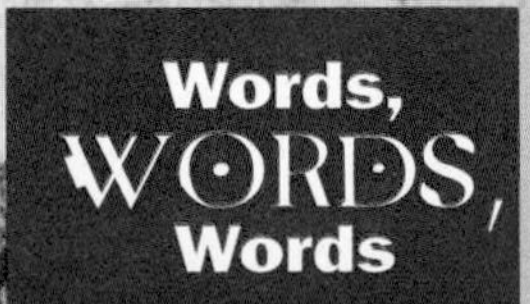

lunged: moved forward quickly and suddenly
surged: rushed forward with force
exhilarated: excited and thrilled

So when it was time for the 200-meter dash, Wilma's graceful long legs were already famous. Her ears buzzed with the sound of the crowd chanting her name. Such support helped her ignore the rain that was beginning to fall. At the crack of the starting gun, she surged into the humid air like a tornado. When she crossed the finish line, she had done it again. She finished far ahead of everyone else. She had earned her second gold medal. Wet and breathless, Wilma was exhilarated by the double triumph. The crowd went wild.

The 400-meter relay race was yet to come. Wilma's team faced the toughest competition of all. And as the fourth and final runner on her team, it was Wilma who had to cross the finish line.

Wilma's teammates ran well, passed the baton smoothly, and kept the team in first place. Wilma readied herself for the dash to the finish line as her third teammate ran toward her. She reached back for the baton—and nearly dropped it. As she tried to recover from the fumble, two other runners sped past her. Wilma and her team were suddenly in third place.

Ever since the day she had walked down the aisle at church, Wilma had known the power of concentration. Now, legs pumping, she put her mind to work. In a final, electrifying burst of speed, she pulled ahead. By a fraction of a second, she was the first to blast across the finish line. The thundering cheers matched the thundering of her own heart. She had made history. She had won for an astounding third time.

At her third ceremony that week, as the band played "The Star-Spangled Banner," Wilma stood tall and still, like a queen, the last of her three Olympic gold medals hanging around her neck.

Wilma Rudolph, once known as the sickliest child in Clarksville, had become the fastest woman in the world. ●

AUTHOR'S NOTE

Wilma Rudolph became, at age twenty, the first American woman to win three gold medals at a single Olympics. When she returned home from Rome, her family was waiting for her, and so was all of Clarksville, Tennessee. The huge parade and banquet held in her honor were the first events in the town's history to include both blacks and whites.

During the time of Wilma's childhood in the 1940s, polio, also known as infantile paralysis, was the world's most dreaded disease. A cure for it was not found until 1955. By then it had killed or crippled 357,000 Americans, mostly children—only 50,000 fewer than the number of Americans who had died in World War II.

After she retired from her career as a runner in 1962, Wilma became a second-grade teacher and a high school coach. She remained a much-admired celebrity, but to prove that there was more to her than just running, she started a company called Wilma Unlimited that gave her opportunities to travel, lecture, and support causes she believed in. Later she founded the nonprofit Wilma Rudolph Foundation to nurture young athletes and teach them that they, too, can succeed despite all odds against them. The story of all she overcame in order to win at the Olympics has inspired thousands of young athletes, especially women.

Wilma Rudolph died in 1994.

WILMA: A VALUABLE LESSON

Wilma Rudolph won against all odds. But it took losing to teach her the greatest lesson of all.

by WILMA RUDOLPH

So, it's 1956, and I'm a fifteen-year-old high school sophomore, and my life has never been better. I couldn't remember being happier. School was fun then. I remember the television show "American Bandstand" was very big with the kids, and once a week somebody would come into the school with a bunch of records and we'd have our own "American Bandstand" show after school. They would give out records to kids who won dance contests doing the latest dances, and I even won a couple myself. All the girls were wearing long, tight skirts, the ones that ended just below the knees, and bobby socks and padded bras. They wore chains around their necks with their boyfriends' rings on them, and if you were going steady with an athlete, the girl wore the guys' letter sweaters or their team jackets. Little Richard was big, and Chuck Berry was big, but truthfully, Elvis Presley had no effect whatsoever. Burt High School was all black, and we just didn't have any kids in the school who identified with Elvis Presley.

The black kids sort of knew that he was just a white guy singing black music, but no black kids had motorcycles or leather jackets, probably because they didn't have the money to buy them.

We had all sorts of little social groups in the school, but none that could be described as being like white greasers. One group was the dressers, the kids who came from fairly affluent homes and who showed it off by wearing the best clothes all the time, even to the point where some of the guys in this group came to school wearing suits and ties. The next group was the regulars, the kids who were looked upon as being regular kids, nothing special, just everyday happy kids. Athletes were another group and they usually stuck with other athletes. The funniest group was the "process" guys. They would go to barber shops and get their hair straightened, and everybody would talk about how the barbers used lye to straighten out their hair. Then they would slick back the straightened hair, and this slick look became known as the "Process Look." The guys thought it gave them a worldly image, the image of being real slick dudes who hung around in nightclubs and traveled with the fastest company. But most of them did just the opposite; they traveled with other process guys only.

My whole life at the time revolved around basketball and my family. Robert was my boyfriend; we went out on dates, and when there was nothing else to do, we'd all go hang out at the local teen-age club. Life seemed so uncomplicated, and happy, then.

As soon as the basketball season ended, I had my track stuff on, and I was running. There was a kid in school everybody called "Sundown"; the reason he was called that was because he was so black. His real name was Edward. Anyway, he and I used to skip out of classes almost every day, and we'd sneak off across the street to the municipal stadium, and we'd throw our books over the big wall that surrounded the stadium, then we'd climb the fence and run over to the track and do some running. If we heard any strange sounds, like somebody was coming, we'd run underneath the stands and hide.

Sometimes, when the college track team from Austin Peay College was using the stadium, the place would be filled with these white guys practicing. "Sundown" and I would show up out of the clear blue sky, and they would look, and sort of blink and then go back about their business. The coach of the college team, this white guy, sort of knew that I was skipping out of classes to practice running; he would give me this little wink, like he knew what was going on but like he also had a little bit of admiration for me because I was so in love with running. Whenever he talked to his team, I would sort of hang around on the fringes and listen, hoping to pick up a pointer or two for free. I think he noticed that, too, and when he saw me sort of hanging around, it always seemed he would start talking a little louder than before.

That taste of winning I had gotten the year before never left me. I was more serious about track now, thinking deep down inside that maybe I had a future in the sport if I tried hard enough. So I thought nothing of cutting classes and going out to run. But one day I got a call to report to the principal's office. I went in, and he said, "Wilma, all of us here know just how important running track is to you. We all know it, and we are all hoping that you become a big success at it. But you can't keep cutting classes and going out to run." I was, well, mortified; the principal had found me out. He finally said that if I continued cutting classes, he would have to tell my father, and I knew what that meant. So I stopped. Even so, I was the first girl out there at practice and the last one to leave, I loved it so. We had some more of those playday-type meets early that season, and I kept on winning all the races I was in. I felt unbeatable.

Then came the big meet at Tuskegee, Alabama. It was the big meet of the year. Girls from all over the South were invited down there to run, and the competition was the best for high school kids. It was a whole weekend type of thing, and they had dances and other things planned for the kids when they weren't out running. Coach Gray was going to drive us all down there to Tuskegee Institute, where the meet was held, and I remember we brought our very best dresses. We all piled into his car until

there wasn't an inch of empty space in that car. Mrs. Allison, my old teacher, came with us; she was going to chaperon us at the big dance after the meet.

All the way down to Alabama, we talked and laughed and had a good time, and Coach Gray would tell us how tough the competition was going to be, especially the girls from Atlanta, Georgia, because they had a lot of black schools down there, and they had these track programs that ran the whole year because of the warm weather. When we got there, all of us were overwhelmed, because that was the first college campus any of us ever saw. We stayed in this big dorm, and I remember just before the first competition, I started getting this nervous feeling that would stay with me for the rest of my running career. Every time before a race, I would get it, this horrible feeling in the pit of my stomach, a combination of nerves and not eating.

When we got to the track, these girls from Georgia really looked like runners, but I paid them no mind because, well, I was a little cocky. I did think I could wipe them out because, after all, I had won every single race I had ever been in up to that point. So what happens? I got wiped out. It was the absolute worst experience of my life. I did not win a single race I ran in, nor did I qualify for anything. I was totally crushed. The girls from Georgia won everything. It was the first time I had ever tasted defeat in track, and it left me a total wreck. I was so **despondent** that I refused to go to any of the activities that were planned, including the big dance. I can't remember ever being so totally crushed by anything.

On the ride back, I sat in the car and didn't say a word to anybody. I just thought to myself about how much work was ahead of me and how I would like nothing better in the whole world than to come back to Tuskegee the next year and win everything. When I got home, my father knew immediately what had happened, and he didn't say anything. Every time I used to come home after a meet, I would rush into the house all excited and

NOBODY GOES UNDEFEATED ALL THE TIME.

bubble over with, "I won . . . I won." This time I didn't say a word. I just walked in quietly, nodded to my father who was sitting there, and went into my room and unpacked.

After so many easy victories, using natural ability alone, I got a false sense of being unbeatable. But losing to those girls from Georgia, who knew every trick in the book, that was sobering. It brought me back down to earth, and it made me realize that I couldn't do it on natural ability alone, that there was more to track than just running fast. I also realized it was going to test me as a person—could I come back and win again after being so totally crushed by a defeat?

When I went back to school, I knew I couldn't continue to cut classes to practice or else I'd be in big trouble. So I would fake sickness, tell the teacher that I didn't feel well and could I please go home? They would let me go, and then I would go over to the track and run. When that stopped working, when they realized that I looked pretty good for being sick all the time, I simply asked them point-blank, "Look, could I cut this class today and go out and run?" Believe it or not, a lot of teachers said, "Okay, Wilma, go, but don't tell anybody."

I ran and ran and ran every day, and I acquired this sense of determination, this sense of spirit that I would never, never give up, no matter what else happened. That day at Tuskegee had a tremendous effect on me inside. That's all I ever thought about. Some days I just wanted to go out and die. I just moped around and felt sorry for myself. Other days I'd go out to the track with fire in my eyes, and imagine myself back at Tuskegee, beating them all. Losing as badly as I did had an impact on my personality. Winning all the time in track had given me confidence; I felt like a winner. But I didn't feel like a winner anymore after Tuskegee. My confidence was **shattered** and I was thinking the only way I could put it all together was to get back the next year and wipe them all out.

But looking back on it all, I realized somewhere along the line that to think that way wasn't necessarily right, that it was kind of extreme. I learned a very big lesson for the rest of my life as well. The lesson was, winning is great, sure, but if you are really going to do something in life, the secret is learning how to lose. Nobody goes undefeated all the time. If you can pick up after a crushing defeat, and go on to win again, you are going to be a champion someday. But if losing destroys you, it's all over. You'll never be able to put it all back together again.

I did, almost right away. There were more playdays scheduled, and I won all the rest of the races I was in the rest of that season. But I never forgot Tuskegee. In fact, I was thinking that anybody who saw me lose so badly at the meet would write me off immediately. I was wrong. One day, right after the track season ended that year, Coach Gray came over to me and he said, "Wilma, Ed Temple, the referee who is the women's track coach at Tennessee State, is going to be coming down to Clarksville to talk with your mother and father."

"What about?" I asked.

"Wilma," he said, "I think he wants you to spend the summer with him at the college, learning the **techniques** of running." ●

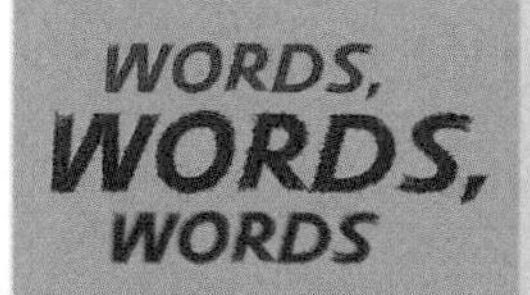

despondent: miserable and depressed
shattered: destroyed completely
techniques: ways of doing something that requires skill

Wrap-UP

Talk About It

Now that you've read "Wilma Unlimited" and "Wilma: A Valuable Lesson," what do you have to say about these questions?

- Are people's accomplishments more impressive if they have to overcome hardships first? Explain your opinion.
- Which of today's great athletes and leaders have inspired you? What are their stories?

Comprehension Check

Write your answers to the questions below. Use information from the biography and autobiography to support your answers.

1. What was Wilma's life like until she was twelve?
2. How would you describe Wilma Rudolph's character?
3. Why do you think Wilma's story has inspired so many young athletes?
4. What lesson does Wilma learn from losing at the track meet?
5. Does Wilma's voice in "Wilma: A Valuable Lesson" sound like the person described in "Wilma Unlimited"? Explain.

Vocabulary Check

Complete each sentence starter below. Before you answer, think about the meaning of the vocabulary word in bold.

1. I became **despondent** after . . .
2. If I had the chance, I would **constantly** . . .
3. One event I would really like to **attend** is . . .
4. I was **exhilarated** because . . .
5. A **lively** person is someone who . . .

Write About It

Choose one of the writing prompts below.

- Write a short article about Wilma Rudolph's performance as if you had been a reporter at the 1960 Rome Olympics.
- Write an eyewitness account of Wilma's first steps without her leg braces.
- Write about a time when a failure you experienced led to a great success. What happened?

More to READ

If you liked these selections about Wilma Rudolph, you can find out more about other inspiring female athletes in these books:

Babe Didrikson Zaharias
by Russell Freedman

Before Wilma, there was Babe. Babe Didrikson won two gold medals at the 1932 Olympics. She played baseball with the boys at a time when women did not play sports.

Jackie Joyner-Kersee
by Geri Harrington

Jackie Joyner-Kersee has also beaten the odds. In spite of her asthma, she became a four-time Olympic champion.

Gail Devers (Overcoming the Odds)
by Bill Gutman

Suffering from Graves' disease and days away from having her feet amputated, this two-time Olympic champion also knows something about making a comeback.

Consumer education

Checking a Sales Receipt

You just bought some new clothes. You can't wait to wear them. But before you leave the store, check your sales receipt carefully. Be sure you were charged correctly. Read about the store's return policy, too.

Look at the receipt below. Then answer the questions on the next page.

Max's Sales Receipt

Super Cool Clothes
555 Big Street
New York, NY 10012
Tel. (212) 555-5555
12/01/05

*** CUSTOMER ***

JEANS	49.99
BLK TNK	32.99
RED SOCKS	2 @ 6.99
SUBTOTAL	96.96
05.25 PERCENT TAX	5.10
TOTAL	102.06
CASH TD	120.00
CASH CHANGE	17.94

PLEASE RETAIN ORIGINAL RECEIPT FOR REFUND, EXCHANGE, OR STORE CREDIT. NO REFUNDS AFTER 30 DAYS.

Check each purchase. Make sure each price is correct. Make sure everything you bought is in your bag, too.

Max bought two pairs of socks at $6.99 per pair. Double this number to find out how much he spent on socks.

Most receipts state the store's return policy. Check to see how many days you have to return or exchange your purchases. Can you get a refund—or store credit only?

"Most receipts include the date you made your purchase. That information may come in handy if you want to return something. Check the date to make sure it's correct."

The Receipt's in the Bag

Stores don't make mistakes that often, but it does happen. Checking the receipt is a good way to protect yourself. Take another look at the receipt on the left and reread the tips that go with it. Then use the receipt to answer the questions below. Write your answers on your own paper.

1. Receipts often use abbreviations. "Blk tnk" stands for
a. blank turtleneck.
b. blinking track lights.
c. black turtleneck.
d. black tennis shoes.

2. What do you think the term "subtotal" means?
a. the total Max pays
b. the total change Max receives
c. the total amount of Max's purchases before sales tax was added
d. the total discount on sale items

3. How much money did Max hand over to the salesperson? How much change did he get back?

4. Which of Max's purchases were on sale?
a. all of them
b. none of them
c. only the socks
d. can't tell

5. Under which of the following circumstances could Max get back $13.98 in cash for the socks?
a. in 3 days without a receipt
b. in 20 days with a receipt
c. anytime
d. never

Write a Receipt

Create a receipt from your favorite store for the following shopping spree: $50 down jacket, $25 swimsuit, $30 ski goggles, and $10 swim goggles. The sales tax on these items is 5%.

Overcharged?

Imagine that a store charged you full price for an item that was on sale. Write a letter to the store. Tell what you want the store to do.

"You'll notice that stores usually print their phone numbers on the receipts. That way you can call the store if you need information or have a problem."

exchange: to return an item to a store and get something else
purchase: an item that has been bought
refund: money given to a customer in exchange for a returned item

magazine article

Body Bugs

Some of nature's strangest critters live on the human body. What are they, and what can you do to get rid of them?

On her twelfth birthday, Amy Wasterlain got the biggest surprise of her life. A bunch of uninvited guests were partying away on her scalp. "My head was pretty itchy," says the teen from Brooklyn, New York. "Then one of my friends saw a louse crawling on my head. We freaked!"

Amy's mom had a nurse examine Amy right away. The nurse spent more than three hours combing through Amy's long brown hair. She picked out each louse, a sesame-seed-size insect, and their tiny eggs, called nits. Many of Amy's friends were also infested. "It was a lice party!" Amy exclaims.

While no official figures are available, Amy and her friends aren't the only ones in a louse-y situation. One recent survey reports six million cases of lice, up almost 10 percent from the year before. To make matters worse, health experts worry that as the number of school cases grow, the tools designed to fight some lice aren't working. Special chemical shampoos designed to wipe some lice out aren't as effective as they used to be, experts say.

Fortunately, the head louse—also called *pediculus capitis* (peh-DIK-yoo-lus ka-PI-tis)—isn't harmful. It's simply one of dozens of parasites that call your body home. Parasites are living organisms that feed off their hosts—in this case, humans. Why are they picking on *you*?

"Your hair provides shelter, the perfect temperature and humidity, and a supply of food," says Richard Pollack, an entomologist (bug scientist). Head lice feature tiny mouthparts that dig into the scalp. "They hang out in your hair and sip a little blood every few hours," he says. Ewww!!!

What other tiny gross-outs thrive on or in your body? On the following pages, you'll meet some critters that call your body home. Don't worry. All of their pictures have been magnified.

FOLLICLE MITE

Scientific Name: *Demodex folliculorum* (DE-muh-deks fo-LIK-yoo-LO-rum)

Classification: Arachnid

Habitat: Follicles (cavities surrounding each eyelash hair); pores on forehead and nose

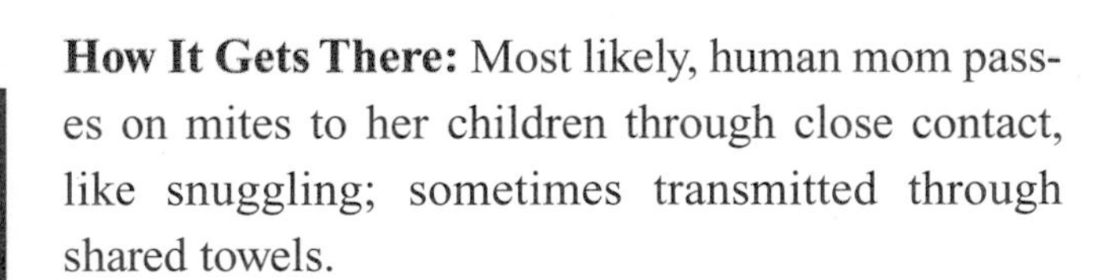

How It Gets There: Most likely, human mom passes on mites to her children through close contact, like snuggling; sometimes transmitted through shared towels.

Actual Size: 0.25 mm (0.01 in.) long, about one-quarter the size of the decimal point in 0.25

Body Count*: Too many to count

Creepy Features: Mouthparts pierce skin and feed on skin cells or oil from sweat glands.

Symptoms: Usually none; sometimes causes red, scaly, wrinkled skin

Treatments: Usually none, unless a serious case

***Body Count** is the number of bugs on an infested body.

Ask YOURSELF

- Which body bug is most gross to you? Why?

Read on and compare the shocking facts about each.

TAPEWORM

Scientific Name: *Taenia echinococcus* (TEE-nee-uh eh-kih-noh-KOH-kus)

Classification: Flatworm

Habitat: Intestinal tract and liver

How It Gets There: Tapeworm eggs are usually found in undercooked meat. When eaten, the egg hatches; larva **burrows** into intestinal lining and forms a cyst (protective sac). Digestive juices found in the stomach **stimulate** growth.

Actual Size: 13 mm (0.5 in.) to 9 m (30 ft.) long

Body Count: One or more

Creepy Features: No mouth or digestive tract; tapeworms **absorb** digested food through their body surface.

Symptoms: Often, no symptoms; sometimes abdominal pain and swelling; nausea

Treatment: Treat with a worm-killing chemical.

Science Glossary

arachnid: a class of eight-legged creatures without a backbone

classification: the assigning of objects or animals to groups and categories

habitat: a place where an animal lives

larva: an insect at the stage of development (when it looks like a worm) between an egg and a pupa

fungus: a group of organisms that has no leaves, stems, or roots

organism: a living plant or animal

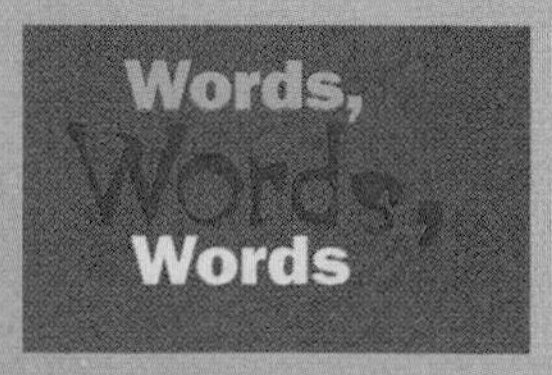

burrows: digs a tunnel or hole
stimulate: to encourage something to grow or develop
absorb: to take in

HUMAN BOTFLY

Scientific Name: *Dermatobia hominis* (der-ma-TOH-byuh HO-mih-nis)

Classification: Insect

Habitat: *Larva* (young botfly) digs into skin.

How It Gets There: Female botfly lays eggs on a mosquito's abdomen. When the mosquito sucks human blood, human body heat causes botfly eggs to hatch on skin. Larvae crawl into the fresh mosquito bite wound and mature.

Actual Size: 3 cm (1 in.) for a mature larva

Body Count: One or more

Creepy Features: Rows of spines on larva help it lodge itself mouth-first into skin. After it matures, the larva wriggles out from under the skin and drops to the ground. Adult botfly emerges and flies off.

Symptoms: Wriggling larvae cause pain under the skin. A boil-like lesion forms at the site of infestation.

Treatment: Covering area with mineral oil, turpentine, or alcohol may force larva to come out for air.

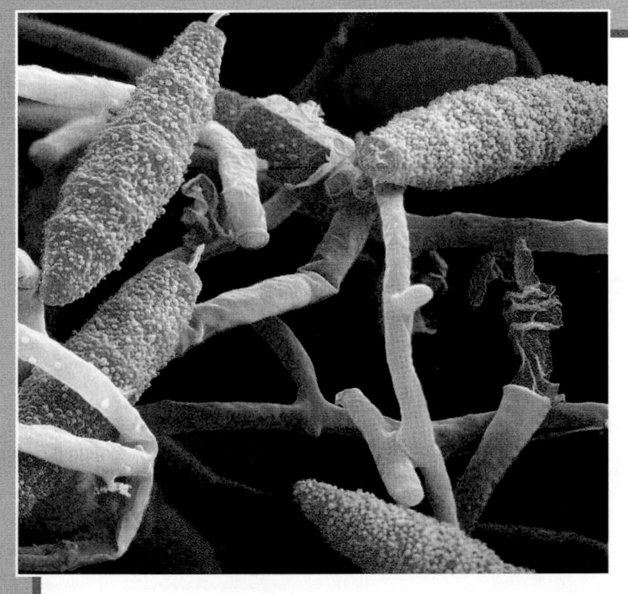

MICROSPORUM GYPSEUM

Scientific Name: *Microsporum gypseum* (my-kroh-SPO-rum JIP-sih-um)

Classification: Fungus

Habitat: Skin, scalp, nails, or forearms

How It Gets There: Transfers from soil to human; can be transmitted from infected pets to humans; occasionally passed through combs or brushes shared with infected person

Actual Size: About 3 to 3.5 microns (1 micron = 1/1,000,000 meter)

Body Count: Thousands

Creepy Features: Fungus can live on skin for years without symptoms, but stress could trigger an inflammation on skin.

Symptoms: Burning and itching; *ringworm,* a red eruption on skin that spreads out from the center

Treatment: Keep infected area clean and dry; use an antifungal treatment.

ITCH MITE

Scientific Name: *Sarcoptes scabiei* (sar-KOP-tis SCAY-be-eye)

Classification: Arachnid

Habitat: Burrows in skin, mostly on fingers, wrists, ankles, elbows, and abdomen

How It Gets There: Close human contact

Actual Size: About 250 to 450 microns

Body Count: Few to hundreds

Creepy Features: Skin-melting *enzymes* (proteins) help the mite burrow through top skin layers and irritate the area with feces and saliva.

Symptoms: Causes an itchy, red, raised rash on skin. Intense itching about one month after **infestation;** scratching can worsen infection.

Treatment: See dermatologist. Treat with **prescription** or over-the-counter lotions containing special chemicals.

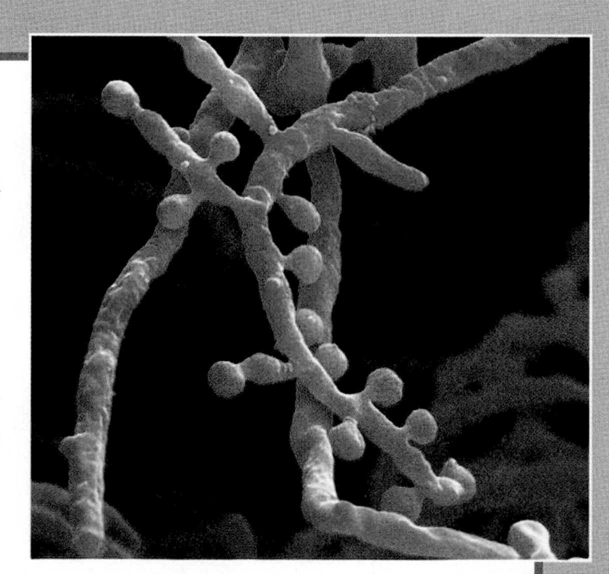

ATHLETE'S FOOT FUNGUS

Scientific Name: *Trichophyton mentagrophytes* (try-koh-FY-ton men-ta-GROH-fy-tis)

Classification: Fungus

Habitat: Most often found in feet

How It Gets There: Walking barefoot on **moist** floors of bathroom and swimming areas; infected skin flakes in shared socks and shoes

Actual Size: About 3 to 3.5 microns

Body Count: Thousands

Creepy Features: Can grow to about an inch or two in 10 to 14 days

Symptoms: Reddish eruption followed by cracked skin

Treatment: Use an antifungal treatment.

HEAD LOUSE

Scientific Name: *Pediculus capitis* (peh-DIK-yoo-lus ka-PI-tis)

Classification: Insect

Habitat: Human hair and scalp

How It Gets There: Hair-to-hair contact; sometimes through shared brushes, hair accessories, and hats

Actual Size: 3 mm (0.12 in.) long as adults

Body Count: From one to more than 100

Creepy Features: Six legs with claws to cling to human hair; mouthparts specialized for sucking human blood

Symptoms: Itching and irritation

Treatment: Comb hair daily for more than two weeks with special louse or nit comb. Use over-the-counter lice-killing shampoos for two treatments about eight to ten days apart. Some lice may be resistant to shampoo. ●

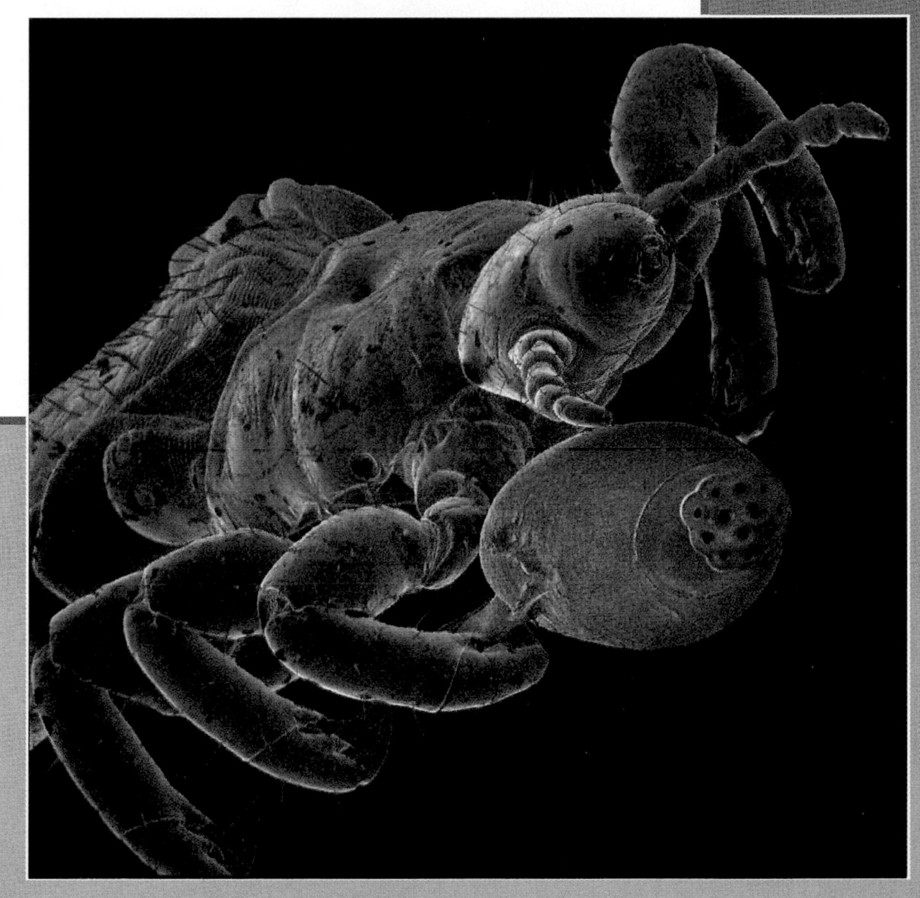

YOURSELF

- Which body bug can you get from eating undercooked meat?

Go back and reread the section "How It Gets There" for each bug.

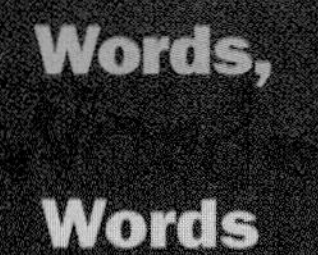

Words, Words

infestation: an object or place that is full of insects
prescription: medicine that is ordered by a doctor
moist: slightly wet

HOT JOB

Photo "Bug" Lady

The story you just read contains some amazing photographs of bugs that live on the human body. Some of those photographs were taken by Darlyne Murawski. Darlyne is a biologist and nature photographer. She works anywhere bugs can be found, including the human body. How did she get into her unusual career? What does she have to do to get the teeny-tiny bugs to look as big as they do in the pictures you see? Why does she love her job? Read the interview to find out.

How did you first get into bugs?

It started when I was very young. I was perhaps five. I was with my mother at our family doctor's office. He had lots of books. One was about tropical parasites. It had lots of really weird pictures of critters: tapeworms, botflies, and other insects that live on the human body. I was hooked!

What schools did you go to?

I earned a master's degree at the Art Institute of Chicago and a Ph.D. in biology at the University of Texas. As a grad student, I researched butterflies in Costa Rican rain forests.

How did you become a photo "bug"?

My parents bought me my first box camera when I was ten. I've been taking pictures ever since.

How do you photograph tiny bugs?

I attach special "macro" lenses to my camera to magnify bugs so you can see fine details. Or I shoot with a camera attached to a microscope. (A microscope can make bugs look thousands of times bigger than they really are.) I have to be careful, though; shine too much light on them and the bugs fry.

Who do you work for?

I'm a freelancer and work for lots of different people. Mostly, I work for *National Geographic*. But I also work for other magazines. I'm developing three books right now. One is for children.

How much do photographers like yourself make?

Nature photographers can earn up to $500 a day when they work.

How do you get an assignment?

First, I come up with a story idea. Then I sell the idea to a magazine. The story has to be fascinating to readers in some way. If the subject is tapeworms, you want to tell something interesting about tapeworms, not just that they are yucky and disgusting. That's where I draw on my biology background.

What qualities does a nature photographer need to have?

Tons of patience. Bugs don't do what you want them to right away. When I was photographing butterflies for *National Geographic* I wanted to show them fighting, which they actually do. So I sat day after day with my cameras and flashes ready, waiting for that to happen. I took a lot of pictures, hoping to get that one shot. My patience paid off.

Do bugs ever give you the creeps?

When I photographed *follicle mites*—insects that live on our pores—I scraped my forehead with a bobby pin to get a sample. When I looked under the microscope, there they were! I scratched myself a lot after that. *To look at Darlyne's buggy photos, see pp. 268 and 273.*

What's the most amazing experience you've ever had as a nature photographer?

One time I was trying to photograph a bola spider fooling the moths that it eats. To attract moths, the spider emits an odor like a female moth. A male moth will come in thinking he's going to find a female. Instead the spider grabs him! I was waiting absolutely still, high up in a tree for hours for this to happen. All of a sudden an owl comes up next to me. He sat and waited with me, about three feet away. Until the owl arrived, it had been lonely up there. It's little things like that that make my work great for me.

Do you have any advice for future bug lovers?

If you love bugs, study them and stick with it. Biologists really enjoy their work. ●

Wrap-Up

Talk About It

Now that you've read "Body Bugs" and "Hot Job: Photo 'Bug' Lady," what do you have to say about these questions?

- Why do you think people are grossed out by body bugs?
- How important is it to do something you love for a living?

Comprehension Check

Write your answers to the questions below. Use information from the article and career profile to support your answers.

1. What are three different bugs that can live on the human body?
2. Why do most body bugs require treatment?
3. Which body bug would be the worst to get? Why?
4. How did Darlyne become interested in bug science?
5. Which of the body bugs does Darlyne have? How do you know?

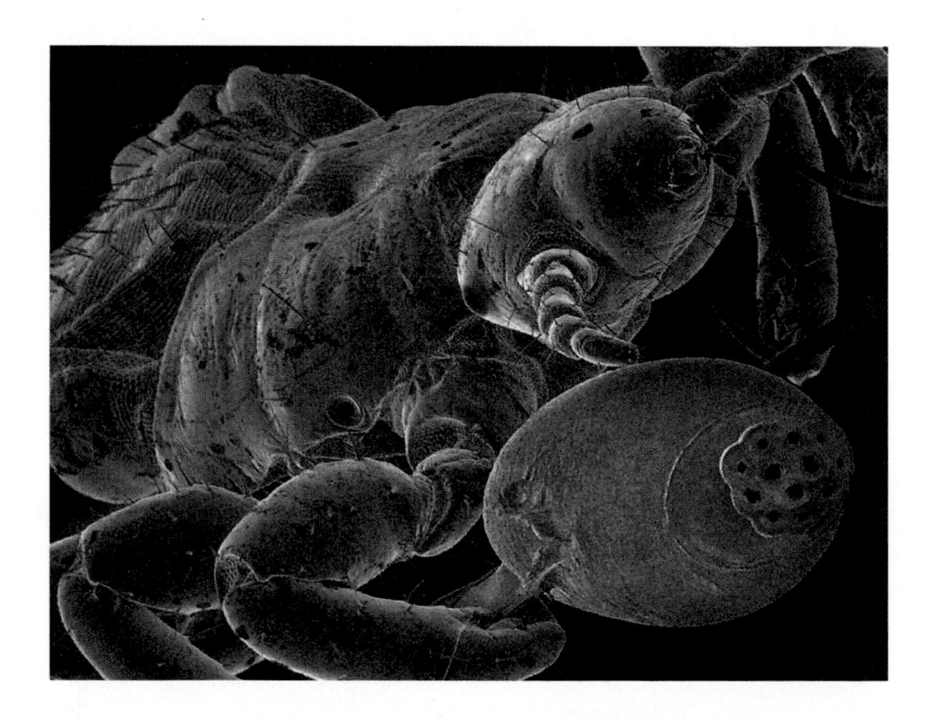

Vocabulary Check

Complete each sentence with the correct vocabulary word.

burrows **stimulate** **absorb**
moist **prescription**

1. On cold mornings, my little brother _______ under the covers.
2. After school I had to stop at the drugstore to pick up some _______ medicine.
3. If you drink plenty of water, your lips will stay _______, instead of getting dry and cracked.
4. Dry skin can _______ a lot of lotion.
5. Word games and puzzles can _______ your mind.

Write About It

Choose one of the writing prompts below.

- Write instructions telling people what to do if they get body bugs (choose three).
- Write a story about invading a human body from one of the body bug's point of view.
- Write a short biography of Darlyne Murawski based on her career profile.

More to READ

If you want to learn more about bugs (the grosser the better!), check out these books:

Ugly Bugs
by Nick Arnold

Have you ever wondered what slugs do with their slime? Or how insects drink your blood? Or what kind of creepy crawlies are hiding behind your wallpaper? This book will reveal the ugly truth about some ugly bugs.

Bizarre Insects
by Margaret Jean Anderson

Welcome to the private world of insects! Find out how everyday insects like houseflies and beetles really look—and behave. You may never hear the buzz of a fly again without shivering.

Bugs in 3-D
by Mark Blum

The creepiest, crawliest, and hairiest bugs are featured in this amazing collection. All sorts of tiny monsters loom into view with fascinating and alarming detail in this 3-D experience.

information searching

Understanding Nutrition Labels

You're training for a sport, or maybe you just want to be healthier. You need to take a look at what you eat. Are you making healthful choices? Food labels can help you find out.

Check out these nutrition labels from some typical snacks. Do they make sense?

Food Labels

"Serving size" is the amount normally consumed by one person. The nutrition facts apply to a single serving.

NUTTY CANDY

Ingredients: milk chocolate (sugar, cocoa butter, chocolate, lactose, skim milk, milkfat, soy lecithin, artificial flavor). Peanuts, corn syrup, sugar, skim milk, butter, milkfat, partially hydrogenated soybean oil, lactose, salt, egg whites, soy protein, artificial flavor.

Nutrition Facts Serv size: 1 bar. Amount per serving: **Calories** 280, **Fat Cal.** 130, **Total Fat** 14g (22% DV), **Sat. Fat** 5g (25% DV), **Cholest.** 5mg (2% DV), **Sodium** 140mg (6%DV), **Total Carb.** 35g (12% DV), **Fiber** 1g (4%DV), **Sugars** 30g, **Protein** 4g, Vitamin A (0% DV), Vitamin C (0% DV), Calcium (4% DV), Iron (2% DV)
Percent Daily Values (DV) are based on a 2,000 calorie diet.

TWISTED PRETZELS

Nutrition Facts
Serving size: 1 oz
(28g/About 12 pretzels)
Servings Per Container 6

Amount Per Serving
Calories 110 Calories from Fat 0

	% Daily Value*
Total Fat 0g	0%
Saturated Fat 0g	0%
Cholesterol 0mg	0%
Sodium 520 mg	22%
Total Carbohydrate 24g	8%
Dietary Fiber 1g	4%
Sugars less than 1g	
Protein 2g	

Vitamin A 0% Vitamin C 0%
Calcium 2% Iron 10%

* Percent Daily Values are based on a 2,000 calorie diet. Your daily values may be higher or lower depending on your calorie needs.

Ingredients: Enriched Flour (Wheat Flour, Niacin, Reduced Iron, Thiamin Mononitrate, Riboflavin, Foilic Acid), Corn Syrup, Salt, Vegetable Oil, (Contains One or More of the Following: Partially Hydrogenated (Soybean or Corn) Oil), Yeast, Malt Extract, Sodium Bicarbonate, Ammonium Bicarbonate, and Artificial Flavor.

Nutrition Facts
Serv. size: 8 fl. oz (240 ml)
Servings Per Container 8

Amount Per Serving
Calories 110 Calories from Fat 0
100% Pure Orange Juice

	% Daily Value*
	0%
Total Fat 0g	2%
Sodium 0 mg	13%
Potassium 450 mg	9%
Total Carbohydrate 26g	
Sugars 22g	
Protein 2g	

Vitamin C 120%		**Calcium**	2%
Thiamin	10%	**Niacin**	4%
Vitamin B6		**Foliate**	15%

Not a significant source of saturated fat, cholesterol, dietary fiber, vitamin A and Iron.

* Percent Daily Values are based on a 2,000 calorie diet.

INGREDIENT: ORANGE JUICE

XLCola

Nutrition Facts
Serv size: 1 Can

Amount Per Serving:
Calories 140

	% Daily Value*
Total Fat 0g	0%
Sodium 50g	2%
Total Carb. 39g	13%
Sugars 39g	
Protein 0g	

* Percent Daily Values are based on a 2,000 calorie diet.

Ingredients: carbonated water, high fructose corn syrup and/or sucrose, caramel color, phosphoric acid, natural flavors, caffeine.

These are the ingredients in the product. The first item on the list is the one that there is the most of in the product.

A healthful diet includes certain amounts of stuff like sugar, fat, and protein. This number tells what percent of a healthful daily intake this food supplies.

"The g's on the labels stand for gram. How much is a gram? A medium-sized paper clip weighs about one gram."

Eat, Drink, and Be Healthy

It's time for a snack. What's it going to be? Review the labels and the tips. Then use them to answer the questions below. Write your answers on your own paper.

1. You're thirsty. You'd like to add protein to your diet, but you want to add as little sugar as possible. Which drink is the better choice for you?
   a. XL Juice
   b. XL Cola

2. Which ingredient does XL Cola have the most of?
   a. corn syrup
   b. juice
   c. carbonated water

3. How many total fat grams are there in one serving of
   a. XL Juice?
   b. Nutty Candy?
   c. Twisted Pretzels?

4. How many servings are there in a container of Twisted Pretzels? About how many pretzels are in each serving?

5. If you were on a low-sodium diet, which would be the worse snack for you?
   a. Twisted Pretzels
   b. Nutty Candy

Look It Up

These words often appear on food labels: **calcium, carbohydrates, cholesterol, fat, fiber, protein,** and **sodium.** Split this list with a partner. Look up your half in the dictionary. Then explain each term to your partner.

Have a Snack

Collect labels from two of your favorite snacks. Then create a chart. Make columns with these labels: fat, sodium, protein, sugar, fiber, calcium, Vitamin A, and Vitamin C. Fill in the columns with the information from your labels.

"Want to know more about food labels? Go to the Web site of the Food and Drug Administration. You can find it at http://vm.cfsan.fda.gov/label.html"

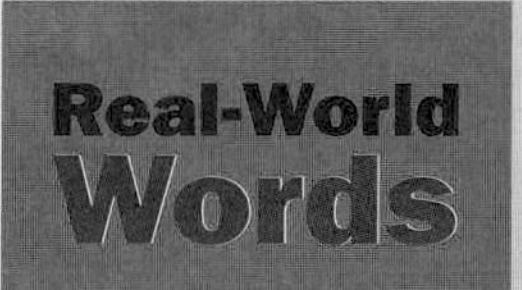

consumed: eaten or drunk
nutrition: the fuel that you provide your body in the form of food and drink
vitamin: one of many natural substances that make your body run

journal

WITHIN

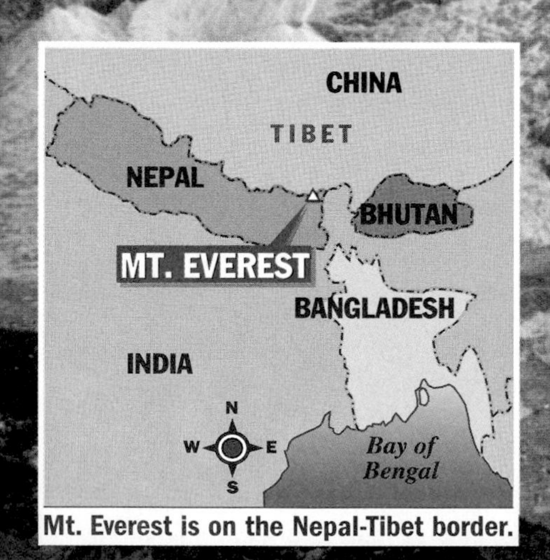

Mt. Everest is on the Nepal-Tibet border.

REACH

My Everest Story

Mark Pfetzer is trying to become the youngest person ever to climb Mount Everest.

But Everest is a mountain that kills.

from the book by
Mark Pfetzer and Jack Galvin

In May 1996, Mark Pfetzer, then 16, stood near the top of Mount Everest. He was determined to become the youngest person ever to climb Everest, the world's highest mountain.

Mark had dreamed of conquering Everest since he was 12. To prepare himself for the tough, dangerous climb, he worked out constantly, learned mountaineering skills, and climbed whenever he got the chance. Mark scaled the highest peaks of Peru, Tanzania, and Equador. He also took on the toughest mountains closer to his home in Massachusetts. Mark's family isn't rich, but he didn't let a lack of money keep him from reaching his dreams. He found corporate sponsors to fund his climbs.

On those days in May, Mark was more than 20,000 feet up on Everest. He was making his way up the mountain from Base Camp to Camps One, Two, and

Three. Within the next couple of days he'd attempt the summit—the top of the mountain. But as he and his Sherpa friend, Jabion, readied themselves for the final climb, a frightening storm began. Mark, sick and disoriented after weeks in the thin mountain air, looked up. He wondered if he'd make it to the top.

Then he remembered that two other teams—led by Rob Hall and Scott Fischer—had started for the summit that morning. Would they make it down in the perilous storm?

The following selection from Mark's autobiography, *Within Reach: My Everest Story,* tells what happened. It is written in the form of journal entries.

GLOSSARY

peak: the pointed top of a mountain

spur: a ridge sticking out of the main part of a mountain

crampon: a spiked iron plate worn on boots to prevent slipping on ice or snow

crevasse: a deep crack in a mountain

gust: a strong, sudden blast of wind

windchill: the temperature felt on the body that is a combination of temperature and wind speed

May 8, 1996

Through the Icefall to Camp One, then to Camp Two. A clear, beautiful day. So calm the mountain is silent, so clear and warm it's driving me crazy. A perfect day to summit. Wasted.

But it feels so good to be moving. I've been at Base Camp since May 4, which is too much time to sit around. If my mom and Carrie weren't there to talk to, I know I'd spend too much time sorting through my stuff, repacking, double checking, listening to music, getting anxious. I don't think I'm going to fall. And I certainly don't think I'm going to die. I have confidence in my climbing skills. You have to. Otherwise forget it. You can't fake it.

I get anxious because I've been too healthy; should have gotten sick earlier in the trip, gotten it out of my system. I have a cold now, and it's getting worse by the hour—a persistent cough, with a lot of phlegm not like last year's cough, which was a dry hack. But I'm strong after all that sitting in Base Camp.

May 9, 1996

On the way to Camp Three, I get some good video of the steep Lhotse Face. The camera is a definite burden, but I'm still trying to get some of the shots the crew wants.

A rescue team brings an injured climber down past Jabion and me. His only mistakes were to climb out of his tent at Camp Three unroped and to forget how steep the terrain was, which is easy to do when your brain's not working very well due to lack of **oxygen** and **fatigue.** He slid hundreds of feet down the angled ice. He's not expected to live.

May 10, 1996

Jabion and I are working our way up the Geneva Spur and across the yellow band of rock to Camp Four (the last stop before the summit). Suddenly we are belted with an unexpected force of wind and snow. What was up to now difficult and uncomfortable takes on a new component: danger.

Every step now becomes a triumph, every minute to Camp Four increasingly painful. In the late afternoon, the wind howls through a snowstorm so intense the snow feels like a solid wall. We manage to stumble toward the faint yellow glow of the lights coming from the tents at Camp Four.

The night goes on, and we have no idea what may be happening outside. . . . Anyone stuck out there will have at least nine more hours of pitch dark, snow driven winds over a hundred miles an hour, and windchill near a hundred below. We doze, we eat, we drink,

and slowly all the **inevitable** questions seep in. Is this just one storm? Has the window of opportunity closed? Are there people hurt? Dead? None of us huddled in our tent know the answers.

I begin to feel my cough steal away more and more of my strength. I have to summit soon, before I lose my strength. We're so close—within reach—and all we can do is hang on to this scab of rocks, 26,000 feet up, and hope that daylight will give us new hope to reach our goal.

ASK YOURSELF

- What are the important events of this climb so far?

Reread the first three journal entries and make a list.

May 11, 1996

Pasang, one of the Sherpas, looks out of the tent, sees a star. He immediately shoves his stuff into his rucksack and is gone into the thundering wind. Jabion says, "Bad luck to see a star that bright in morning." He may be right. Jabion, Graham, and I decide to go down too. . . .

[Mark has decided against summitting in the storm, but going back down the mountain is dangerous as well.]

I get out of the tent, feeling very spaced out and weak after coughing all night, struggling to get my backpack and oxygen mask on. Have to rest after each effort.

Words, WORDS, Words

oxygen: a colorless gas found in the air
fatigue: great tiredness
inevitable: sure to happen

Shocked to see Pete Athans, one of the best climbers, coming up the mountain. "Rob Hall's still up there," he says. I look up and see in the early light, a string of black dots working up the slope. It's a rescue team. Pete says, "At least nine people are missing." Pete is amazingly strong to go up in that storm. I stand watching him for a moment. Nine people? Who?

I look up the mountain, imagine trying to grope through a whiteout with dark coming on, imagine trying to find our tents, the smallest possible needle in the huge haystack of Everest, especially when your brain can hardly function, and I realize how lucky I was to be in a tent.

Jabion and I go back over the Geneva Spur, fighting the wind for balance on each rocky step. How strong that wind is, trying to pluck us off the mountain with one gust, trying to flatten us with the next. And then, once across, we round a corner and are suddenly wind free, protected by the spur we just traversed. . . .

Lack of appetite and coughing have weakened me to the point that I can only take about ten steps before I have to rest. Jabion stays with me, and it's very slow going. In fact, a group of climbers from Scott Fischer's team pass me. They look awful, in much worse shape than I am. They tell me they had been caught by the storm, were lucky to make it back to camp. And then one guy tells me Scott is dead. One of the best in the world, a climber who's survived some terrible situations, has died. . . .

The route from Base Camp to the summit.

When Jabion and I get to Camp Three, Fischer's team have already set their backpacks into the **steep** slope and are sitting on them in the sun. They have just lost their great friend and leader, are lucky to be alive themselves, and they just sit there, numb. . . . I just can't talk right now. Neither can they. We all just sit there a while, hacking. . . .

I load up all my equipment: sleeping bag, clothes, oxygen tank, accessories, and the video camera, and start to leave Camp Three. . . .

I tell Jabion to go ahead. I'll go down myself. Let momentum pull me. Hold on to rope, slide down. Rest. I meet David Breashears going up for rescue. He congratulates me. My legs are cramping, my eyes hurt, the roof of my mouth is burned, I'm coughing, my back hurts from the heavy pack, and I'm so weak I can walk only ten steps before resting. Congratulations? He must think I summitted. "I didn't summit," I mumble.

"So what," he says. "You're alive." And takes off.

I watch him go and think: He's right. Don't feel sorry for yourself. You wanted to be here. Your **pilgrimage.** And you are still alive. So pay attention and get down the mountain!

That's what I do. I pay attention. Even though I'm really scared for the first time, with crevasses everywhere, alone, unroped, fatigued. I won't let Scott Fischer into my mind. I won't think about falling. I won't panic. I go fast. I have to get to Camp Two. . . .

I send a message to my mom to let her know I'm OK, crawl into my sleeping bag, and go to sleep.

ASK YOURSELF

- What do you think will happen to Mark on his way back down Everest?

Think about what you know about the setting and the story events to make a prediction.

May 12, 1996

For a while everything seems normal, as if all those people hadn't died, as if no one was missing, as if the horrible night had never happened. Maybe that's what people do when someone dies—maybe they still laugh and kid around. That's what seems to be happening here. We're ignoring death.

Halfway across a crevasse in the Icefall, my crampon gets stuck on a ladder. It's a wide, very deep crevasse, spanned by three ladders tied together. That's the problem. I wedge the back edge of my crampon into the overlap of two rungs. It won't budge. Kind of **symbolic** of this trip. Get stuck in Camp Four very near the summit, now stuck in the Icefall, with Base Camp within sight. My weak condition makes it worse, of course, but it's tricky enough. I'm on a swaying ladder. Kami, our lead Sherpa, who has caught up to me, cannot come out and free me, because the ladder might pull away from its anchor with the weight of the two of us and send us both down into a crevasse that seems to go all the way to Kathmandu.

Finally, I take the crampon off and just leave it there. When I get off the ladder, Kami tries to work it free. One little nudge from him and it goes flying down onto an ice ledge about twenty feet down, leaving me to slip and slide the rest of the way down.

Once into Base Camp, reality roars back. My mother finds me, gives me a big hug, blurts out, "Thank God. You're alive!" She hadn't known if I was safe or not during the storm—she hadn't eaten or slept at all for two days. She and my sister Carrie wandered from camp to camp, their hopes rising and falling with each rumor. Someone would tell her I was dead, then someone would tell her I was alive.

Elated after finally learning I was OK, she and Carrie were saddened again when they listened, as so many did in Base Camp, to Rob Hall speak his last words to his wife on the phone.

Rob had stayed near the summit to help one of his climbers, Doug Hansen. Both were far beyond the reach of any rescue. After Doug died, Rob lived long enough to radio down to Base Camp and ask to speak to his wife in New Zealand.

I want to respond to my mother's sense of relief, to her happiness, to her running around and getting me hot drinks and food, but I can't. I have little to say. I'm far too numbed by fatigue and my cough to think of anything but sleep. No food. Just a little water and sleep.

May 14, 1996

I am talking to Morton Dean of *Good Morning America;* we are live across the United States. He's asking me about surviving the storm, about the temperatures and winds, and what I know. ABC wants me because I am the youngest climber, but they should get someone who knows more. I tell him I'm not sure of the temperature; I was in a tent and didn't see most of the problems, and even now I'm not sure of the final death toll. I'm distracted during our phone call because I don't want to be here. I want to be at a memorial service for Scott Fischer, which is being held as I talk. The whole Base Camp is there for a great guy and climber, but because we had technical problems, my call was delayed, and now I'm on the phone saying stupid things like "Yeah. It was very cold and windy up there."

Words, WORDS, Words

steep: sharply sloping up or down
pilgrimage: a long journey in search of something
symbolic: serving as a symbol of something

As I talk, I can picture our crew standing in the afternoon sun, the wind blowing their hair, everyone battle weary—Sherpas, climbers, support people—all together. I'm battle weary, too—in a tent reporting back to headquarters about this great battle that the enemy won, which left some scarred, some dead, all of us shaken.

Maybe it's appropriate that I get stuck with a media problem—the kid who gets all the publicity because he's so young and his parents must be irresponsible to let him climb the world's highest mountain. But I'm not one of the dead climbers, or even one of the frostbitten ones. And I know I'll be back next year. They say you always make it on the third try. Most people learn how to acclimate, to be patient, and they summit on the third try.

Next spring for me. The magic of the third try.

When I finish talking to *Good Morning America,* I realize that the phone I've been using in the tent is the one used to get Rob Hall's final call to his wife just before he died. It's hard to think anything positive about Everest right now, a force that tricks people into tranquil sunshine, then smacks them with a killer wind. Enemy. That's all I can think of. An enemy I want to get away from.

Epilogue:

Mark and everyone in his climbing team made it down the mountain alive. He was very disturbed by the deaths on Everest. He was also saddened by the death of his father, one of his biggest supporters, from cancer in July 1997. But he hasn't let the disaster or his personal loss stop him from pursuing his goal. He's started training and plans to climb Everest again in the spring of 2000.

Here's Mark's advice for young people with equally big goals:

"No matter how may reps it takes, no matter how many stairs I have to run, I'm going to reach my goal. Every kid has the same chance—but too many of us think we have so much time ahead, we kill off the present. I see a lot of guys my age putting themselves into the future, always saying 'Can't wait till I get my license,' or 'Can't wait till I get out of high school,' or 'Can't wait till I get away from home.' The whole time they're idling like a car at a stoplight. . . . Then when the light finally changes, they're not used to moving.

The point is that I'm heading somewhere. Just as in mountain climbing, I'll put one foot in front of the other and keep going. Always climbing, training, exploring new ways to challenge myself.

"I think my father would be proud."

FAST FACTS: TOP OF THE WORLD

Sir Edmund Hillary and Tenzing Norgay

- Mount Everest is part of the Himalaya mountain chain.
- The summit of Everest rises 29,028 feet above sea level.
- Sir Edmund Hillary of New Zealand, and Sherpa Tenzing Norgay of Nepal, were the first to climb Everest on May 29, 1953.
- Since then, nearly 800 people have reached the summit.
- Nearly 150 people have died trying to reach the summit.
- Temperatures near Everest's summit can reach 100 degrees below zero. Winds can reach 150 miles per hour.

Once, only the world's best climbers tried to scale the world's highest mountain. Today, anyone with enough money to hire a guide can give Mount Everest a try. Every year, more and more people do just that. That's good for the economies of Nepal and Tibet, where Everest is located. But it may not be so good for the mountain. It's littered with trash. What's more, inexperienced climbers are putting themselves and their guides in danger. Many are dying. Some people say inexperienced climbers should be banned from Everest. Others say the mountain should be open to anyone who can afford the trek.

What do you think? Read this debate and decide for yourself.

yes

Climbing the world's highest mountain is the ultimate physical challenge. Anyone who feels up to it has the right to try. Of course it's a risk. But where would we be today if everybody always decided to play it safe?

As for the all the litter, climbers are taking steps to clean up the mountain. Many groups make it a goal to take some trash away when they leave.

And don't forget about Tibet and Nepal. Both countries are very poor. They really need the money they make selling climbing permits and assisting climbers. Don't limit human achievement. Keep Everest open to everyone!

If you said yes:

- How can deaths by inexperienced climbers and their guides be prevented?

no

Only expert climbers belong on Everest. Now that anyone with some cash can climb, record numbers of climbers are dying. At one point, Everest got so crowded that some people died because they couldn't get down quickly enough.

Today, climbers who pay big money expect to reach the summit. Guides feel pressured to keep going even when the weather is bad and ill-prepared clients have trouble.

What's more, the mountain itself is littered with empty oxygen tanks and garbage. It's time to set some limits. There are just too many people on Everest!

If you said no:

- What about the Sherpas of Tibet and Nepal who depend on climbers to make a living?

What's your point of view?

Talk About It

Now that you've read *Within Reach* and "Should Inexperienced Climbers Be Allowed To Scale Mount Everest?" what do you have to say about these questions?

- Mark Pfetzer's personal "pilgrimage" was climbing Mount Everest. What might your personal "pilgrimage" be?
- Would you risk your life to fulfill a dream like climbing Mount Everest? Explain your answer.

Comprehension Check

Write your answers to the questions below. Use information from the reading to support your answers.

1. Why do Mark and Jabion decide not to attempt to summit?
2. Why is Mark so disappointed that he didn't summit?
3. What do you think drives people to attempt difficult physical challenges like climbing Mount Everest?
4. Why do some people believe that not just anyone should be allowed to climb Everest?
5. Where do you think Mark Pfetzer would stand on the Everest debate?

Vocabulary Check

Complete each sentence with the correct vocabulary word.

inevitable **pilgrimage** **fatigue**
steep **oxygen**

1. I felt overcome by _______ after the tough workout the coach gave us.
2. The clouds grew dark and thick, and rain seemed _______.
3. We went on a _______ from store to store, looking for a perfect gift.
4. The hill was so _______ that I had to get off my bike and walk.
5. In science class today we learned that there isn't any _______ in outer space.

Write About It

Choose one of the writing prompts below.

- Write a journal entry as if you were Mark's mother, waiting at base camp for Mark to return.
- Write a short essay explaining your opinion about who should be allowed to climb Mount Everest. Give reasons to support your opinion.
- Create copy for six signs that might be posted along the way to Everest's peak. On them, include safety tips or other reminders.

Fact FILE

May 10, 1996, was one of the deadliest days in Mount Everest's history. Eight climbers died on the mountain that day. They were killed by a sudden storm that no one had predicted. Was it poor judgment from oxygen-starved minds? Or was there really no way to tell that this killer storm was coming? The question remains.

If you're interested in learning more, the disaster is well documented. Other climbers on the mountain that day included a journalist, Jon Krakauer, and a moviemaker, David Breashears. They both survived. Krakauer wrote a book about the tragedy called *Into Thin Air*, and Breashears made an IMAX movie called *Everest*. Both of these works created interest in the debate over whether just anyone should be allowed to climb the world's tallest mountain.

Check out the book or catch the movie to learn more about that deadly day on Everest.

Planning a Budget

You have a new job, and you can't wait to get your first paycheck. What will you do with the money? Make sure expenses are covered before you spend money for fun. Making a budget will help you to spend your money wisely.

Take a look at the budget below. Are you ready to be a smart spender?

Nola's Weekly Budget

When you get a paycheck, the government takes money out for taxes. Your net income is what's left.

"Fixed expenses" are things you must pay for. "Flexible expenses" are fun things you don't really have to spend money on.

What if you want to buy something one paycheck can't cover? Set aside a little money each week.

WEEKLY NET INCOME	
net income	$75
FIXED EXPENSES	
bus fare (to and from work), 4 times a week; $1 each way	8
$2.50 for lunch, 5 times a week	12.50
total fixed expenses	$20.50
FLEXIBLE EXPENSES	
one CD	16
fast food with friends	6
one movie ticket and popcorn	9
total flexible expenses	$31
WEEKLY SAVINGS	
new bike (total: $190)	10
end-of-school class trip (total: $150)	10
general savings	3.50
total savings	$23.50

"Making a budget will help you keep track of your money. You'll be able to see where you're spending too much, or where you can cut corners when you need to."

Dollars and "Sense"

You can't wait to go on a shopping spree. But before you spend all your hard-earned dollars, make sure your fixed expenses are covered. How do you do that? Reread the budget and the tips that go with it. Then use them to answer the questions. Write your answers on your own paper.

1. Which of the following is true about Nola's weekly income?
  a. She makes $75 a week before taxes are taken out.
  b. She makes $75 a week after taxes are taken out.
  c. She makes $20.50 a week after taxes are taken out.
  d. Her income is not taxed.

2. How much money is left in Nola's budget after she has paid for all of her necessary expenses?
  a. $3.50 **c.** $54.50
  b. $20.50 **d.** $75

3. How much does Nola spend on the following items?
  a. one regular lunch?
  b. one movie ticket and popcorn?
  c. bus fare for one day?

4. Two really great movies came out this week. Nola wants to see them both, but she also wants to have at least $23.50 left for savings. How would you recommend that she cut her expenses?

5. Nola worked some extra hours, so her paycheck is larger than usual this week. Should she save the extra money or find something fun to spend it on? Explain your answer.

Just Save It!

Everyone says, "Save, save, save." But why? List three good reasons that a person should save money.

Plan Your Budget

Do you work or get an allowance? What is your weekly net income? What are your fixed expenses? What else do you spend money on? Plan a weekly budget for yourself. Suppose you want to save money. Which expenses could you cut?

"Many computer programs have a function that allows you to make and keep a budget."

Real-World Words

expenses: items or services that cost money
income: money you earn or receive
taxes: money paid to support a government

A GRAPHIC CLASSIC BY
ADAM GRANT AND TERRY M. WEST

BASED ON THE NOVEL BY
JULES VERNE

What will the future be like? What new inventions will people use? Many science fiction writers have tried to answer these questions. One of the most famous was Jules Verne. He had an amazing ability to dream up the right answers.

About 100 years ago, Verne wrote ***20,000 Leagues Under the Sea.*** It told of a crazed inventor named Captain Nemo.

Nemo built an amazing ship that could travel undersea. On board there were many inventions. There was a tank that let the crew breathe underwater. There was a machine that made electricity.

At the time, Nemo's inventions were just dreams. Now they're real.

I'VE TRIED TO TELL MANY PEOPLE THIS STORY. BUT NO ONE WILL BELIEVE ME. MAYBE YOU WILL. IT ALL STARTED A FEW YEARS AGO. I WAS A PROFESSOR. I WAS AN EXPERT ON THE OCEANS. I HAD A LOYAL HELPER NAMED CONSEIL....
Good morning, Professor Aronnax. I have your mail.
Good morning, Conseil. Did you read the newspapers today? Another ship has been sunk. That's the third one this week!

ASK YOURSELF

- What is Professor Aronnax planning to do?

Think about the problem he has been asked to solve.

WE SEARCHED FOR MONTHS AND MONTHS.

BUT WE FOUND NOTHING.

FINALLY, ONE DAY, OUR CAPTAIN SPOKE TO THE CREW.
We must head for home—

JUST THEN ONE OF THE MEN, NED LAND, SPOTTED SOMETHING IN THE WATER.
Ahoy!!! It's the monster!!!
Men, get ready!

ASK YOURSELF

- What kind of monster do you think this might be?

Clues from the illustrations can help you figure this out.

THEN THE BEAST RUSHED AT US. IT HIT US VERY HARD. CONSEIL, NED, AND I FELL OUT OF THE SHIP.

I AWOKE IN THE OCEAN. I SAW OUR SHIP SAILING AWAY WITHOUT US. THEY HAD NOT SEEN US FALL OVERBOARD.
Help! Help! Come back!
Try to be calm, Professor!

THEN WE HEARD A VOICE. IT WAS NED.
Conseil! Professor! Up here!

You won't believe it. But this whale is made of iron! Come aboard.
Ned, have you killed the whale?
It looks like some kind of underwater ship! I've never seen one like it!

Who are you people?
A MOMENT LATER, A DOOR OPENED. A CREW OF MEN CAME OUT.

THEY FORCED US INTO THE SHIP ...
Get your hands off me!

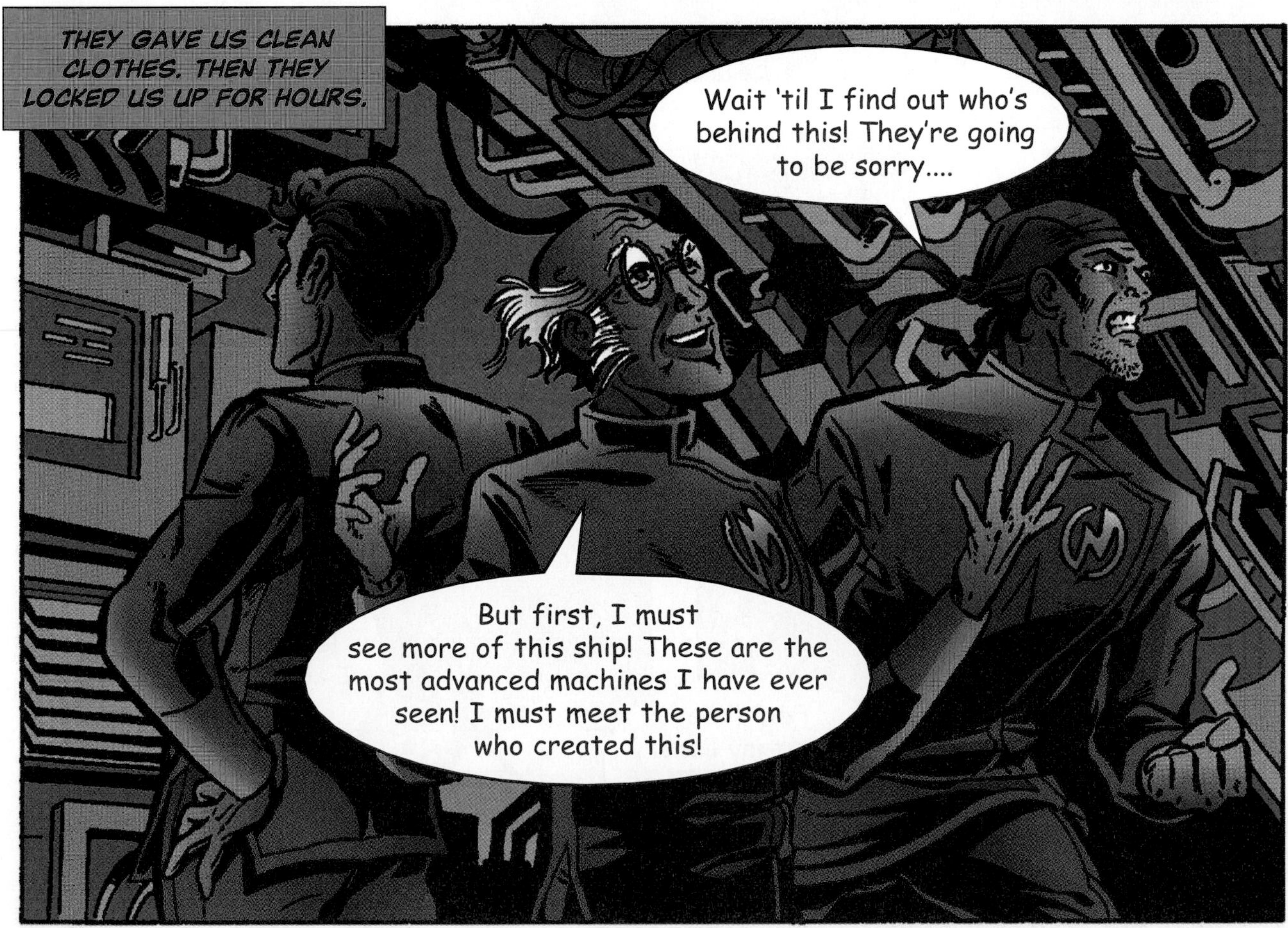
THEY GAVE US CLEAN CLOTHES. THEN THEY LOCKED US UP FOR HOURS.
Wait 'til I find out who's behind this! They're going to be sorry....
But first, I must see more of this ship! These are the most advanced machines I have ever seen! I must meet the person who created this!

ASK YOURSELF

- What new problem does Professor Aronnax have?

Think about what Captain Nemo says.

THE NEXT DAY, NEMO CALLED ME TO HIS OFFICE.
Professor, could I interest you in a tour of the ship?
Of course!

NEMO STARTED HIS TOUR IN THE ENGINE ROOM.
The lights and engines are run by batteries. The batteries run on salt from the sea.
How can we breathe in here?
We go to the surface each day and fill our huge air tanks. We also have extra tanks that store enough air for about four days. That's in case we have to stay underwater.

It's simple, but smart! How does the ship go up and down in the water?
We have large water tanks. When we want to go under, the tanks are filled with seawater. The weight makes the ship sink. When we want to rise, pumps push the water out.
That's perfect!

NEMO CONTINUED TO SHOW ME AROUND THE SHIP. AT ONE POINT, HE PUSHED A BUTTON. A WALL SLID AWAY. THERE WAS A HUGE WINDOW TO THE OCEAN.
Now, Professor, here's a view for your scientific mind!
Amazing!
But don't you ever go to land? How do you get food and other supplies?
All our food is from the sea. We eat fish and vegetables from our undersea farms. And our clothes are made of sea fibers. You see, Professor, almost everything we need is in the sea.

Where do you get the money to pay for all this, Captain?
We collect gold and treasures from shipwrecks.

I'm sorry, Captain, but I must ask you something. Did you sink all those ships I've read about?
Yes. I'm afraid that's an ugly part of my mission. I take the ships' treasures. I use some of it. And I give the rest to people who need it.

WHAT NEMO SAID BOTHERED ME. BUT I PUT IT OUT OF MY MIND.
THE NEXT FEW MONTHS, WE HAD MANY AMAZING ADVENTURES.

WE TRAVELED ALL OVER THE WORLD. WE STUDIED THE SECRETS OF THE DEEP.

WE EVEN TRAVELED TO THE SOUTH POLE.
Don't worry, men. The *Nautilus* can cut through ice.

I WAS VERY INTERESTED IN EVERYTHING I SAW. BUT I COULDN'T FORGET THAT WE WERE PRISONERS. AND MY FRIENDS COULDN'T FORGET IT, EITHER.
I can't stay on this ship much longer.
We've got to find a way out of here.
I do not trust Nemo. We must escape soon.

I DECIDED TO TALK WITH NEMO ABOUT LETTING US GO.
Captain, could I speak with you? It's important.
Not now, Professor. I'm finishing my life story.

Your life story?
Yes. When I finish it, I will put it in a waterproof box and throw it in the sea. Someday, someone will find it.
Why take such a risk? Give us our freedom. We'll take your book with us.

Your freedom?!
I told you that no one may ever leave the *Nautilus*!!!

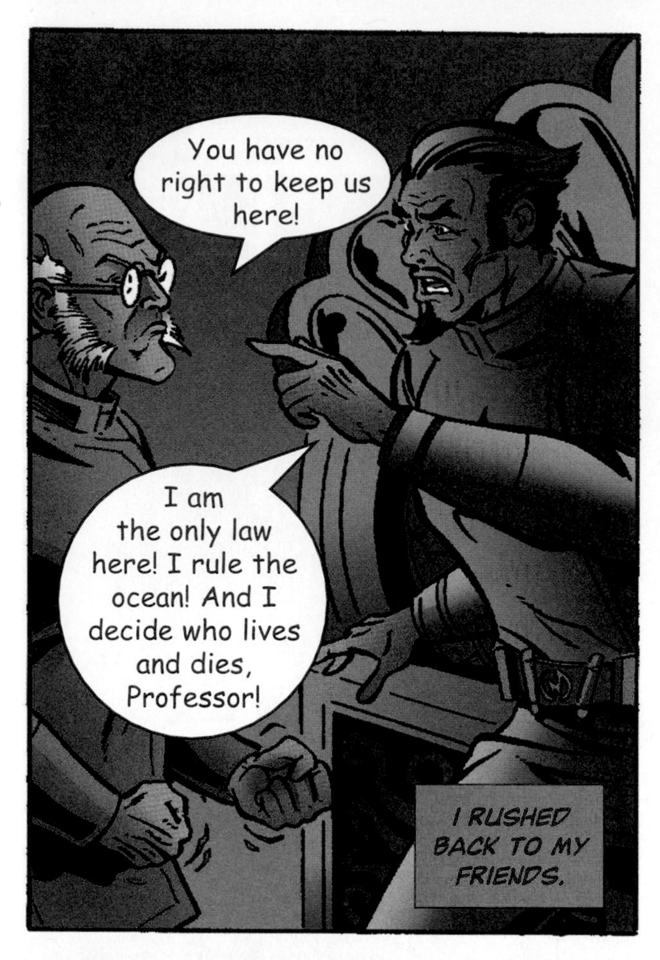
You have no right to keep us here!
I am the only law here! I rule the ocean! And I decide who lives and dies, Professor!
I RUSHED BACK TO MY FRIENDS.

You two were right. We are in danger. We must escape.

BUT THE NEXT DAY, WE HAD OTHER THINGS ON OUR MINDS. WE SAW A SHIP IN THE DISTANCE. ITS CREW SENT A SIGNAL. IT SAID THAT THEY WERE FRIENDLY. BUT NEMO ORDERED AN ATTACK.
Prepare to ram the ship!!!
Captain, you must not!!!
Get out of my way, Professor! Remember that I am captain of this ship! I am ruler of the seas! Get back or I will have you killed!

ASK YOURSELF

- Is Captian Nemo lying when he says that he was only defending his ship?

Reread what's happened, and decide for yourself.

THAT NIGHT, THE NAUTILUS WAS STILL ON THE SURFACE.
WE KNEW IT WAS OUR CHANCE TO ESCAPE.
Look!
WE SNEAKED OUT AND GOT INTO ONE OF THE NAUTILUS'S LIFEBOATS.

SUDDENLY, THERE WAS A HUGE WHIRLPOOL. IT WAS SPINNING THE NAUTILUS AROUND.
A whirlpool! There are lots of them in these waters! They can drag a ship to the bottom and smash it into a million pieces!

SOMEHOW, WE ROWED OUT OF DANGER.
We're free!

BUT THE NAUTILUS WAS NOT AS LUCKY.

THE NEXT DAY, WE SAW LAND.
Land, ho!

WE NEVER FOUND OUT WHAT HAPPENED TO CAPTAIN NEMO....
MAYBE ONE DAY SOMEONE WILL FIND HIS BOOK, OR MAYBE HE AND HIS NAUTILUS ARE STILL TRAVELING ON THE BOTTOM OF THE SEA....

Talk About It

Now that you've read *20,000 Leagues Under the Sea,* what do you have to say about these questions?

- Would you have wanted to join Captain Nemo on his undersea adventures? Explain why or why not.
- What might the *Nautilus* be like if Jules Verne were writing a sequel today? Tell how it might be the same . . . or different.

Comprehension Check

Write your answers to the questions below. Use information from the graphic classic to support your answers.

1. How are Captain Nemo and his crew able to exist under the sea?
2. Why didn't Professor Aronnax and his friends try to escape right away?
3. What made Professor Aronnax and his friends finally decide to escape?
4. Why do you think Nemo was afraid for others to learn his secret?
5. What do you think might have happened if the world had learned about the *Nautilus?*

Write About It

Choose one of the writing prompts below.

- Create a message in a bottle that Professor Aronnax might have written while he was on board the *Nautilus.* In the message, explain his situation and what he has learned.
- Write a letter to Jules Verne telling him about one recent invention that you think might amaze him.
- The professor had some great adventures on board the *Nautilus.* Write an ad for a trip on Captain Nemo's submarine.

About the AUTHOR

Jules Verne was a nineteenth century author who was one of the most popular writers of his generation. Almost one hundred years after his death, Verne's books are still read and loved worldwide.

Many of Verne's books foretell inventions and technology of the 20th century. He wrote of undersea exploration and travel to outer space long before it actually occurred. He is thought to have foreseen the invention of the airplane and the car. Verne is often credited with inventing science fiction.

Filling Out Mail Forms

Amy's got a summer job at a photo studio. Sometimes, customers want their pictures fast! Luckily, many shipping services send packages overnight. But the sender has to fill out special shipping forms that sometimes get complicated.

Check out the form below. Could you fill one out?

Speedy Ship Overnight Shipping Form

Hang on to this number. If a package gets lost, Speedy Ship will use the tracking number to find it.

Speedy Ship USA Airbill Tracking Number 8188325673M

1 From (please print)
Date 9/23/01 Sender's Account Number
Sender's Name Amy Perez Phone 802 555-8943
Company Picture This
Address 329 13th Avenue
City New York State NY Zip 10001

2 To (please print)
Recipient's Name Katelyn Queen Phone 914 555-3122
Company
Address 22 Gravy Lane
(We cannot deliver to Post Office Boxes)
To "HOLD" at Speedy Ship location, print Speedy Ship address here)
City Ossining State NY Zip 10562

Call 1-800-555-SHIP
Visit our Web site

3 Express Service *Packages up to 125 lbs.*
☐ Overnight Rush (Next Morning)* ☒ Regular Overnight
☐ 2nd Day (day after tomorrow)
*Business days only

4 Packaging
☒ Speedy Ship letter ☐ Speedy Ship Box ☐ Customer's Packaging

5 Special
☐ Saturday Delivery ☐ Sunday Delivery ☐ HOLD at Speedy Ship office
Speedy Ship will not ship dangerous goods

6 Payment
Bill: ☒ Sender ☐ Recipient ☐ Third Party ☐ Credit Card ☐ Cash/Check
Speedy Ship Account No. Credit Card No. 12345678 Exp. 02/04

Number of Packages	Total Weight	Total Value*
1	1 lb	$ 14.00

*We are liable for $100 only, unless you declare a higher value.

7 Release Signature Okay to deliver without signature.

Use section 3 or 5 to tell Speedy Ship when your package must arrive.

Tell Speedy Ship who to bill for this shipment. Write down the account or credit card number to be charged.

Get It in the Mail

Amy needs to send some packages—fast! You're going to help her out. Review the form and tips. Then use them to answer these questions. Write your answers on your own paper.

1. Katelyn Queen's pictures wouldn't fit in a Speedy Ship box. So Amy used the photo studio's packaging. Which box should Amy check in section 4 of the form?

2. Katelyn Queen is using a credit card to pay for this shipment. Which box should Amy check in section 6 of the form? What other information must she write in section 6?

3. A customer's package will arrive on Friday. She won't be home. She wants to pick it up at Speedy Ship. Which box should Amy check in Section 5 of the form?

4. Another customer wants her package delivered to her home on Sunday. What section of the form should Amy use to tell this to Speedy Ship? What box should she check?

5. Katelyn Queen calls the office two days after Amy sends the pictures. She complains that she hasn't gotten them yet. What should Amy do?
   - **a.** Apologize and ask Katelyn to be patient. The package will show up soon.
   - **b.** Apologize and use Katelyn's credit card number to trace the missing package.
   - **c.** Apologize and use the Speedy Ship tracking number to trace the missing package.

Fill It Out

It's Wednesday. Joe Pito wants his pictures by Friday. He wants to pay for the shipping with his credit card, number 3984 8423, which expires 11/11. The order fits in a Speedy Ship box and weighs four ounces. It's worth about $40. How would you fill out sections 3 through 6?

Find Out

You need to send a package overnight. But you don't even know the name of a mail service. How could you find one? Write down a few ideas.

"Did a package get lost? Most express mail services have Web sites that allow you to track packages on line."

Real-World Words

account: an agreement letting you charge goods or services
recipient: a person who gets or receives something
third party: a person who's not sending or receiving a package

A Vaquero of the Southwest (at left)

Women Workers of World War II

THEY BUILT AMERICA

Chinese Workers of the Transcontinental Railroad

They were clever, brave, and tough. You may not have read about these little-known men and women in your history book. Now's your chance.

Do you know that the American cowboy wasn't born in America at all? Have you heard that women helped America win one of its most dangerous wars? Do you know how courageous Chinese workers helped build the first railroad line across America?

Railroad builders, war workers, and even cowboys . . . These may seem like very different groups of people with very different stories. But they all played an important role in making America what it is today.

Just turn the page and you'll read about . . .

Vaqueros of the Southwest

The Time: 1500s to 1800s
The Problem: Controlling vast herds of cattle and horses
Their Contribution: Pioneered the ranching skills later used by American cowboys

Americans love cowboys. Nothing seems more red, white, and blue than a John Wayne movie or a man on horseback herding cattle. And yet, like so many things that are considered American, cowboys came from somewhere else. Their true birthplace is in Mexico, where they were originally called "vaqueros" (vah-KEHR-ohs).

"Vaquero" comes from "vaca," the Spanish word for cow. During the 1500s, Spain conquered the areas known today as Mexico and the southwestern United States. After their conquest, the Spanish brought over cows and horses. These creatures had never before been seen in the Americas. Herds of both animals grew to enormous sizes, and the need for vaqueros grew with them.

The first vaqueros were nothing like the cowboys you see in movies about the Old West today.

Vaqueros like these were the original cowboys.

Instead, they were laborers given the job of guarding cattle. In addition to the Spanish, vaqueros eventually included Native Americans and descendants from African slaves. Over the next two centuries, they invented the cowboy lifestyle. They learned how to catch cattle using a looped rope called a *lazo*—which Americans turned into "lasso." They also created heavy leather pants to protect their legs called *chaparreras*, which was later shortened to "chaps."

Living in the Saddle

In the 1600s and 1700s, cattle herds moved northward from

Mexico to Spanish-controlled Texas and California. The vaqueros who moved the herds practically lived in their saddles. As a result, they became some of the best horsemen in the world. "I have seen some very good riders in Mexico, but these vaqueros in California are much better," one American wrote in 1832. "It is said that they will throw the lasso better with their feet than Mexican vaqueros can with the hand."

Vaqueros became known for their colorful outfits and their willingness to face death. One favorite game was to ride up to a running steer, grab its tail, and flip it. Risks were definitely part of the job. Vaqueros became handy at killing the grizzly bears that attacked cattle herds and at taming wild horses. "In this business," wrote an American in 1808, "there is no one in the world superior to the Spanish vaqueros of Texas."

During the 1830s and 1840s, the U.S. won control of Texas, California, and the rest of the Southwest. Americans poured into the area, but most knew little about cattle. Vaqueros taught them what kind of ropes and knots to use. They also taught them how to herd an angry longhorn, a type of cattle common in the Southwest.

The Americans who learned those lessons at first called themselves vaqueros as well. But by the 1860s, most Americans who worked with cattle were called cowboys. Between 1860 and 1890, those cowboys raised more than nine million head of cattle to help feed the United States.

ASK YOURSELF

- Who were the vaqueros and what did they do?

Think about what you've read so far and put it into your own words.

Where Did They Go?

What happened to the vaqueros? Unfortunately, most of them could not read or write, so few personal stories have been handed down. Many stayed and worked in the United States even though they were greatly **outnumbered** by cowboys. Many others left for Mexico, Chile, Argentina, or other Spanish-speaking countries.

Today, a handful of skilled vaqueros can still be found riding and roping in northern Mexico. They proudly hang on to their traditions which have been handed down over many generations.

Leaving Their Mark

Before they faded away in the U.S., the vaqueros had an **enormous** impact on the business of being a cowboy. They invented the cowboy's saddle as well as important tools like branding irons.

Vaqueros also invented the cattle drive, and the methods for raising cattle on the open range. In fact, many of the first cattle rustlers—or thieves—were vaqueros. They learned how to change a cow's brand in order to cover their tracks.

Vaqueros liked to sing sad, sweet songs as a way of passing the time. They sang songs like "Cielito Lindo," a famous Spanish song which tells listeners to "sing and don't cry" despite life's **hardships.** That tradition of song helped give Americans "singing cowboys" like Roy Rogers and Gene Autrey.

Today, vaqueros live on mostly through the language of the American cowboy. English words like *ranch*, *rodeo*, *bronco*, *mustang*, *corral*, and *lariat* all got their start in Spanish. Along with their words, though, vaqueros handed down a tradition of skill, toughness, and daring that helped make the cowboy a legend.

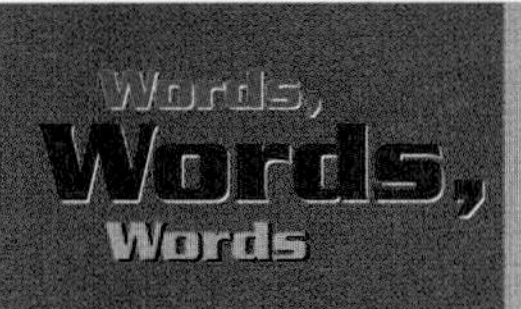

outnumbered: to be smaller in number than another group
enormous: very large
hardships: conditions that one suffers through

Women Workers of World War II

The Time: 1941 to 1945
The Problem: Defeating Japan and its allies, Germany and Italy
Their Contributions: Produced the weapons that won the war; helped to change attitudes about working women

On December 7, 1941, a Japanese sneak attack on Pearl Harbor in Hawaii plunged the United States into World War II. Almost overnight, thousands of young men left home to fight as soldiers and sailors. But their sudden departure sparked a crisis. With so many men gone, who would keep the country going as policemen, farmers, and taxi drivers? Who would produce the planes, tanks, and other weapons needed to win the war?

Two women take a break from welding.

There was only one answer: women. But in 1941, that wasn't an easy answer for Americans to accept. Most women at that time did not work outside the home. They raised children while men supported their families.

During the 1930s, an economic slowdown called the Great Depression had made jobs **scarce.** People felt that a working woman—especially a married woman—kept a job away from a man. In 1936, one poll found that most Americans favored passing laws that would **forbid** wives from working.

From Baking to Bombs

World War II helped end the unemployment of the Great Depression. Suddenly, there were plenty of jobs and not enough workers. But attitudes about women working did not change overnight. Many companies did not want to hire women, and many women did not want to work.

The U.S. government launched an ad campaign to solve the problem. One billboard about making ammunition declared: "If you've followed recipes exactly in making cakes, you can learn to load a shell."

Women answered the government's call to action in a big way. By 1943, they made up nearly one-third of the U.S. workforce. Nearly two million women worked in factories producing weapons alone.

Before the war only certain jobs were considered "ladylike," such as secretary or schoolteacher. That changed.

During the war, women served in the armed forces fixing trucks and flying airplanes. As civilians, women became firefighters and bus drivers. Some even became lumberjacks—though they were called "lumberjills." Many developed a new-found **confidence.** "I decided if I could learn to weld like a man," one woman recalled, "I could do anything it took to make a living."

Posters like this encouraged women to work during WW II.

Producing a Miracle

The **enthusiasm** of women workers created a miracle. The U.S. produced enough supplies not just for its own armies, but for several other countries as well. The news media heaped praise on female war workers and a tune called "Rosie the Riveter" became their unofficial theme song.

Most Americans assumed that all the Rosies would give up their jobs once the soldiers returned home. After all, a woman's place was with her family. "I wanted to be home with those kids—they were too precious to leave for work," remembers one woman.

When the war ended in August 1945, women all over the U.S. were thrown out of work. Those women who wanted to keep working usually had to settle for low-paying, unimportant jobs. These were often jobs men didn't want. Over time, many Americans chose to forget the women's role in winning the war.

But the women, the Rosies, did not forget. They had proven themselves and tasted independence. Many could not go back to the way things were before. "I was head of a household, and it made a different person of me," said one woman of her work during the war. "I have never been without a job since that day."

Without Rosie the Riveter America couldn't have won the war. Because of her, working in America has never been the same.

ASK YOURSELF

- How did women workers help America win the war?

Think about what they did and describe it in your own words.

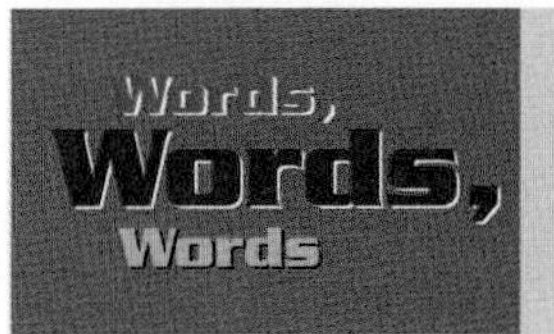

scarce: hard to find
forbid: to order someone not to do something
confidence: a belief in one's own ability
enthusiasm: great interest and excitement

Chinese Railroad Workers

Hundreds of Chinese died building the Transcontinental Railroad.

The Time: 1862 to 1869
The Problem: Building a railroad across America that would connect the East Coast to the West Coast
Their Contribution: Supplied the manpower to do the job

The Transcontinental Railroad was one of the greatest **achievements** in American history. Completed in 1869, the railroad connected America's East and West Coasts for the first time ever. People and goods would now be able to cross the country in a matter of days, not months. Because of the 1,744-mile long ribbon of track, America and the West would never be the same.

Creating an East to West link was especially historic because of the many hardships workers had to endure. Thousands of brave men worked 12-hour days and risked their lives. But no one paid a bigger price than Chinese railroad workers did to get the job done. Many sacrificed their lives building the railroad.

From 1865 to 1869, the Chinese endured everything from bitter cold, **avalanches,** and blizzards to scorching desert heat while they worked. They braved deadly explosives to blast through rock mountains and laid mile after mile of track. Without the Chinese, the Transcontinental Railroad would never have become a reality.

A Race to Build

In 1862, the U.S. government announced it was going to set aside money to build a coast-to-coast railroad. The government would pay for each mile of track laid. This created a fierce competition between two companies to see which could build faster. The Union Pacific started its tracks in Nebraska and built westward. The Central Pacific started in California and built eastward. Eventually, they would meet in the middle.

But the Central Pacific had several problems. The company would have to blast through high mountain passes in order to build its part of the tracks. Finding people to do the dangerous work wouldn't be easy. Few people lived in the West. In order to find enough workers, the company's boss, Charles Crocker, decided to take a chance on hiring Chinese immigrants.

Chinese workers in the West made up 90 percent of the railroad workforce.

Coming to America

Many Chinese first came to the U.S. during the California Gold Rush of 1849. Few made their fortunes in gold so they were willing to work for Crocker.

The Chinese had a difficult time getting accepted in America. Their language, clothes, food and foreign customs set them apart culturally. Some people believed they might not be able to handle heavy work. Crocker found just the opposite was true. "They prove nearly equal to white men in the amount of labor they perform, and are much more reliable," he said.

At the Central Pacific, Chinese workers soon made up 90 percent of the workforce. More than 10,000 of them courageously tunneled through miles of mountain rock. And when winter hit, they dug through 60-foot snow drifts. "Snow slides carried away our camps and we lost a good many men in those slides," one company official reported.

End of the Line

The Transcontinental Railroad was finally completed on May 10, 1869, sparking nationwide celebrations.

For the Chinese-Americans though, the celebrations quickly turned sour. **Prejudice** against them grew as people flooded westward on the new rail line. The Chinese were unfairly blamed when bad economic times hit. Western states passed anti-Chinese laws that made it hard to work or count as citizens.

Still, nobody could deny that Chinese-Americans had made coast-to-coast travel a reality. Despite facing tough conditions, the Central Pacific workers were able to lay 742 miles of track. Those who watched the Transcontinental Railroad being built knew who deserved the credit. "Without [the Chinese]," California's governor wrote at the time, "it would be impossible to complete the western portion of this great national enterprise." ●

ASK YOURSELF

- What dangers did the Chinese face in building the Transcontinental Railroad?

Remember what you read and explain it in your own words.

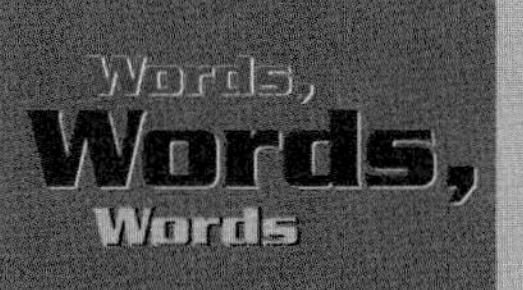

achievements: things done successfully with great effort or courage
avalanches: large masses of snow, ice, or earth that suddenly move down a mountain
prejudice: an unfair opinion about a group of people based on their race or religion

Talk About It

Now that you've read "They Built America," what do you have to say about these questions?

- ▶ What historical facts surprised you most as you read these articles?
- ▶ How do you think these groups might be honored for what they did?

Comprehension Check

Write your answers to the questions below. Use information from the articles to support your answers.

1. What skills did the cowboys learn from the vaqueros?
2. Why did so many women enter the workforce during World War II?
3. How would you describe the Chinese workers' jobs on the Central Pacific railroad?
4. How did the Rosies help change women's roles?
5. What do the vaqueros and the Chinese railroad workers have in common? Explain.

Vocabulary Check

Answer each question with a complete sentence. Before you answer, think about the meaning of the vocabulary word in bold.

1. What do you consider your greatest **achievements**?
2. Why is having **confidence** important?
3. How do you deal with **prejudice**?
4. Why might someone eat an **enormous** dinner?
5. What can you do when faced with **hardships**?

Write About It

Choose one of the writing prompts below.

- Write a journal entry describing one day in the life of a vaquero.
- Write a letter from one of the Rosies to a husband or brother who is fighting in the war. In the letter, explain what type of job you have and how you feel about it.
- Write a short speech thanking the Chinese railroad workers for their contribution to the Transcontinental Railroad.

More to READ

If you want to learn more about the vaqueros, the women workers, or the Chinese workers, check out these books:

Charro: The Mexican Cowboy
by George Ancona

This book tells the story of today's Mexican cowboys, complete with fabulous photographs of vaqueros in action.

Rosie the Riveter: Women Working on the Home Front in World War II
by Penny Colman

Told through the eyes of a young girl named Dot Chastney, everything you always wanted to know about the Rosies is contained in this fascinating book.

Dragon's Gate
by Laurence Yep

This award-winning novel tells the story of Otter, who flees China for California in 1865 and learns firsthand about the dangers of working on the Transcontinental Railroad.

Reading an Ad

If it sounds too good to be true, it probably is. Smart shoppers know that they have to read ads carefully.

Here are three typical ads. Read all about them—and don't forget the fine print. Are the items for sale really bargains?

Ads From *The Neighborhood News*

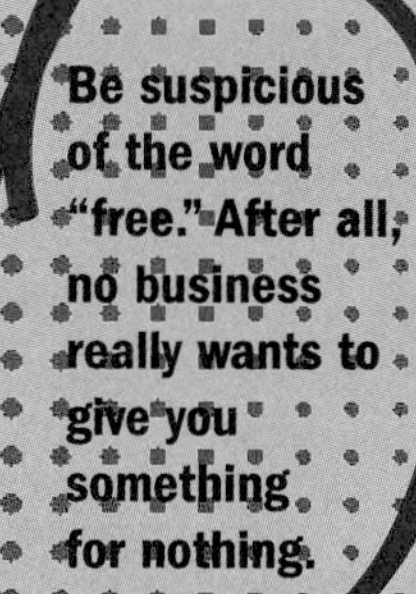

Bargain Basement
Jeans $10
All styles
Women's Sizes 6–8 only
Men's waist sizes 36–42 only
Values $59 to $89
All items on sale 12/24 thru 12/26

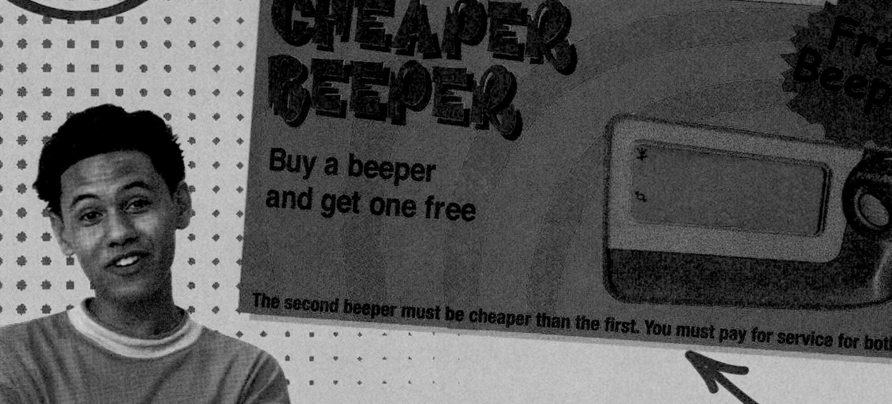

These words are really big because the advertiser wants them to catch your eye.

These words are so small that it's easy to ignore them—and that's just what the advertiser hopes you'll do.

"Notice how the beeper ad says you must pay for service. Before you make this kind of purchase, find out how much the service costs."

Test Your Shopping Smarts

Have you read the fine print? Are the deals really deals? Be a savvy shopper. Reread the ads and review the tips that go with them. Then read the questions below and use the ads to answer them. Write your answers on your own paper.

1. The Bargain Basement is selling jeans in all sizes for only $10.
   a. true
   b. false

2. What is the cost of a bucket of burgers at Burger Bonanza? What is the value of the free toy?

3. Let's say you want a beeper. You go to Cheaper Beeper. Which two statements are true about Cheaper Beeper?
   a. If you pay for one beeper, you'll get the second one for free.
   b. If you buy one beeper, you can get two more beepers for free.
   c. If you buy a beeper and get one free, you must pay for service for both.

4. Read about the following people. Which two of them might find Bargain Basement a real bargain?
   a. Yolanda wears women's size 6.
   b. Patrick wears men's jeans with a waist size of 38.
   c. Sally wears women's size 14.

5. Look at the date of the sale at Bargain Basement. Why might it be tough to take advantage of this sale?

Buyer Beware
Find a newspaper or magazine and choose some ads. Read them carefully. Do you think the deals they are offering are bargains or not? List your reasons.

Bad Business
Create an ad. Think of ways you could trick a shopper into buying a product. Then trade ads with a partner. Would you buy your partner's product? Why or why not?

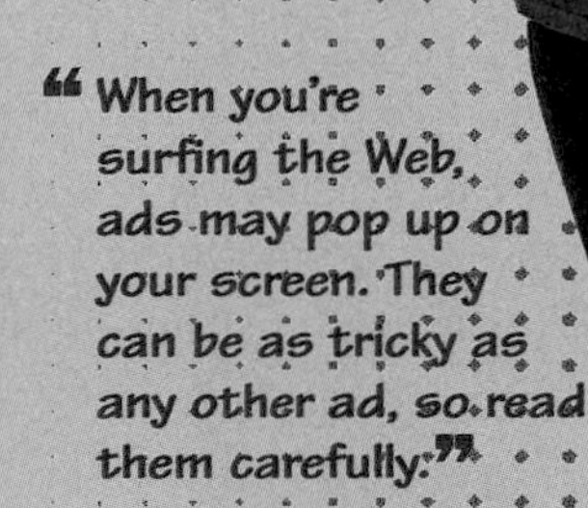

"When you're surfing the Web, ads may pop up on your screen. They can be as tricky as any other ad, so read them carefully."

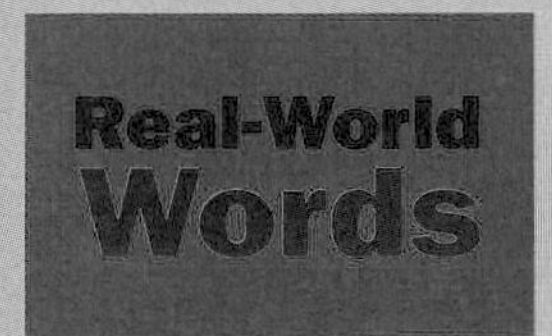

Real-World Words

advertiser: a person who places an advertisement
bargain: a purchase made for less than the usual price
savvy: well-informed and smart

Glossary

You will find all your vocabulary words in alphabetical order in the Glossary. Look at the sample entry below to see how to use it.

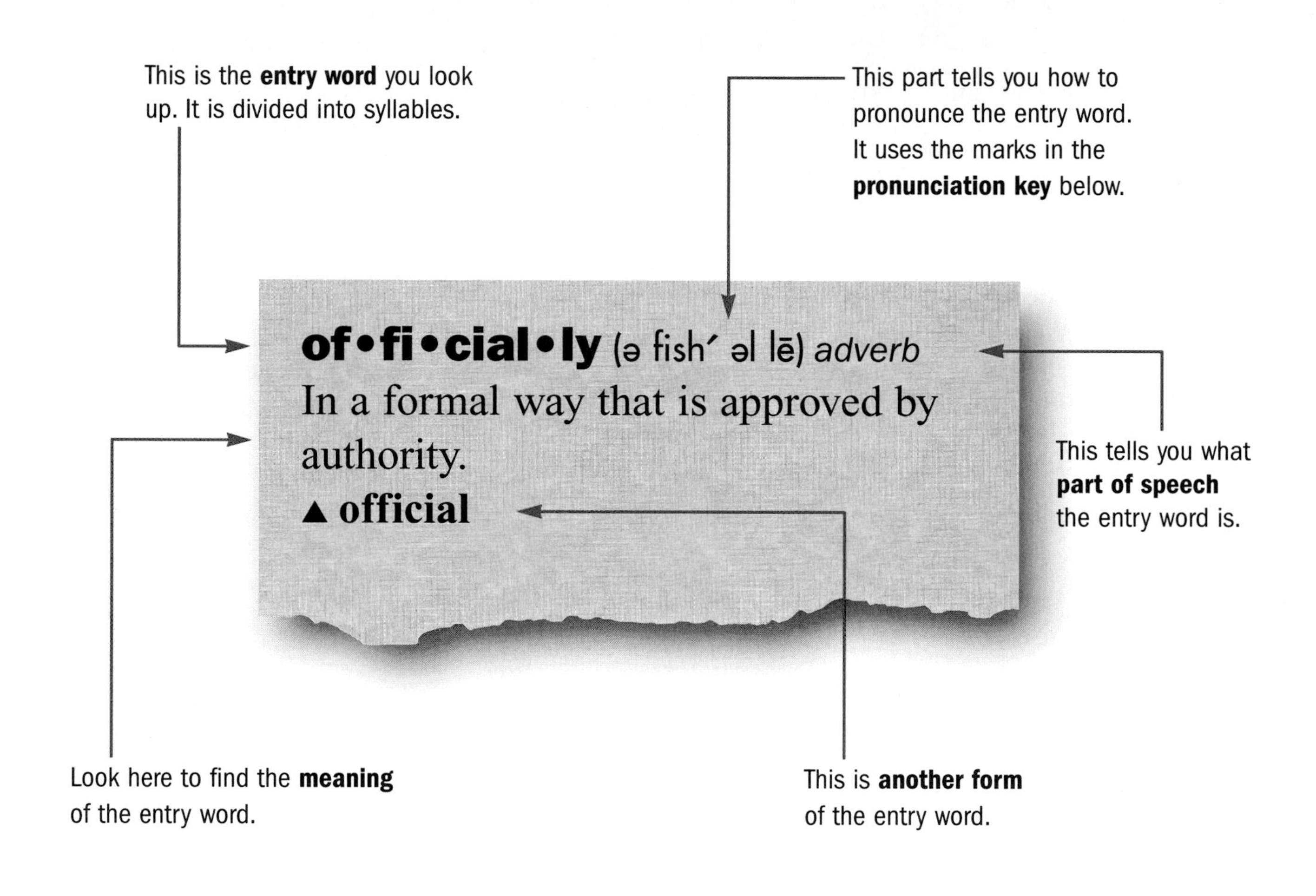

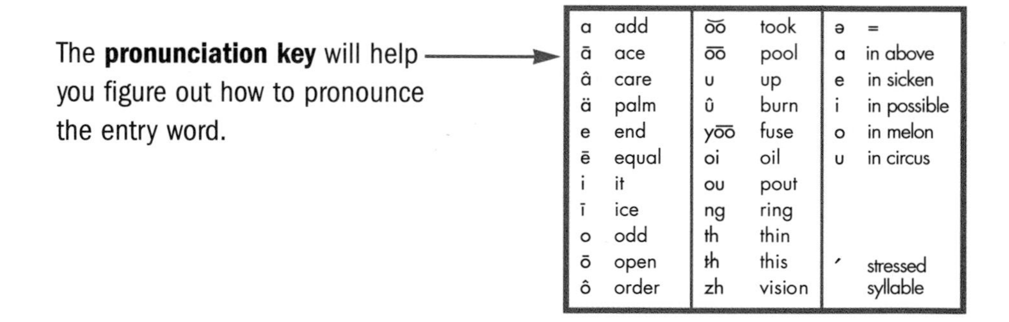

a	add	o͝o	took	ə	=
ā	ace	o͞o	pool	a	in above
â	care	u	up	e	in sicken
ä	palm	û	burn	i	in possible
e	end	yo͞o	fuse	o	in melon
ē	equal	oi	oil	u	in circus
i	it	ou	pout		
ī	ice	ng	ring		
o	odd	th	thin		
ō	open	t͟h	this	′	stressed syllable
ô	order	zh	vision		

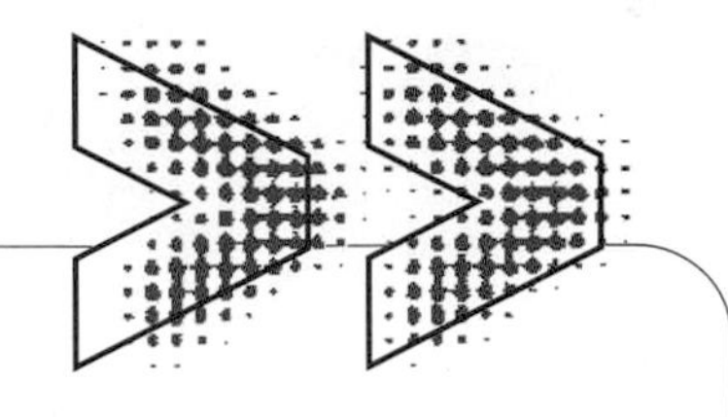

ab•sorb
(ab sôrb′) *verb*
To take in.

ac•cept•ance
(ak sep′ təns) *noun*
Feeling like you belong.

ac•ci•den•tal•ly
(ak′ si dən′ tl lē) *adverb*
Unexpectedly.
▲ **accidental**

ache
(āk) *verb*
To feel pain.

a•chieve•ments
(ə chēv′mənts) *noun*
Things done successfully with great effort or courage.
▲ **achievement**

ac•quaint•ed
(ə kwān′ tid) *verb*
Having been brought into social contact.
▲ **acquaint**

ad•ja•cent
(ə jā′ sənt) *adjective*
Close or next to something.

al•ler•gic
(ə lûr′ jik) *adjective*
Reacting to something by sneezing, coughing, or breaking out in a rash.

an•ces•tors
(an′ ses tərz) *noun*
Members of your family who lived a long time ago.
▲ **ancestor**

an•guish
(ang′ gwish) *noun*
A strong feeling of sadness and nervousness.

anx•ious•ly
(angk′ shəs lē) *adverb*
With worry.
▲ **anxious**

ap•point
(ə point′) *verb*
To choose someone for a job.

ap•pre•ci•ate
(ə prē′ shē āt′) *verb*
Enjoy or value something.

at•tend
(ə tend′) *verb*
Go to.

au•thor•i•ty
(ə thôr′ i tē) *noun*
A high position of power.

Thesaurus

authority
command
influence
power

av•a•lanch•es
(av′ ə lanch′ əs) *noun*
Large masses of snow, ice, or earth that suddenly move down a mountain.
▲ **avalanche**

bliz•zard
(bliz′ ərd) *noun*
A heavy snowstorm.

bur•den
(bûr′ dn) *noun*
A heavy load.

bur•rows
(bûr′ōz) *verb*
Digs a tunnel or hole.
▲ **burrow**

Word Origin

The word **burrow** comes from the German word **burgs** which originally meant “fortress”.

a	add	o͝o	took	ə	=
ā	ace	o͞o	pool	a	in above
â	care	u	up	e	in sicken
ä	palm	û	burn	i	in possible
e	end	yo͞o	fuse	o	in melon
ē	equal	oi	oil	u	in circus
i	it	ou	pout		
ī	ice	ng	ring		
o	odd	th	thin		
ō	open	t͟h	this	′	stressed
ô	order	zh	vision		syllable

Glossary

cam•paign
(kam pān′) *noun*
A series of actions that lead to achieving something important.

chant
(chant) *noun*
A phrase said or sung over and over again.

clutch•ing
(kluch′ ing) *verb*
Holding on tightly.
▲ **clutch**

co•ma
(kō′ mə) *noun*
A deep sleep that is very hard to wake up from.

con•cen•trat•ed
(kon′ sən trāt′ id) *verb*
Directed toward one point; focused.
▲ **concentrate**

con•fi•dence
(kon′ fi dəns) *noun*
A belief in one's own ability.

con•sid•ered
(kən sid′ ərd) *verb*
Believed that something is true.
▲ **consider**

con•sist•ed
(kon sist′ id) *verb*
Made up of.
▲ **consist**

con•stant•ly
(kon′ stənt lē) *adverb*
All the time.
▲ **constant**

con•vert
(kən vûrt′) *verb*
To make something into something else.

Thesaurus

convert
change
transform
translate

con•vic•tion
(kən vik′ shən) *noun*
A strong belief in something.

coo•ing
(ko͞o′ ing) *verb*
The sound a pigeon makes.
▲ **coo**

co•or•di•na•tion
(kō ôr′ dn ā′ shən) *noun*
Ability to combine two or more things successfully.

cop•ing
(kōp′ ing) *verb*
Dealing with something successfully.
▲ **cope**

dan•gling
(dan′ gling) *verb*
Swinging or hanging down loosely.
▲ **dangle**

de•cent
(dē′ sənt) *adjective*
Thoughtful or kind.

des•per•ate
(des′pər it) *adjective*
Willing to do anything to change your situation.

de•spond•ent
(di spon′dənt) *adjective*
Miserable and depressed.

de•ter•mi•na•tion
(di tûr′ mə nā′ shən) *noun*
A strong passion to complete a task despite its difficulty.

di•a•bol•i•cal
(dī′ ə bol′ i kl) *adjective*
Extremely wicked.

dip•lo•mat
(dip′ lə mat′) *noun*
A person who represents his or her country's government in a foreign country.

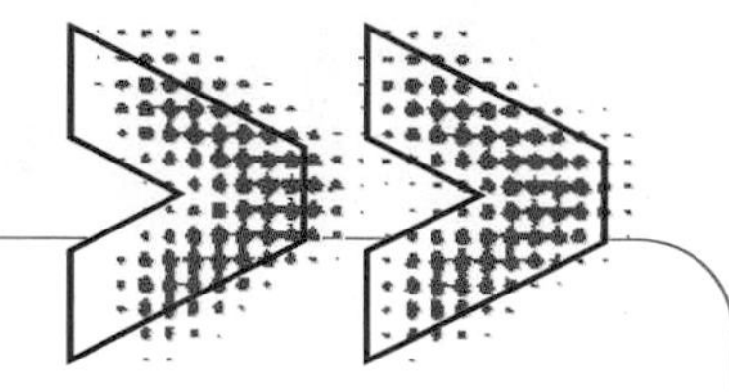

dis•cour•aged
(di skûr′ ijd) *verb*
Caused to give up hope or confidence.
▲ **discourage**

dis•o•bey
(dis′ ə bā′) *verb*
To go against the rules or someone's wishes.

dis•play
(di splā′) *verb*
Show.

dis•sect
(dī sekt′) *verb*
To cut apart a human body in order to examine it.

dis•tinc•tive
(di stingk′ tiv) *adjective*
Clearly different.
▲ **distinct**

dis•tract
(di strakt′) *verb*
To weaken a person's concentration.

em•braced
(em brāst′) *verb*
Hugged.
▲ **embrace**

e•mo•tions
(i mō′ shən) *noun*
Strong feelings of any kind.

en•cour•ag•es
(en kûr′ ij əz) *verb*
Shows approval for one's actions.
▲ **encourage**

e•nor•mous
(i nôr′məs) *adjective*
Very large.

en•sured
(en sho͝ord′) *verb*
Made sure.
▲ **ensure**

en•thu•si•asm
(en tho͞o′ zē az′ əm) *noun*
Great interest and excitement.

e•quiv•a•lent
(i kwiv′ ə lənt) *adjective*
Equal in value.

es•tab•lished
(i stab′ lisht) *verb*
Experienced.
▲ **establish**

e•ter•nal
(i tûr′ nl) *adjective*
Lasting forever.

et•i•quette
(et′ i kit) *noun*
Rules of polite behavior.

ex•haust•ed
(ig zôst′ id) *adjective*
Very tired.
▲ **exhaust**

ex•hil•a•rat•ed
(ig zil′ ə rāt′ id) *adjective*
Excited and thrilled.
▲ **exhilarate**

fa•tigue
(fə tēg′) *adjective*
Great tiredness.

fool•proof
(fo͞ol′ pro͞of) *adjective*
Something that cannot fail.

Word Usage

Foolproof is a compound word. A **compound word** is a word that is made up of two smaller words. **Foolproof** is made from **fool** and **proof,** which is a term for something that can't fail.

a	add	o͝o	took	ə	=
ā	ace	o͞o	pool	a	in above
â	care	u	up	e	in sicken
ä	palm	û	burn	i	in possible
e	end	yo͞o	fuse	o	in melon
ē	equal	oi	oil	u	in circus
i	it	ou	pout		
ī	ice	ng	ring		
o	odd	th	thin		
ō	open	t͟h	this	′	stressed syllable
ô	order	zh	vision		

Glossary

for•bid
(fər bid′) *verb*
To order someone not to do something.

fru•gal
(fro͞o′ gəl) *adjective*
Careful not to waste money.

fu•ri•ous•ly
(fyo͝or′ ē əs lē) *adverb*
Intensely or fiercely.
▲ **furious**

gazed
(gāzd) *verb*
Looked at something for a long time.
▲ **gaze**

grins
(grinz) *verb*
Cheerfully smiles.
▲ **grin**

guar•an•teed
(gar′ ən tēd′) *adjective*
Certain that something will happen.
▲ **guarantee**

hard•ships
(härd′ships) *noun*
Conditions that one suffers through.
▲ **hardship**

har•mo•ny
(här′ mə nē) *noun*
Agreement.

haz•ard
(haz′ ərd) *noun*
A danger or a risk.

hic•cups
(hik′ ups) *noun*
Sounds in the throat caused by a spasm of the diaphragm.
▲ **hiccup**

hi•lar•i•ous
(hi lâr′ ē əs) *adjective*
Very funny.

Thesaurus

hilarious
extremely funny
lively
witty

hon•or
(on′ ər) *noun*
Honesty and fairness.

host•ess
(hō′ stis) *noun*
A woman who entertains guests.

hu•mor•ous
(hyo͞o′ mər əs) *adjective*
Funny.

i•den•ti•fied
(ī den′ tə fīd) *verb*
Considered as the same.
▲ **identify**

il•le•gal
(i lē′ gəl) *adjective*
Against the law.

il•lu•sions
(i lo͞o′ zhənz) *noun*
Things that appear to exist but really do not.
▲ **illusion**

im•pact
(im′pakt) *noun*
A strong effect.

im•plant•ed
(im plant′ id) *verb*
Put something in or on your body by surgery.
▲ **implant**

im•pressed
(im prest′) *verb*
Affected strongly; influenced.
▲ **impress**

im•prove
(im pro͞ov′) *verb*
To make better.

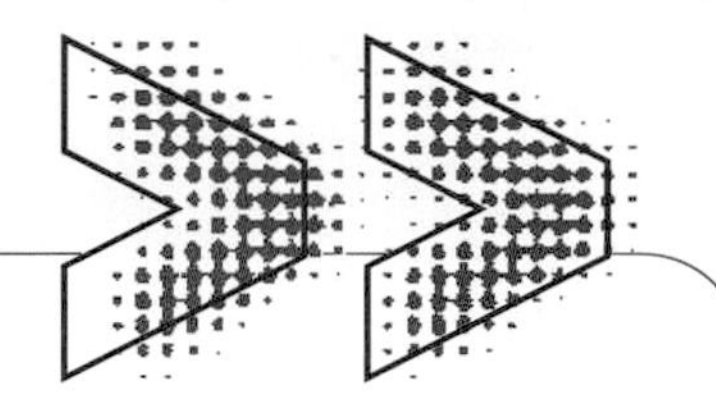

im•pulse
(im′ puls) *noun*
A sudden desire to do something.

in•dif•fer•ent
(in dif′ rənt) *adjective*
Not caring or concerned about something.

in•ev•i•ta•ble
(in ev′ i tə bəl) *adjective*
Sure to happen.

in•fes•ta•tion
(in′ fes tā′ shən) *noun*
An object or place that is full of insects.

in•flu•ence
(in′ flo͞o əns) *verb*
Have an effect upon; affect; change.

in•i•ti•at•ed
(i nish′ ē āt′ id) *verb*
Started.
▲ **initiate**

in•va•sion
(in vā′ zhən) *noun*
Taking over a country by armed force.

jeered
(jērd) *verb*
Shouted in a rude way.
▲ **jeer**

jus•tice
(jus′ tis) *noun*
Fair treatment.

lin•gered
(ling′ gərd) *verb*
Stayed or waited around.
▲ **linger**

live•li•hood
(līv′ lē ho͝od′) *noun*
The way you make money to support yourself.

live•ly
(līv′ lē) *adjective*
Active and full of life.

lunged
(lunjd) *verb*
Moved forward quickly and suddenly.
▲ **lunge**

mas•ter•piece
(mas′ tər pēs′) *noun*
A person's finest piece of work or achievement.

me•di•o•cre
(mē′ dē ō′ kər) *adjective*
Less than average quality.

merged
(mûrjd) *verb*
Joined together.
▲ **merge**

mis•sion
(mish′ ən) *noun*
A special job or task.

moist
(moist) *adjective*
Slightly wet.

mor•ti•fied
(môr′ tə fīd′) *adjective*
Embarrassed enough to feel one's pride is hurt.
▲ **mortify**

muf•fler
(muf′ lər) *noun*
Something that reduces the noise made by a car engine.

non•sense
(non′ sens) *noun*
Silly or annoying behavior.

oath
(ōth) *noun*
A serious promise.

a	add	o͝o	took	ə	=
ā	ace	o͞o	pool	a	in above
â	care	u	up	e	in sicken
ä	palm	û	burn	i	in possible
e	end	yo͞o	fuse	o	in melon
ē	equal	oi	oil	u	in circus
i	it	ou	pout		
ī	ice	ng	ring		
o	odd	th	thin		
ō	open	t͟h	this	′	stressed syllable
ô	order	zh	vision		

Glossary

oc•cu•pa•tion•al
(ok´ yə pā´ shə nl) *adjective*
Having to do with a job.
▲ **occupation**

of•fi•cial•ly
(ə fish´ əl lē) *adverb*
In a formal way that is approved by authority.
▲ **official**

op•po•nents
(ə pō´ nənts) *noun*
People who fight against a cause or person.
▲ **opponent**

op•por•tu•ni•ty
(op´ ər tōō´ ni tē) *noun*
A chance to do something.

Word Origin

Opportunity comes from the Latin word **opportunitas,** which means "convenience".

out•num•bered
(out´num´bərd) *verb*
To be smaller in number than another group.
▲ **outnumber**

o•ver•whelmed
(ō´ vər hwelmed´) *adjective*
Having too many problems and worries to deal with.
▲ **overwhelm**

ox•y•gen
(ok´ si jən) *noun*
A colorless gas found in the air.

pag•eant
(paj´ ənt) *noun*
A public show.

par•a•lyzed
(par´ ə līzd) *verb*
Helpless or unable to function.
▲ **paralyze**

pas•sion•ate
(pash´ ə nit) *adjective*
Having or showing very strong feelings.

peer•ing
(pēr´ ing) *verb*
Looking at something that is difficult to see.
▲ **peer**

Word Usage

To **peer** means "to look at something that is difficult to see." **Peer** is also used to mean "a person of the same age, rank, or standing as another." Words that are spelled the same but have different meanings are called **homographs.**

pe•nal•ized
(pen´ l īzd) *verb*
Punished for something done wrong.
▲ **penalize**

per•ma•nent•ly
(pûr´ mə nənt lē) *adverb*
Forever.
▲ **permanent**

pil•grim•age
(pil´ grə mij) *noun*
A long journey in search of something.

po•lit•i•cal
(pə lit´ i kəl) *adjective*
Having to do with the government.

port•ly
(pôrt´ lē) *adjective*
Heavy or stout.

prawns
(prônz) *noun*
Shrimp.
▲ **prawn**

pre•car•i•ous•ly
(pri kâr´ ē əs lē) *adverb*
In an unsafe and risky way.
▲ **precarious**

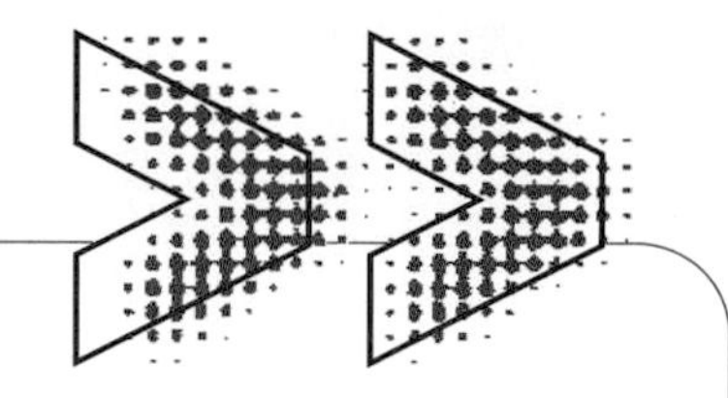

prej•u•dice
(prej′ə dis) *noun*
An unfair opinion about a group of people based on their race or religion.

pre•scrip•tion
(pri skrip′shən) *noun*
Medicine that is ordered by a doctor.

pre•serve
(pri zûrv′) *verb*
To protect something so that it stays in its original state.

pre•tend•ed
(pri ten′ did) *verb*
Made believe.
▲ **pretend**

pro•ceed
(prə sēd′) *verb*
To begin and continue an activity.

rag•ged•y
(rag′ i dē) *adjective*
Torn and worn out.
▲ **ragged**

ran•cid
(ran′ cid) *adjective*
Spoiled.

rat•tling
(rat′ ling) *verb*
Moving noisily.
▲ **rattle**

re•al•is•tic
(rē′ ə lis′ tik) *adjective*
Concerned with the way things really are.

rea•son•a•ble
(rē′ zə nə bəl) *adjective*
Fair.

re•de•fin•ing
(rē′di fīn′ ing) *verb*
Giving new meaning to.
▲ **redefine**

ref•er•ence
(ref′ rəns) *noun*
A mention of someone or something.

re•gret
(ri gret′) *verb*
To be sad or sorry about something.

re•lief
(ri lēf′) *noun*
A bringing of comfort or a reduction of pain.

re•marks
(ri märks′) *noun*
Comments about something.
▲ **remark**

res•i•dence
(rez′ i dəns) *noun*
A place where someone lives.

Thesaurus

residence
abode
dwelling
home

re•sis•tance
(ri zis′ təns) *noun*
Fighting back.
▲ **resist**

re•strict•ed
(ri strik′ tid) *adjective*
Stopped from doing something.
▲ **restrict**

sa•cred
(sā′ krid) *adjective*
Deserving great respect.

a	add	o͝o	took	ə	=
ā	ace	o͞o	pool	a	in above
â	care	u	up	e	in sicken
ä	palm	û	burn	i	in possible
e	end	yo͞o	fuse	o	in melon
ē	equal	oi	oil	u	in circus
i	it	ou	pout		
ī	ice	ng	ring		
o	odd	th	thin		
ō	open	th	this	′	stressed syllable
ô	order	zh	vision		

Glossary

sas•sy
(sas′ ē) *adjective*
Being rude or fresh to someone.

scarce
(skârs) *adjective*
Hard to find.

scent
(sent) *noun*
A pleasant smell.

Word Usage

The words **scent** and **sent** are homophones. **Homophones** sound the same but are spelled differently and have different meanings. **Scent** means "a pleasant smell," while **sent** means "to have made someone or something go someplace."

set•tled
(set′ ld) *verb*
Made one's self comfortable.
▲ **settle**

shat•tered
(shat′ərd) *verb*
Destroyed completely.
▲ **shatter**

sheep•ish•ly
(shē′ pish lē) *adverb*
Acting in an embarrassed way for having done something foolish.
▲ **sheepish**

sig•na•ture
(sig′ nə chər) *noun*
Your full name written in script.

si•mul•ta•nē•ous•ly
(sī′ məl tā′ ne əs lē) *adverb*
Happening at the same time.
▲ **simultaneous**

smear•ing
(smēr′ ing) *verb*
Rubbing something around an area.
▲ **smear**

snubs
(snubz) *noun*
Attempts to ignore and reject a person.
▲ **snub**

so•lar
(sō′ lər) *adjective*
To do with the sun.

spe•cial•ty
(spesh′ əl tē) *noun*
Something you are good at doing.

sprint
(sprint) *noun*
A fast run for a short distance.

star•tled
(stär′ tld) *verb*
Surprised.
▲ **startle**

steep
(stēp) *adjective*
Sharply sloping up or down.

stench
(stench) *noun*
A strong, unpleasant smell.

stim•u•late
(stim′yə lāt′) *verb*
To encourage something to grow or develop.

strick•en
(strik′ ən) *verb*
Affected suddenly by an illness.

strides
(strīdz) *noun*
Gains or improvements.
▲ **stride**

sub•tle
(sut′ l) *adjective*
Fine or delicate in meaning.

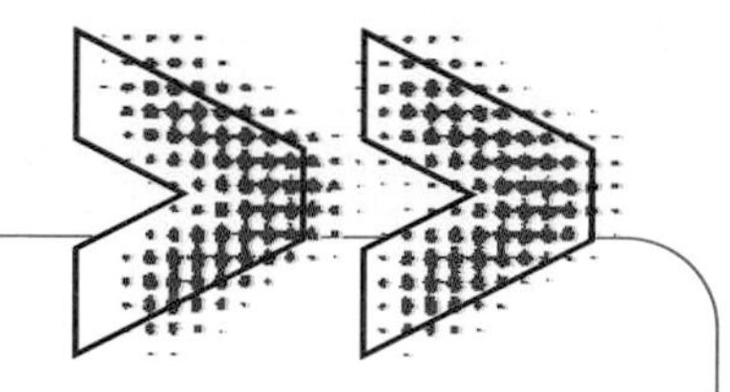

surged
(sûrjd) *verb*
Rushed forward with force.
▲ **surge**

sus•pi•cious
(sə spish′ əs) *adjective*
Feeling as if something is wrong with little or no proof.

sym•bol•ic
(sim bol′ ik) *adjective*
Serving as a symbol of something.

sys•tem•at•ic
(sis′ tə mat′ ik) *adjective*
Having a method or a plan.

taunts
(tônts) *noun*
Mean and insulting remarks.
▲ **taunt**

tease
(tēz) *verb*
To say mean and hurtful things to someone.

tech•niques
(tek nēks′) *noun*
Ways of doing something that requires skill.
▲ **technique**

tem•per•a•ture
(tem′ pər ə chər) *noun*
The degree of heat or cold in weather.

tempt•ed
(tempt′ id) *verb*
To want something or want to do something; attracted.
▲ **tempt**

tor•tured
(tôr′ chərd) *verb*
Caused extreme pain and suffering.
▲ **torture**

trag•e•dy
(traj′ i dē) *noun*
A very sad event.

trans•mit
(tranz mit′) *verb*
To send.

trudged
(trujd) *verb*
Walked slowly with effort.
▲ **trudge**

tur•quoise
(tûr′ koiz) *noun*
A blue-green color.

up•hol•ster•y
(up hōl′ stər ē) *noun*
The stuffing, springs, and covering put on furniture.

ur•gen•cy
(ûr′ jən sē) *noun*
Needing immediate attention.

vet•er•i•nar•i•ans
(vet′ ər ə nâr′ ē ənz) *noun*
Doctors who take care of sick animals.
▲ **veterinarian**

won•der
(wun′ dər) *noun*
Someone who is talented at something.

writh•ing
(rīth′ ing) *verb*
Twisting and turning in pain.
▲ **writhe**

a	add	o͝o	took	ə	=
ā	ace	o͞o	pool	a	in above
â	care	u	up	e	in sicken
ä	palm	û	burn	i	in possible
e	end	yo͞o	fuse	o	in melon
ē	equal	oi	oil	u	in circus
i	it	ou	pout		
ī	ice	ng	ring		
o	odd	th	thin		
ō	open	th	this	′	stressed syllable
ô	order	zh	vision		

Literary & Reading Terms

author A person who writes a short story, play, poem, novel, article, essay, or book.

autobiography An account of a person's life written by that person. An autobiography is an example of nonfiction.

base word A word from which other words can be made. By adding a prefix to the beginning of a base word or a suffix to the end of a base word, you can change a word's meaning (such as *view/preview/viewing*).

biography An account of a person's life written by another person. A biography is a form of nonfiction.

cause and effect The *cause* is something that makes another thing happen. What happens is called the *effect*. The reader figures out why an event happened or how one event caused another to occur.

characterization The way the author presents the personality of a character. The reader learns about a character through descriptions, actions, speech, and thoughts. *Character traits* are the qualities that a character possesses.

characters People in a story, play, novel, etc. There are *major* and *minor* characters in a story, major characters being more important than minor ones. The *main character* is the most important character.

compare and contrast To compare is to figure out how events, characters, or ideas are similar. To contrast is to find out how they are different.

compound word A word that is made up of two or more smaller words, such as *homework.*

conflict A struggle between characters, between a character and a force of nature, or between opposing views held by different characters. *Internal conflict* lies in the mind of a character who must resolve something.

connotation The implied meaning of a word or phrase as opposed to its exact dictionary meaning or *denotation.* The connotations of a word are the ideas and feelings associated with it.

contraction A word formed by leaving out and combining parts of other words. For example, the word *can't* is made from the words *can* and *not*. The *n* and the *o* in *not* are dropped and are replaced by the apostrophe.

debate A discussion between sides with different opinions or points of view.

denotation The exact dictionary meaning of a word as opposed to its implied meaning, or *connotation.*

dialogue The conversation in a story or play. The exact words the characters say. In a story, quotation marks point out the dialogue.

diphthong Two vowels that spell a sound that is formed by a gliding action in the mouth (such as *oy, oi, ou, ow*).

draw conclusions To make decisions about a story and its characters. To draw conclusions, a reader thinks about events and details in a story and comes to a new understanding.

editorial An article or a statement that reflects the opinions of a newspaper, magazine, or other information source.

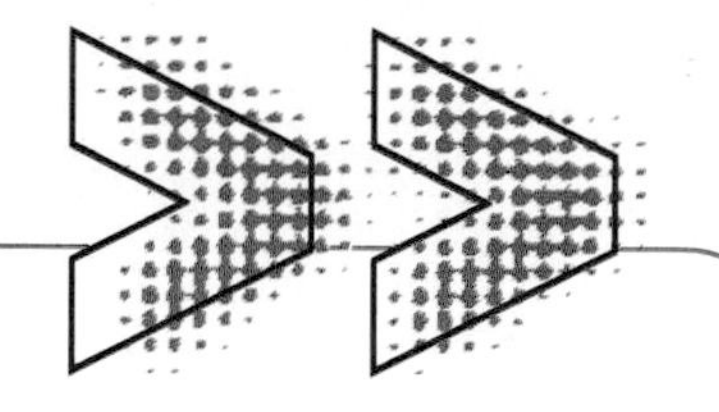

encyclopedia entry Informative article found in an encyclopedia (a set of books with alphabetized entries about many different subjects).

essay A short, nonfiction piece of writing on a subject or theme that expresses a specific point of view.

exaggeration Overstatement of an idea beyond the limits of truth.

fiction An invented story. Although fiction may be based on actual personal experience, it involves invented characters, actions, and settings.

figurative language Words used in a special way to give added meaning. In figurative expressions such as "I'm up to my ears in homework," the words are not intended to be interpreted in a word-for-word, or *literal,* sense. Stories, and especially poems, use figurative language to create images, or mental pictures. See also **metaphor, personification, simile.**

flashback A technique that interrupts the present action in a story, play, or novel to tell about something that happened in the past.

foreshadowing A storytelling device that an author uses to give the reader advance warning of events to come.

graphic classic A well-known story told through pictures in a comic-book format.

historical fiction A story or novel whose setting is in some period in the past. Often real people from the past or important historical events are used in works of historical fiction.

homophone A word that sounds like another word but has a different meaning and spelling (such as *hear* and *here*).

humor The quality of being comical or funny.

imagery Words that create mental pictures, or images, that appeal to one or more of the reader's five senses. For example, "The moon floated above the clouds like a ship lost on the stormy seas" appeals to the reader's sense of sight.

irony The contrast, or difference, between what is said and what is meant. For example, if we say in conversation that something feels good when it really feels bad, we are using irony.

lyrics The words of a song. Lyrics often express personal thoughts or feelings. Originally, lyric poems were sung and accompanied by a musical instrument called a lyre.

main idea The most important idea in a paragraph or selection. The reader may find the main idea in a topic sentence or heading and will find details that support the main idea in the rest of the paragraph or selection.

make inferences A reader makes an inference when he or she combines text information with his or her own prior knowledge to figure out something that is not directly stated in a story.

media literacy An understanding of the ways in which mass communication is used in society.

metaphor A figure of speech in which there is an indirect or implied comparison between two things. "Her eyes were stars in the midnight sky" is a metaphor.

mood The general atmosphere or feeling in a work of literature. Mood is created largely through description and setting.

Literary & Reading Terms

motivation The reason a character in a work of literature acts in a particular way. The character's motivation may be stated directly or hinted at by what he or she does, thinks, or says.

myth A story told by people in ancient times to explain life and nature. Many myths, including Greek myths, are about gods and goddesses.

narrative poem A poem that tells a story or relates a sequence of events.

narrator The teller of a story.

nonfiction Writing about real people and factual events. Journal accounts, diaries, essays, interviews, articles, textbooks, biographies, autobiographies, and letters are examples of nonfiction.

novel A book-length piece of fiction that usually has a plot and deals with human experience.

personal narrative A true story about a person's life told in the first person.

personification A figure of speech that describes an object, idea, or animal as if it had human characteristics. For example: "The light spring rain danced upon our heads."

photo essay A collection of photos and words that tells a story or presents information.

play A work written to be performed before an audience. A play may be written in parts called *acts.* Acts may be divided into smaller parts called *scenes. Stage directions* tell the director or actors how the stage is to look and how the characters are to move and speak. The *dialogue,* or *lines,* are the words the characters speak.

plot The sequence of events in a short story, novel, play, or poem. The major element in a plot is the *conflict,* or struggle, between opposing forces. Rising action is the part of the plot in which the action builds and a problem, or conflict, develops. The turning point is the part of the plot in which the struggle between the forces comes to a head in some incident—the crisis, or climax. The resolution is the part of the plot in which the problem is solved.

plot twist A turn of events in the structure of a story, novel, or play that is unexpected, yet logical based on the reader's knowledge of the plot and character.

poetry Literature that uses language chosen for its sound and for its ability to express and evoke emotion. Many poems use images, or mental pictures, which appeal to the senses. Most poetry is written in lines that have a particular rhythm, or pattern of stressed syllables. Poetry can either be rhymed or unrhymed.

point of view The vantage point from which the narrator tells the story. In the *first-person* point of view, the narrator is usually a character in the story. This narrator tells the story by using the pronouns "I" or "we." In the *third-person* point of view—the most common form of telling a story—the narrator may or may not be a character in the story. This narrator uses the pronouns "he," "she," or "they." When the narrator, in the third-person point of view, seems to know what every character is thinking and feeling, this narrator is called *omniscient* or *all-knowing.*

possessive The form of a noun or pronoun that shows possession or ownership.

prefix A word part added to the beginning of a word to change its meaning (such as *view/preview*).

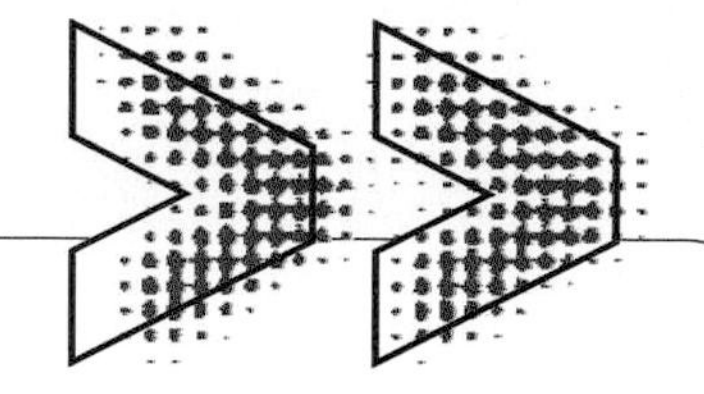

problem and solution A *problem* is a difficult situation that a character in a story has to solve. The *solution* is how the problem is solved.

profile A brief account of someone's life or accomplishments.

read for detail A *detail* is a small piece of information. Details help the reader to better understand the who, what, when, how, where, or why of a part of a story or piece of nonfiction.

root A word or word part from Latin or another language that is the basis of an English word. One example of a root is *port,* which means "to carry" (such as *import/portable*).

science fiction A fantasy story that is often set in the future, on other planets, or in other dimensions in time. Scientific impossibilities may be used in the plot.

sequence of events The order in which events occur. The reader can look for time–order words, such as *first, then* or *next,* and other clues to determine the sequence of events.

setting The time, place, and general environment of a story. The setting tells when and where the story takes place. The reader determines setting by noticing descriptions and events.

short story A brief piece of fiction, usually of 500 to 5,000 words in length.

simile A figure of speech in which two things are compared directly, using *like, as,* or *than.* "Her eyes sparkled like diamonds" is a simile.

stanza A group of two or more lines in a poem that are printed as a unit and held together by length, rhyme scheme, and meter.

style The individual, creative way an author expresses ideas and presents characters, setting, and action.

suffix A word part added to the end of a word to change its meaning (such as *slow/slowly*).

summarize To identify, organize, and combine the most important parts of a story so they can be retold in a brief statement.

suspense The tension readers feel because they are uncertain as to how events are going to turn out.

symbol Something that has meaning in itself and yet stands for something else. For example, in a story, a heart may also stand for love.

theme An important truth about life expressed by the author of a work of literature. It may be the author's thoughts about a certain topic, or the author's view of human nature. The theme is conveyed by the whole story—by the title, the plot, the characters, the setting, and the mood.

Author & Title Index

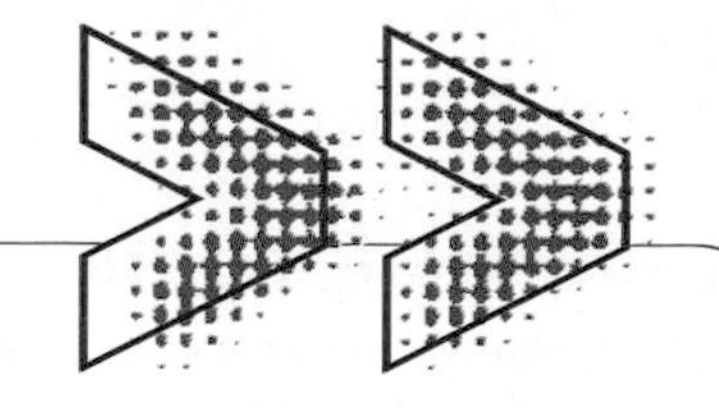

Acknowledgments

Grateful acknowledgment is made to the following sources for permission to reprint from previously published material. The publisher has made diligent efforts to trace the ownership of all copyrighted material in this volume and believes that all necessary permissions have been secured. If any errors or omissions have inadvertently been made, proper corrections will gladly be made in future editions.

"Seventh Grade" from BASEBALL IN APRIL. Copyright © 1990 by Gary Soto. Reprinted by permission of Harcourt, Inc.

Cover from PACIFIC CROSSING by Gary Soto. Copyright © 1992 by Gary Soto. Reprinted by permission of Harcourt, Inc.

Cover from CRAZY WEEKEND by Gary Soto. Cover illustration copyright © 1994 by Dan Gonzalez. Published by Scholastic Inc.

"Fighting Fire" from FIGHTING FIRE by Caroline Paul. Copyright © 1998 by Caroline Paul. Reprinted by permission of St. Martin's Press, LLC.

"Help Is Here!" from EMERGENCY! by Joy Masoff. Copyright © 1999 by Joy Masoff. Reprinted by permission of Scholastic Inc.

"Only a Dollar's Worth" by Herma Werner. Copyright © 1993 by Herma Werner. Originally published as "Just a Dollar's Worth" in *Scholastic Action* magazine, April 2, 1993. All rights reserved.

"Just a Pigeon" by Dennis Brindell Fradin. Copyright © 1996 by Dennis Brindell Fradin. Originally published in *Scholastic Scope* magazine, December 6, 1996. Reprinted by permission of the author.

"A Matter of Honor" by Barbara Seiger. Copyright © 1994 by Barbara Seiger. Originally published in *Scholastic Action* magazine, April 8, 1994. Reprinted by permission of the author.

"Confessions of a Gym-Class Dropout" from CONFESSIONS OF A GYM-CLASS DROPOUT by Chuck Ranberg and Patrick Daley. Text copyright © 1992 by Scholastic Inc. Illustrations copyright © 1999 by Scholastic Inc. Originally published as "Ultrabodies" in *Scholastic Action* magazine, May 1, 1992. Reprinted by permission of Scholastic Inc.

"Heart-Thumping Workouts" by Bob Hugel from *Scholastic Choices* magazine, January 1999. Copyright © 1999 by Scholastic Inc. Reprinted by permission of Scholastic Inc.

"Smelly Feat" from UNBEARABLE! MORE BIZARRE STORIES by Paul Jennings. Copyright © 1990 by Paul Jennings. Reprinted by permission of Penguin Putnam Inc.

"Helping Sea Turtles Cope with Birth, Sickness and Storms" from "Topsail Beach Journal: Helping Sea Turtles Cope with Birth, Sickness and Storms" by Emily Yellin from *The New York Times*, September 2, 1999. Copyright © 1999 by the New York Times Co. Reprinted by permission.

"The High Cost of Cheap Labor" by Joe Layden from *Scholastic Scope* magazine, September 6, 1996. Copyright © 1996 by Scholastic Inc. Reprinted by permission of Scholastic Inc.

"The Man Who Changed America" by John Scher. Adapted from *Sports Illustrated For Kids*, February 1997. Copyright © 2000 by Time Inc. All rights reserved. Reprinted courtesy of *Sports Illustrated for Kids*.

"The Latino New Wave" by Peter Vilbig, Mireya Navarro, Barbara Whitaker, and Susan Brenna from *The New York Times Upfront* magazine, November 1, 1999. Copyright © 1999 by the New York Times Co. and Scholastic Inc. Reprinted by permission of *The New York Times Upfront*/Scholastic Inc.

"Stomp Your Feet to the Latin Beat" and "Say it en español" from "Dancin' La Vida Loca" by Jennifer Smith and "Latin Lingo" by Leila Cobo from *react* magazine, October 4–10, 1999. Copyright © 1999 by Advance Magazine Publications Inc. Reprinted by permission of *react* magazine, a Parade Publication. All rights reserved.

"Jodie's Revenge" from "The Corpse in the Classroom" by R. L. Stine from *Scholastic Thrills and Chills* magazine, Nos. 5/6. Copyright © 1995 by Scholastic Inc. Play adaptation originally published in *Scholastic Action* magazine, October 20, 1995. Reprinted by permission of Scholastic Inc.

"Meet the Skull Man" adapted from "Bringing the Dead Back to Life" by Tod Olson from *Scholastic Scope* magazine, March 22, 1999. Copyright © 1999 by Scholastic Inc. Reprinted by permission of Scholastic Inc.

"Passage to Freedom: The Sugihara Story" from PASSAGE TO FREEDOM: THE SUGIHARA STORY by Ken Mochizuki, illustrated by Dom Lee. Text copyright © 1997 by Ken Mochizuki. Illustrations copyright © 1997 by Dom Lee. Permission arranged with Lee & Low Books Inc., New York, NY.

"Hero" from MUSIC BOX by Mariah Carey. Copyright © 1993 by Sony Songs Inc./Rye Songs (BMI). Used by permission of Sony/ATV Music Publishing. All rights reserved.

"My Friend's Got This Problem, Mr. Candler" from MY FRIEND'S GOT THIS PROBLEM, MR. CANDLER by Mel Glenn. Text copyright © 1991 by Mel Glenn. Published by Clarion Books/Houghton Mifflin Co. Reprinted by permission of the author.

"What Would You Do?" from *Scholastic Action* magazine, October 4, 1996, October 18, 1996, January 10, 1997, January 24, 1997, and April 11, 1997. Copyright © 1996, 1997 by Scholastic Inc. Reprinted by permission of Scholastic Inc.

"Young Blue Eyes" by Susan Beth Pfeffer from FROM ONE EXPERIENCE TO ANOTHER by M. Jerry Weiss and Helen S. Weiss. Copyright © 1997 by M. Jerry Weiss and Helen S. Weiss.

"Hi-Tech Eyes" from "Hi-Tech IDs" by Miguel Vilar from *Science World* magazine, October 4, 1999. Copyright © 1999 by Scholastic Inc. Reprinted by permission of Scholastic Inc.

"Don't Be Fooled" from "Shopping 101" by Pearl Gaskins from *Scholastic Choices* magazine, April 1999. Copyright © 1999 by Scholastic Inc. Reprinted by permission of Scholastic Inc.

"Where Teens Get Their Money" and "What They Spend it On" graphs from *The New York Times Upfront* magazine, September 6, 1999. Copyright © 1999 by the New York Times Co. and Scholastic Inc. Reprinted by permission of *The New York Times Upfront*/Scholastic Inc.

"Meet the Weird Watsons" from THE WATSONS GO TO BIRMINGHAM—1963 by Christopher Paul Curtis. Copyright © 1995 by Christopher Paul Curtis. Used by permission of Dell Publishing, a division of Random House, Inc.

Cover from THE WATSONS GO TO BIRMINGHAM—1963 by Christopher Paul Curtis. Copyright © 1995 by Christopher Paul Curtis. Used by permission of Dell Publishing, a division of Random House, Inc.

Cover from BUD, NOT BUDDY by Christopher Paul Curtis. Copyright © 1999 by Christopher Paul Curtis. Used by permission of Delacorte Press, a division of Random House, Inc.

"The All-American Slurp" by Lensey Namioka from VISIONS: NINETEEN SHORT STORIES BY OUTSTANDING WRITERS FOR YOUNG ADULTS, edited by Donald Gallo. Copyright © 1987 by Lensey Namioka. Reprinted by permission of Lensey Namioka. All rights are reserved by the author.

Cover from DEN OF THE WHITE FOX by Lensey Namioka. Copyright © 1997 by Lensey Namioka. Reprinted by permission of Harcourt, Inc.

Cover from TIES THAT BIND, TIES THAT BREAK by Lensey Namioka. Copyright © 1999 by Lensey Namioka. Used by permission of Delacorte Press, a division of Random House, Inc.

"My Name," "Our Good Day," "Papa Who Wakes Up Tired in the Dark," and "Mango Says Goodbye Sometimes" from THE HOUSE ON MANGO STREET by Sandra Cisneros. Copyright © 1984 by Sandra Cisneros. Published by Random House, Inc. Reprinted by permission of Susan Bergholz Literary Agency. All rights reserved.

"Eleven" from WOMAN HOLLERING CREEK by Sandra Cisneros. Copyright © 1991 by Sandra Cisneros. Published by Random House, Inc. Reprinted by permission of Susan Bergholz Literary Agency. All rights reserved.

"Teasing Isn't Funny" from STORIES FROM MY LIFE: CASSANDRA WALKER TALKS TO TEENS ABOUT GROWING UP by Cassandra Walker. Copyright © 1997 by Cassandra Walker. Reprinted by permission of the author. All rights reserved.

"Don't Give Up" from BECOMING MYSELF: TRUE STORIES ABOUT LEARNING FROM LIFE by Cassandra Walker. Copyright © 1994 by Cassandra Walker. Reprinted by permission of the author. All rights reserved.

Cover from BECOMING MYSELF: TRUE STORIES ABOUT LEARNING FROM LIFE by Cassandra Walker. Copyright © 1994 by Cassandra Walker. Reprinted by permission of the author. All rights reserved.

Cover from STORIES FROM MY LIFE: CASSANDRA WALKER TALKS TO TEENS ABOUT GROWING UP by Cassandra Walker. Copyright © 1997 by Cassandra Walker. Reprinted by permission of the author. All rights reserved.

"My Native Tongue" by Karen Sorensen from *Scholastic Scope* magazine, January 10, 1997. Copyright © 1997 by Scholastic Inc. Reprinted by permission of Scholastic Inc.

"The Navajo" from SCHOLASTIC ENCYCLOPEDIA OF THE NORTH AMERICAN INDIAN by James Ciment, PhD with Ronald LaFrance, PhD. Copyright © 1996 by Scholastic Inc. Reprinted by permission of Scholastic Inc.

"Wilma Unlimited" from WILMA UNLIMITED: HOW WILMA RUDOLPH BECAME THE WORLD'S FASTEST WOMAN by Kathleen Krull, illustrated by David Diaz. Text copyright © 1996 by Kathleen Krull. Illustrations copyright © 1996 by David Diaz. Reprinted by permission of Harcourt, Inc.

"Wilma: A Valuable Lesson" from WILMA by Wilma Rudolph and Bud Greenspan. Copyright © 1977 by Bud Greenspan. Reprinted by permission of Dutton Signet, a division of Penguin Putnam Inc.

"Body Bugs" by Chana Stiefel from *Science World* magazine, September 6, 1999. Copyright © 1999 by Scholastic Inc. Reprinted by permission of Scholastic Inc.

"Hot Job: Photo 'Bug' Lady" from *Science World* magazine, September 6, 1999. Copyright © 1999 by Scholastic Inc. Reprinted by permission of Scholastic Inc.

"Within Reach: My Everest Story" from WITHIN REACH: MY EVEREST STORY by Mark Pfetzer and Jack Galvin. Text copyright © 1998 by Mark Pfetzer and Jack Galvin. Reprinted by permission of Penguin Putnam Inc.

"20,000 Leagues Under the Sea" from 20,000 LEAGUES UNDER THE SEA, a graphic classic by Adam Grant based on the novel by Jules Verne. Copyright © 1999 by Scholastic Inc. Reprinted by permission of Scholastic Inc.

Photo Credits

pp. 6-7, 12, 14, 15, 25, 33 (all photos), 36-37, 50-51, 66-67, 76-77, 87, 98-99, 112-113, 126-127, 140-141, 154-155, 158 (basketball), 164-165, 174-175, 188-189, 200-201, 210-211, 222-223, 238-239, 266-267, 278-279, 290-291, 312-313, 324-325: Ken Karp for Scholastic Inc.; p. 11: Courtesy of Scholastic Trade Department; pp. 16ml, 23: ©David Roth; pp. 16-17: ©George Hall/CORBIS; pp. 19, 22: ©Bill Stormont/The Stock Market; p. 20 ©Peter Escobedo; p. 21tl: ©Frank Marchese; p. 21tr: ©Roger Ball/The Stock Market; p. 28 (nickel): John Lei for Scholastic Inc.; p. 28 (all other coins): Halley Ganges for Scholastic Inc.; p. 31: ©Kevin Kushel/Bruce Coleman Inc.; p. 46: ©David Leach/Tony Stone Images; p. 63: ©Wilmington Star-News/Ken Blevins; p. 68: Courtesy of Reebok Youth in Action Awards; p. 69: ©K. M. Choudary/AP/Wide World Photos; pp. 70, 74: Courtesy of Ron Adams; p. 71: ©Jim Bourg/Gamma Liaison; pp. 72-73: ©Marie Dorigny/REA/SABA; p. 78: ©UPI/Bettmann/CORBIS; p. 78 (background): ©2000 PhotoDisc, Inc.; p. 79tr: ©AP/Wide World Photos; p. 79mr: ©Hy Peskin/Life Magazine; p. 79br: ©Manny Millan/Sports Illustrated; pp. 80tr, 82tr, 84: ©Bettmann/CORBIS; p. 80bl: ©Tom Dipace/Sports Illustrated; p. 81tl: ©Jack Zehrt/FPG International Corp.; p. 81br: ©UPI/Bettmann/CORBIS; p. 82tl: ©David E. Klutho/Sports Illustrated; p. 83: ©Doug Pensinger/Allsport USA; pp. 88-89: ©Reed Saxon/AP/Wide World Photos; p. 90: ©Norm Detaff/AP/Las Cruces Sun-News; p. 92, 96: ©Dirk Edgar Shadd; p. 94: ©Carlos Goldin/The Stock Market; p. 95: David Mager for Scholastic Inc.; p. 97 ©2000 PhotoDisc, Inc.; pp. 108-109: ©Michael Bryant / Philadelphia Inquirer; pp. 128-129: ©Bob Rowan; Progressive Image/CORBIS; p. 130tc: ©2000 PhotoDisc, Inc.; p. 130ml: ©Michael J. Bernstein; p. 131tc: ©2000 PhotoDisc, Inc.; p. 131mr: ©Michael J. Bernstein; pp. 132, 138: ©2000 PhotoDisc, Inc."; p. 133tc: ©Ian Shaw/Tony Stone Images; p. 133mr: ©Michael J. Bernstein; pp. 134-135tc: ©Alan Schein/The Stock Market; p. 135mr: ©Michael J. Bernstein; p. 150: ©Juan Silva Productions/The Image Bank; p. 151 (all photos): Courtesy of John Daugman/Cambridge University; pp. 156-157, 162: ©Chip Simons; p. 158(cell phone, sneakers), p. 159 (pizza): David S.Waitz for Scholastic Inc.; p. 158 (walkman): John Lei for Scholastic Inc.; p. 159 (cd): ©2000 PhotoDisc, Inc.; p. 159 (sunglasses): Grant Huntington for Scholastic Inc.; p. 159 (skateboard, camera): Bie Bostrom for Scholastic Inc.; p. 160 (ticket, hamburger, bag): ©2000 PhotoDisc, Inc.; p. 160 (girl, boy): Rubberball; p. 161: ©Mike Chew/The Stock Market; pp. 166 (all photos), 168, 172 (all photos): Courtesy of Doctors Without Borders; p. 185: ©Curtis Photographic/ Courtesy of Bantam Doubleday Dell; pp. 190-191, 193, 194, 198 (all collages): Daryl Hair for Scholastic Inc.; pp. 190-191c: ©Mark Harmel/FPG International Corp.; p. 191 (chopsticks): ©2000 PhotoDisc, Inc.; p. 191 (celery): ©Michael Nelson/FPG International Corp.; p. 193 (jeans): Francis Clark Westfield for Scholastic Inc.; p. 193 (T-shirt): David Lawrence for Scholastic Inc.; p. 194 (soup): ©2000 PhotoDisc, Inc.; p. 196 (fork): John Lei for Scholastic Inc.; p. 196 (bowl & chopsticks): ©2000 PhotoDisc, Inc.; p. 197: ©Don Perkins/Courtesy of Harcourt Brace & Co.; p. 202: ©Fredrich Cantor/Courtesy of Vintage Contemporaries; p. 204: David E. Franck for Scholastic Inc.; p. 205: Bie Bostrom for Scholastic Inc.; p. 207: ©D. William Hamilton/The Image Bank; p. 208 (all photos): Ana Esperanza Nance for Scholastic Inc.; p. 209: ©Rubén Guzmán/ Courtesy of Vintage Contempories; pp. 212, 215: Courtesy of Free Spirit Publishing; p. 217: Courtesy of Cassandra Walker; p. 224: ©UPI/Bettmann/CORBIS; pp. 227, 236: Courtesy of Cumberland County Historical Society; p. 229: Courtesy of the U.S. Dept. of Defense; pp. 230-231: ©Kenji Kawano; pp. 234, 235: ©Hulton Getty/Liaison Agency; pp. 260, 262: ©Bettmann/CORBIS; pp. 268, 269, 274: ©Darlyne Murawski; pp. 268-277 (backgrounds): ©2000 PhotoDisc, Inc.; p. 270: ©Manfred Kage/Peter Arnold, Inc.; 271tr: ©Ah Rider/Photo Researchers, Inc.; pp. 271bl, 272 (all photos): ©Oliver Meckes/Photo Researchers, Inc.; pp. 273, 276: ©David Scharf/Peter Arnold, Inc.; pp. 280-281 (Mt. Everest): ©Wild Country/CORBIS; pp. 281 (inset photo), 283, 288: Courtesy of Mark Pfetzer; p. 286: ©Hulton-Deutsch Collection/CORBIS; p. 287: ©Robert Holmes/CORBIS; p. 309: ©Bettmann/CORBIS; pp. 314tl, 320: ©Culver Pictures; pp. 314-315tc, 319: Courtesy of the National Archives; p. 315tr: Courtesy of the Library of Congress; pp. 316, 321, 322: ©The Granger Collection; p. 318: Gordon Parks/Courtesy of The Library of Congress

Illustrations Credits

pp. 14, 36, 86, 126, 164, 210, 238, 266, 312: Deb Lofaso; pp. 25, 140, 174, 188, 200, 324: Glen Davis; pp. 27, 34: Patrick Faricy; pp. 38, 40, 43, 48: Peter Spacek; pp. 50, 76, 98: Joe Borzetta; pp. 52-53, 56, 61, 64: Mike Lester; p. 66: Bennett/Christian Science p. 91: U.S. Bureau of the Census; pp. 100-101, 102, 104-105, 110: Anni Matsick; pp. 113, 290: Elana Goren-Totino; pp. 114-121, 124: Dom Lee; pp. 122-123: Ida Habtemichael; pp. 136-137: Leslie Harris; pp. 142-143, 146, 147, 149, 152: John Euland; p. 154: Yahooligans!; pp. 171, 234, 280: Jim McMahon; pp. 176-177, 180, 182-183, 186, 187: Sally Wern Comport; pp. 210, 278: Elliot Kreloff; pp. 240-258, 264-265: David Diaz/Cecilia Zeiba-Diaz; p. 284: Robin Bernstein; p. 293: Mike Lilly/ Unstoppable Prod.; pp. 294-309: Greg Follender/ Unstoppable Prod.

Cover Credits

tl (firemen): ©Bill Stormont/The Stock Market; bl (boy), tr (girl): Ken Karp for Scholastic Inc.; c (mountain climber): ©Robert Holmes/CORBIS; mr (louse): ©Darlyne Murawski; br (baseball game): ©Jack Zehrt/FPG International Corp.